RENEWING THE WO...

Water

K. LUSK BROOKE

Dedication

This work is dedicated to Frank P. Davidson,
founder of the field of Macro Engineering

Frank Davidson's extraordinary vision and life work was not just about building large projects or inspiring others to think bigger—although that certainly was one result. His frequent use of the word *macro* meant to him THE WHOLE, that which is good for the whole. To my father, Frank Davidson, macro didn't just mean big; he saw it as a larger, holistic connection that benefits all humanity.

—Roger Davidson

Table of Contents

The Water Planet

Image of Earth taken by *Apollo 17* spacecraft crew, NASA, 1972.
Attribution: p. 159.

Preface

This work is a sequel to *Building the World*, exploring 3,000 years of engineering, scientific, and technical achievements that shaped history. In fact, the present book was originally titled "Rebuilding the World." It is certainly true that the world needs rebuilding. Energy grids are inadequate to current needs; water systems leak; bridges and roads need repair. With climate change, increasingly devastating storms demand rebuilding. Sea level rise will further force rebuilding.

But we must do more than just rebuild. We must renew.

Early attempts to harness and share essentials like water and energy were based on an assumption that these natural elements were infinite. We pumped water with no fear of scarcity. We struck oil, and it gushed in such abundance that we built a whole world powered by an energy source that seemed infinite. Now, we are draining more water for agriculture, drinking, industry, and sanitation than we can replenish. We are squeezing out remaining coal, gas, and oil with a clock ticking. A time bomb is also ticking. The changes we must make demand building with a new vision, one of renewal.

Humans, by nature, tend to delay acting until a crisis. This has been true throughout history. As seen in *Building the World*, China did not develop the Grand Canal until grain and fresh water were needed in the arid north, and it became clear that an internal waterway from the south could satisfy both needs. Ancient Rome did not seek an alternative to the increasingly polluted Tiber River until that water source was threatened by poison during a time of war. The Roman aqueducts, bringing fresh water to the growing city and empire, were the result. Crisis is a time for action. Now is such a time.

The study of success may be quickly summarized: success causes go-ahead action; failure causes a stop and then a change. We may experience success and failure as opposites, but they are poles of a shared system. Failure tells us what we didn't know, didn't see, and now can change; if well examined, failure is the secret to success. Failure is a window; success is a door.

Renewing the World offers a window to look at some of the problems we face, providing a glimpse of emerging solutions. Its companion, *Leadership Casebook,* offers a door. These two books are meant to be used together. There can be no understating the challenge ahead. But the very urgency demanding change may also open the greatest opportunity humanity has ever seen for truly sustainable renewal. It's not just an opportunity for one country or even one region. It is, and must be, a globally shared opportunity. Together, perhaps only together, we can renew the world.

K. Lusk Brooke
Center for the Study of Success

Overview

It is time to rebuild, and renew, the world. The essential systems of civilization were built for, and based upon, a former era. Climate change is now upon us, shaking our foundations and challenging our resilience. Now is the moment in history to rebuild, redesign, reimagine, and renew our world.

A previous work, *Building the World*, explored the past 3,000 years through great engineering and scientific breakthroughs that changed history. From the Roman aqueducts to the New River of England, humans have continued to develop water systems. One might similarly view the history of humankind from the spark of Promethean fire to the forms of energy developed since then; many believe we must solve problems related to energy in this century. The world became connected through transport. If cars changed history, how much more will airplanes or the internet? Water, energy, and transport come together in cities. Historian Arnold Toynbee, in *Cities of Destiny*, suggested that some of civilization's most significant achievements happened in cities. Finally, what is a greater leap in civilization than stepping onto the moon? We will continue to expand our frontiers in space. This may bring us full circle because space is the only place from which we can see Earth as a nexus of dynamic, interacting systems.

It should be stated that these five are not the only, or even the most important, foundations of civilization: education, environment, health, justice, and rights are essential. But water, energy, cities, transport, and space are things we can build to make a better world possible. It is time to renew the world.

— When we build, let us think that we build forever.
John Ruskin, 1849
The Seven Lamps of Architecture

— Most of us will first experience climate change through water.
MIT *Technology Review*
The Water Issue, January 2022

How to Use This Book

Digital and Printed Versions

This book is available in both digital and print versions. In the digital version, sources and references are mainly live links, inviting exploration into topics. There are, of course, many important printed works that are not available digitally at this time, and in those cases reference will be made to publication and ISBN. Many readers prefer a printed version, but in this case it is recommended that a digital version also be obtained because it will provide instant access to sources.

Please scan this QR code to visit the website where you will find a link to obtain print and digital versions.

Sources

Sources are presented in every topic area so users and consumers may delve more deeply into key areas of interest. At the time of publication, all web-links were tested and found fully operational.

Case Studies

Over the course of history, humans have built—and rebuilt—essential systems. From the climate migrants of Cyrene to the innovators of the New River, water problems have been a major reason for change. Energy discoveries often began with water and progressed to other sources, including atomic energy. London Bridge was built, and rebuilt, many times. Ships, trains, cars, aircraft, and rockets characterize eras of transport, each requiring unique approaches to financing, management, and environmental concerns.

Each topic—Water, Energy, Cities, Transport, Space—presents a historic case study that includes issues bearing on today's challenges. ***Historic case studies*** have the advantage of availability of original contracts that detail successes (and failures) of decisions regarding resources, including financial, human, and natural.

In addition, ***contemporary case studies***, such as "Planetary Resources Inc., Property Rights, and the Regulation of the Space Economy" included in the volume on Space, help to elucidate current issues.

Case studies, contracts and laws, and models of systems may be explored individually, but may also serve as common frameworks for synchronous group interaction.

Contracts and Laws

Many of us have seen photos of the Taj Mahal, but have you read the real estate contract? *Building the World* presented the original agreements, contracts, decrees, and laws for some of history's greatest achievements. This book is a sequel, and curates a selection of key laws that may serve as precedent for the future. These laws address issues like environment, profit, public/private ownership, stakeholder rights, and timeframe.

System Models

Global and regional systems like water, energy, and transport, present complexities that may be best explored through a systems framework. Therefore each volume includes a system model as a guide to some of the factors that may determine future decisions.

Windows on the Economy

Throughout the book you will see *Windows on the Economy* that offer a view of the impact of problems and significant opportunities for solutions and actions. Economic data presented should be considered as estimates and trends, with provided sources offering documentation of current figures and future projections. All the *Windows on the Economy* offer video links.

Voices of the Future

Jeff Bezos, Gro Harlem Brundtland, Matt Damon, Christiana Figueres, Bill Gates, and Ingrid Waldron are among the forward thinkers whose messages highlight ideas in this book and contribute to the call to action. The links in *Voices of the Future* open to speakers who share their insights and thoughts directly.

VOICE OF THE FUTURE
—Paul Hawken

"We see global warming not as an inevitability but as an invitation to build, innovate and effect change, a pathway that awakens creativity, compassion, and genius."

—Paul Hawken, environmentalist, author, editor of *Drawdown* (2017, p. xi)

VIDEO: Paul Hawken and Bill Maher, "Paul Hawken: Project Drawdown/Real Time with Bill Maher (HBO)" 30 September 2017. https://www.youtube.com/watch?v=k1wXHx2DsSU

PROBLEMS WE MUST SOLVE

WATER

"Splash" by José Manuel Suárez, 2008.
Attribution: see p. 159

Every two minutes, a child dies of a water-related disease. More than 2.1 billion people lack access to safe drinking water (3 in 10 people), and more than four billion (6 in 10 people) live without safe sanitation. If you have a kitchen tap, be mindful that 83% of household water contains plastic in some form.

If unchecked, rising seas will drown coastal cities around the globe. Jakarta, Indonesia, is sinking faster than any other big city. Sea levels around Indonesia's capital have risen approximately 10 feet (3 meters) in the last three decades.

Safe drinking water and access to effective sanitation continue to be a problem. It is estimated that solving the problem would produce $30 billion in health and economic benefits each year.

Earth is the water planet. Water innovations have powered every advance from ancient cities built on rivers and ports, to ships as an early means of global transport, to hydroelectric energy, to the quest for water in space. As we protect and sustain water, so will we sustain Earth's future.

ENERGY

"Electricity (sanded and polished)"
by Andrew Fysh, 2013.
Attribution: see p. 159

The water-food-energy nexus will greatly influence the future. Did you know it takes between 3,000 and 6,000 gallons of water to power a 60-watt incandescent bulb for 12 hours a day over the course of a year? Or that globally, 940 million people do not have access to electricity? Three billion use wood to cook and heat indoors, causing (among other things) health problems from indoor pollution. Power choices influence climate change. Clean, safe, renewable energy is an urgent matter and a major opportunity.

"Skyscrapers with Lit Windows at Night,"
By Vita Vilcina, 2012.
Attribution: see p. 159

CITIES

By 2050, 68% of all people on Earth will live in cities. Asia will be home to more than 30 urban centers with 10+ million people. Cities may grow beyond their ability to handle urban populations. Sydney, Australia, once considered a plan to split into three cities. Capitals like Port-au-Prince, Haiti; Mexico City, Mexico; and Tokyo, Japan sit on earthquake-prone land. Cities located on coasts may also be threatened by rising seas.

Cities cause serious pollution, but they can also change laws and mandate improvements faster than nations. Cities have the capability to offer education and public health systems. The future of Earth may be determined by cities.

"Heatpipe tunnel Copenhagen 2009.jpg"
by Bill Ebbesen, 2009.
Attribution: see p. 159

TRANSPORT

Someone is killed in a vehicular accident every 25 seconds. Traffic emissions are choking cities. Old roads and bridges are crumbling. Antiquated train tracks need rebuilding and new forms of conveyance planned. A proposal in France may outlaw short-haul air transport in favor of advanced high-speed trains.

Global supply chain complexities were formerly almost invisible to consumers except for labels reporting origin and assembly. But in 2020-2021, the global pandemic revealed problems that could bring changes in supply chain management and transport, including pivoting from global resourcing and just-in-time inventory planning to more local operations. Another development? Autonomous trucking that may ease pressures of labor shortages. Highways will be transformed with the installation of charging stations for electric cars and trucks. Cities may be redesigned for autonomous vehicles and human-powered transport.

"Solar System Montage – High Resolutions 2001 Version"
Jet Propulsion Laboratory, 2001.
Attribution: see p. 160

SPACE

In 1969, humans walked upon Earth's moon. They left behind a few footprints, objects, and proof that space could be safely explored. Now there are more than 20,000 orbiting devices, and space debris has become a concern: there are some 23,000 particles larger than 3-9 inches (10 cm) and 100 million larger than 0.04 inches (1 mm)—all moving at more than 17,000 miles (27,354 km) per hour. In November 2021, a failing orbiting satellite was destroyed in space, adding thousands more pieces of floating debris, some endangering the International Space Station. In the same month, in an effort to deflect an asteroid with the potential to impact Earth, the U.S. National Aeronautics and Space Administration (NASA) launched its DART (Double Action Redirection Test) mission to move Dimorphos from its current orbit—a space "target practice" to test ways to alter the course of asteroids that may endanger Earth. Traveling nearly seven million miles, DART is expected to reach its destination in September 2022.

Space laws need updating as private enterprise joins with governments to expand space transport, energy generation and transmission, celestial mining, and habitation. Space dangers include asteroids, debris, satellite traffic, and war. A resolution to prevent a space arms race was approved by the United Nations First Committee in 2021 and intended for completion in 2023. The group convened a working group to make recommendations on norms, principles, and rules to keep space safe. In the next decade, we can expect to see innovations in space achievements as well as advances and refinements in space law.

Space is the only place from which we can view Earth as a complete system. From space, we can measure climate change and test solutions. From space, we can see planetary cycles of interactive causes and effects that may reveal how Earth regenerates and renews.

Causal Factors

Aging Infrastructure

There are several known weaknesses in aging global infrastructure: lead is leaking from aging water pipes that need replacing; old energy grids are outdated, often collapsing in times of power surges; transport infrastructure, including roads and bridges, needs repair. In 2019, there were 178 million daily crossings over 46,100 structurally deficient bridges in the United States (ARTBA, 2019). In 2021, 40% of American roads were deemed in need of upgrading. While we can put off rebuilding old bridges and roads by mending and patching, there can be no such delay when floods ravage and seas rise to destroy coastlines and lives.

Population Growth

Despite numerous warnings, world population continues to grow. Today many people live in cities: in 1800 only 2% of the population was urban; in 2000, 50%; by 2050, 68% (UN, 2020). Climate migrants and refugees may need to flee flooding coasts and island nations, settling in new locations that may be safer but also make them more dense. As cities accommodate more people, there will be pressures but there may also be hope, because throughout history cities have often been the first responders in times of crisis.

Disasters

Unexpected, dire events, whether by natural or human causes, have always caused rebuilding. But disasters impact all systems at once, stopping the clock on life as normal—destroying buildings, tainting water, decimating food supplies, and threatening public health, sometimes for years. Industrial disasters, nuclear meltdowns, oil spills, and human disasters caused by attacks, paralyze recovery. After Haiti's 2010 earthquake, the rebuilding cost was pegged at $11.5 billion— and rebuilding continues, complicated by yet another earthquake in 2021. Scientists predict more extreme weather and environmentally caused disasters. During a hurricane in 2017, fragile power grids in Puerto Rico collapsed leaving areas of the island without electricity and reliable water for months; in 2021, electricity on the island still remains erratic. Every kind of disaster requires rebuilding because multiple systems may be in crisis at the same time.

Climate Change

Climate change is a slow-moving disaster, perhaps not visible until it is inevitable. Climate change makes us aware of the interactive nature, the nexus, of our basic foundations. We now see rising seas, but to stop inundation of the water planet, we have to change global energy practices. Changing water and energy use changes cities and transport. Water, energy, cities, transport—clearly these systems are severely impacted by the climate crisis, and by each other. But space? While some may see space as an exit strategy, it is actually the opposite. Space is the only place from which we can assess and measure global climate. With weather satellites, we can now detect methane hot spots, see pollution clogging urban skies, take the oceans' temperature. Space is the dashboard for driving solutions to the climate crisis.

Crises

It is hopeful to note that many of history's greatest innovations were developed in response to crisis. Rome knew the Tiber River was getting dirty, but nothing was done about it until the threat of a possible poisoning of the river's water. Similarly, atomic energy became a reality through the Manhattan Project, initiated in an urgent time of war.

While climate change is a slow-moving disaster, it is still something that will cause a crisis that will continue to escalate. Response will be increasingly important, and innovation will continue to develop. It is time to rebuild.

Building Macro Systems

"What we're asking ourselves to do here is change energy—and that includes all of transport, all of electricity, all of household usage, and all of industrial usage," stated Bill Gates (2015), principal founder of Microsoft Corporation, environmental leader, and philanthropist. Global and regional energy and water systems; transport networks for land, shipping, and aviation; mega-cities; space exploration and potential habitation—these are macro in scope. Several qualities characterize macro endeavors and systems:

- **Long Time Frame**

  Spanning decades, sometimes centuries, macro projects have long time frames. Architects, constructors, developers, engineers, financiers, government, legislative regulators, and those who live in contiguity to a project may need to take different approaches than the customary ways of thinking about beginnings and ends. Consider the Grand Canal of China—the longest continuous engineering project in history, and still evolving.

- *Planning and Profit*

  Because of long time delays, costs of building macro systems can escalate due to unforeseen delays, among other reasons. For example, if the Channel Tunnel linking France and England had been built when designed in 1959, the cost would have been far lower than at completion in 1994. Japan's *Shinkansen* high-speed train system was on schedule and profitable from day one. The Suez Canal was efficiently conceived and built; the Panama Canal, initiated by the same entrepreneur, was not well planned and required several leadership changes. There is a correlation between depth of planning and degree of success. Historic case studies may reveal approaches to success and ways to avoid failure.

- **Many Voices**

  Like a large stone cast into a pond, a macro project creates waves that affect its galvanizing cause. Foundational systems like water, transport, energy, or space, require vast resources: natural, material, and human. Hundreds and thousands of people are employed; millions and billions are affected. Bridging continents and uniting regions, macro systems can have a unifying effect.

- *One Vision*

  Even though they involve many people, macro works are often ignited by the vision of an individual: in earliest times, perhaps an empress or regent, high priest or czar; more recently, an entrepreneur, legislator, or visionary who believes ardently in the difficult but possible.

- *Environmental Concerns*

  Environmental structural change is a major consideration of macro foundational systems. For example, dams generate hydroelectric power and increase water supplies for people and agriculture. However, salinity can later become an environmental problem, as seen in the High Dam at Aswan or the Snowy Mountains Hydroelectric power project of Australia. The earliest projects barely recognized environmental implications, but more recently, design is influenced by environmental concerns and rights.

- *Technical and Scientific Innovations*

  Foundational systems such as energy or transport present scientific and technical challenges because of their size and scope, often requiring the development of new technologies. While environmental, scientific, and technical issues for these foundational systems can be demanding, they are also sources of innovation.

- *Cooperative Advantage*

  While one pillar of strategy is competitive advantage, macro also demands cooperation. In his book *Macro*, Frank P. Davidson articulated the idea of macro-engineering and how this field influences the interconnection of systems. Mobilizing macro endeavors requires shared purpose, as suggested by George H. Litwin, John J. Bray, and Kathleen Lusk Brooke in *Mobilizing the Organization*. L. Sprague De Camp, in *The Ancient Engineers*, observed that as humans began to farm, communities settled in one place long enough to develop expertise for building beyond the scope of one generation. Edward O. Wilson, in *Sociobiology*, traced the evolution of the instinct to devote action to the well-being of those beyond one's immediate circle and time frame. As we solve the macro issues we face in water, energy, cities, transport, and space, we may see visible signs of evolution pointing the way to a future that rebalances, rebuilds, reimagines, and reunites the world.

Sources:
American Road & Transportation Builders Association (ARTBA). Bridge Report, 2019.
https://artbabridgereport.org/reports/2020%20ARTBA%20Bridge%20Report.pdf.

American Society of Civil Engineers. "Infrastructure Report Card." https://infrastructurereportcard.org.

Biden, Joseph R. "Fact sheet: The American Jobs Plan," 31 March 2021. https://www.whitehouse.gov/
briefing-room/statements-releases/2021/03/31/fact-sheet-the-american-jobs-plan/.

Building the World: A Finding Aid for the Research Collection. University of Massachusetts Boston Healey
Library, February 2013. Note: this extensive collection allows users to request scanned copies of documents
that may not be available elsewhere but are valuable to researchers. https://cpb-us-
w2.wpmucdn.com/blogs.umb.edu/dist/5/707/ files/2012/07/Finding-Aid-2jaiazs.pdf .

Carrington, Damian. "Plastic fibres found in tap water around the world, study reveals." 5 September 2017.
The Guardian. https://www.theguardian.com/environment/2017/sep/06/plastic-fibres-found-tap-water-
around-world-study-reveals.

Davidson, Frank P. *Macro: A Clear Vision of How Science and Technology Will Shape Our Future*. New
York: William Morrow, 1983. ISBN: 0-688-02182-4.

Davidson, Frank P. and Kathleen Lusk Brooke. *Building the World: An Encyclopedia of the Great
Engineering Projects in History*. Greenwood/ABC-CLIO, 2006. ISBN: 0313333548.

De Camp, L. Sprague. *The Ancient Engineers*. London: Ballantine Books, Random House, 1960.
ISBN: 0-345-32029-8.

Gates, Bill. Quoted in: Bennet, James. " 'We need an energy miracle' – Bill Gates has committed his fortune to
moving the world beyond fossil fuels and mitigating climate change." November 2015. *The Atlantic*.
https://www.theatlantic.com/magazine/archive/2015/11/we-need-an-energy-miracle/407881/

Hadley, Greg. "UN committee advances proposal on rules governing behavior in space." 2 November 2021.
Airforce Magazine. https://www.airforcemag.com/united-nations-votes-working-group-space-rules/.

Hall D. O., and Patricia A. Moss. "Biomass for energy in developing countries." *GeoJournal*, vol. 7, no. 1
(January 1983): 5-14. https://link.springer.com/article/10.1007/BF00191854#page-1.

Hawken, Paul, ed. *Drawdown: The Most Comprehensive Plan Ever Proposed to Reverse Global Warming*.
Penguin Book, 2017. ISBN-10: 9780143130444.

Hawken, Paul, and Bill Maher. Video. "Paul Hawken: Project drawdown/real time with Bill Maher" HBO. 30
September 2017. https://www.youtube.com/watch?v=k1wXHx2DsSU.

Hotz, Robert Lee. "There's a speeding mass of space junk orbiting earth, smashing into things." 12 September
2017. *Wall Street Journal*. https://www.wsj.com/articles/we-need-satellitesa-speeding-mass-of-space-junk-
puts-them-at-risk-1505226427.

International Energy Agency. "World Energy Outlook." Energy Database.
https://www.iea.org/reports/world-energy-outlook-2020.

Ivanova, Maria. *The Untold Story of the World's Leading Environmental Institution: UNEP at Fifty*.
Cambridge: MIT Press, 2021. ISBN: 9780262542104.

Langley, Winston E. "Declaration on the Right of Peoples to Peace," p. 93. In: *Encyclopedia of Human Rights
Issues Since 1945*. Westport, CT: Greenwood Press, 1999. ISBN: 0313301638.

Litwin, George, John J. Bray, Kathleen Lusk Brooke. *Mobilizing the Organization: Bringing Strategy to Life*.
London: Prentice Hall, 1996. ISBN: 0131488910.

Lo, Andrea. "Why is Sydney being split into three cities?" 12 April 2018. *CNN.* https://www.cnn.com/2018/04/12/asia/sydney-three-cities/index.html.

Lobe, Jim. "Haiti: Recovery Bill Estimated at 11.5 Billion Dollars." Institute for Policy Studies. https://ips-dc.org/haiti_recovery_bill_estimated_at_115_billion_dollars/.

Luhby, Tami. "The cost to fix America's crumbling infrastructure? Nearly $2.6 trillion, engineers say." 30 March 2021. CNN. https://www.cnn.com/2021/03/30/politics/infrastructure-us-investment-cost-engineers/index.html .

Meador, C. Lawrence, and Arthur C. Parthé, Jr. "Managing macro-development policy, planning and control system implications," 78-108. In: *How Big and Still Beautiful? Macro-Engineering Revisited.* Edited by Frank P. Davidson, C. Lawrence Meador, and Robert Salkeld. American Association for the Advancement of Science. Boulder, CO: Westview Press, 1980. ISBN: 0-89158-792-6.

NASA. "The Artemis Accords: Principles for cooperation in the civil exploration and use of the moon, mars, comets, and asteroids for peaceful purposes." October 2020. https://www.nasa.gov/specials/artemis-accords/img/Artemis-Accords-signed-13October2020.pdf.

NASA. "Space Debris and Human Spacecraft." https://orbitaldebris.jsc.nasa.gov/faq/.

Raymond, John (Jay) W. "As space activity—and its debris—increases, the U.S. works to establish international norms and rules." 29 November 2021. *Washington Post.* https://www.washingtonpost.com/opinions/2021/11/29/space-activity-its-debris-increases-norms-rules/.

Revkin, Andrew C. "Disaster Awaits Cities in Earthquake Zones." 24 February 2010. *New York Times.*

Rincon, Paul. "Nasa Dart asteroid spacecraft: Mission to smash into Dimorphos space rock launches," 23 November 2021. BBC.com, Science & Environment.

Ritchie, Hannah and Max Roser. "Access to Energy." 2019. *OurWorldInData.org.* https://ourworldindata.org/energy-access.

Thornton, Alex. "10 cities are predicted to gain megacity status by 2030." 6 February 2019. World Economic Forum. https://www.weforum.org/agenda/2019/02/10-cities-are-predicted-to-gain-megacity-status-by-2030/.

Timmons, David, Jonathan M. Harris, and Brian Roach. "The Economics of Renewable Energy." Global Development and Environment Institute, Tufts University, Medford, MA. 2014. https://sites.tufts.edu/gdae/.

Toynbee, Arnold, ed. *Cities of Destiny.* London: Thames & Hudson, 1967. Library of Congress Catalog Card Number: 67-21688-65125.

United Nations. "68% of the world population projected to live in urban areas by 2050, says UN" 16 May 2018. *Department of Economic and Social Affairs, United Nations.* https://www.un.org/development/desa/en/news/population/2018-revision-of-world-urbanization-prospects.html.

United Nations. Committee on the Peaceful Uses of Outer Space. "Debris Mitigation Guidelines" 27 June 2018. A/AC.105/2018/CRP.20. Text document: https://www.unoosa.org/res/oosadoc/data/documents/2018/aac_1052018crp/aac_1052018crp_20_0_html/AC105_2018_CRP20E.pdf.

United Nations. First Committee. "Delegates Approve 5 Draft Resolutions, as First Committee Takes Action on Peaceful Use, Non-Weaponization of Outer Space, Chemical Weapons." 1 November 2021. https://www.un.org/press/en/2021/gadis3676.doc.htm.

United Nations. Institute for Disarmament Research. 2021 Outer Space Security Conference. September 2021. https://www.unidir.org/events/2021-outer-space-security-conference.

United Nations. "World Water Development Report 'Water and Climate Change'." 21 march 2020. https://www.unwater.org/world-water-development-report-2020-water-and-climate-change/

Wilson, Edward O. *Sociobiology*. Cambridge, MA: Belknap Press. 1980. ISBN: 0-674-81623-4.

World Health Organization (WHO). "2.1 billion people lack safe drinking water at home, more than twice as many lack safe sanitation." 12 July 2017. https://www.who.int/news/item/12-07-2017-2-1-billion-people-lack-safe-drinking-water-at-home-more-than-twice-as-many-lack-safe-sanitation

Younger, Paul L. *All that Matters: Water*. London: Hodder & Stoughton, 2012. ISBN: 9781444155812.

WATER

"Splash!" by José Manuel Suárez, 2008.

DID YOU KNOW. . .?

➤ Every two minutes, a child dies of water-related disease.

➤ More than two billion people do not have safe drinking water.

➤ Water has been identified as the #1 at-risk element of the world's changing climate.

➤ Groundwater under the Sahara Desert is some of the oldest fresh water on Earth—200,000 to 1 million years old.

➤ Only 3% of water on Earth is drinkable, with 1% accessible and the rest in ice caps and glaciers.

➤ Water has been discovered on the moon, Mars, and many asteroids.

➤ Growing certain produce requires enormous amounts of water: asparagus, 22 gallons per ounce; cherries, 14 gallons per ounce.

➤ Every gallon of bottled drinking water requires two gallons of water to produce it.

Water is the driving force of all nature.
—Leonardo da Vinci

The cure for anything is salt water: sweat, tears, or the sea.
—Isak Dinesen

*Nothing is softer or more flexible than water,
yet nothing can resist it.*
—Lao Tzu

*All water has a perfect memory and is forever trying
to get back to where it was.*
—Toni Morrison

WHY WATER IS IMPORTANT

We can live for three weeks without food, but only three days without water. All of human history may be traced through people's need for innovations concerning the use (or misuse) of water. Solomon's Temple could not have been built without the water that floated the cedars of Lebanon to the sacred site. Cyrene was founded because ancient Greek residents of Thera (now Santorini) fled land devastated by drought and found fertile ground in Libya. What would Rome be without its fountains? The word "pontiff" refers to the special authority the pope had to build bridges (*pontifex*) over the Tiber River. Waterways, such as the Grand Canal of China and the Canal des Deux Mers of France, were forerunners of floating transport routes that changed the world as much as the Suez and Panama Canals.

Water is power. As world population increases, demand for water will continue to magnify. Problems with supplies of potable water are beginning to appear, even in developed areas, due to aging infrastructure. Flint, Michigan; Benton Harbor, Michigan; Baltimore, Maryland; and Sebring, Ohio are recent examples of U.S. cities where old pipelines have leached lead into local water supplies.

Water is not just for drinking. It is also the fundamental resource used for human sanitation. If this basic need goes unmet, public health suffers severely. The United Nations set a goal to eliminate by 2025 the scourge of insufficient water for sanitation.

Aerial view of the Innoko River in summer.
By Keller Jo, U.S. Fish and Wildlife Service, 2013.

Attribution: see p. 160

Water is a key element of the world economy. Approximately half of all world jobs depend on water, which sustains agriculture, farming, and food supply. Water is vital to industry: it takes between 13,000 and 21,000 gallons of water (49,210 to 79,493 liters) to manufacture a car; 2.5 gallons (9.46 liters) of water to refine 1 gallon (3.79 liters) of gasoline; 62,000 to 75,000 gallons (234,695 to 283,905 liters) to produce a ton of steel.

Water is energy. Hydroelectric achievements, such as those by Nikola Tesla at Niagara Falls, created new forms of energy. Gazing at the falls, Tesla proclaimed: "Someday I'll harness that power." Hydroelectric energy forever changed the culture and character of the country when Tesla and George Westinghouse won the contract for the Niagara Falls Power Project. On 16 November 1896, 1,000 horsepower surged from the waterfall to be successfully transmitted to Buffalo, New York. Within ten years, New York City was powered by electricity. In 1984, the dam at Itaipú was built by Brazil and Paraguay to harness the Sete Quedas waterfalls on the Paraná River and generate electricity.

"Niagara Falls, from the American Side,"
by Frederic Edwin Church, 1867.

Attribution: see page 160

Water is transport. One of the first great transit routes, the Grand Canal of China, continues to unite that nation and to serve the needs of north and south. New canals are being considered in many areas of the world; shipping lanes and ocean transport are under development, and investigation.

Water has implications for space. Hydrogen is a rocket fuel. Imagine how expensive and limited such fuel would become if it were necessary to transport liquid energy into space for use in rocketry. It would be a limit akin to carrying with you all the water you need to hike the Grand Canyon—you could not go far. On the other hand, what if rocket fuel ingredients were already aloft? Hydrogen found on planets and asteroids could provide fuel for staying and progressing in space. Mars has water: Planetary Resources found it on asteroids, NASA found it on the moon. In addition to fuel, water would of course support habitation.

The phrase "water planet" reminds us that every system we have on Earth is powered in some way by water. As David H. Marks, inaugural director of MIT's Laboratory for Energy and the Environment, and the research team including Kelly Gallagher, Paul Kirshen, William Moomaw, Edward Spang, observed: "As an energy sector changes or expands, the mix of technologies deployed to produce fuels and electricity determines the associated burden on regional water sources" (Spang, 2014).

Not only is world water in a crisis of scarcity, it is also enduring an assault on sustainability and safety. Oceans are becoming increasingly acidic and filled with debris and plastic; rivers are parched by drought and overuse; lakes are shrinking; underground aquifers are tapped for non-potable uses, including hydraulic fracturing. Floods and droughts occur more frequently, exacerbated by climate and environmental imbalance. All these scenarios provide plenty of reasons for concern. But there is also hope.

Sources:
Environmental Protection Agency. "All the Water in the World." 2015.
https://www.epa.gov/sites/production/files/2015-08/documents/mgwc-ww-intro.pdf/

Reed, Christopher. "How The Steel Industry Uses Billions Of Gallons Of Pennsylvania Water." 30 September 2016. Fresh Air/ WESA fm. https://www.wesa.fm/economy-business/2016-09-30/how-the-steel-industry-uses-billions-of-gallons-of-pennsylvania-water

Ritchie, Hannah and Max Roser. "Water Use and Stress: Share of freshwater withdrawals used in agriculture." July 2018. *Our World in Data.* https://ourworldindata.org/water-use-stress

Scutti, Susan, "Study: Public water supply is unsafe for millions of Americans." *CNN*. Available from: http://www.cnn.com/2016/08/09/health/contaminated-water/index.html

Spang, Edward, William Moomaw, Kelly Gallagher, Paul Kirshen, David H. Marks. "The water consumption of energy production: An international comparison." 2014. Environmental Research Letters. 9. 105002. 10.1088/1748-9326/9/10/105002.
https://www.researchgate.net/publication/266620784_The_water_consumption_of_energy_production_An_international_comparison

UNICEF and World Health Organization. "Progress on Sanitation and Drinking Water – 2015 update and MDG assessment." ISBN: 9789241509145; https://apps.who.int/iris/handle/10665/177752

Water.org. "Effects of the Water Crisis on Health. 2020. https://water.org/our-impact/water-crisis/health-crisis/

WHO/UNICEF Joint Monitoring Program for Water Supply, Sanitation and Hygiene. "1 in 3 people globally do not have access to safe drinking water: New report on inequities in access to water, sanitation, and hygiene also reveals more than half of the world does not have access to safe sanitation services." *World Health Organization.* https://www.who.int/news/item/18-06-2019-1-in-3-people-globally-do-not-have-access-to-safe-drinking-water-unicef-who.

VOICE OF THE FUTURE
—Matt Damon

"It struck me that water undergirded all the issues of extreme poverty."

Sources:
Dizikes, Peter. "Q&A: Matt Damon on making a difference in the world." *MIT News*, 3 June 2016. http://news.mit.edu/2016/qa-matt-damon-making-difference-world-0603.

Forbes. https://www.forbes.com/sites/jeffconway/2021/10/25/matt-damon-announces-waterorg-partnership-with-cryptocom/

VIDEO: Damon, Matt. "Every 90 seconds," *National Geographic.* YouTube. 25 July 2017. https://www.youtube.com/watch?v=fn016bAJ4Z4/.

PROBLEMS

In an era of expanding population compounded by increasing climate change, difficulties related to water security are many and require solutions. Throughout history, many of the world's greatest achievements were attempted—and accomplished—in response to danger, disaster, or failure. In the next decades, innovations to resolve water problems may rebuild the world.

Lack of Water for Drinking

A child dies every two minutes from a water-related disease. Infants, with developing but not yet mature immune systems, are particularly vulnerable. Worldwide, more than two billion people drink water contaminated by fecal matter. Diseases like cholera and typhoid spread in contaminated drinking water, causing an estimated 500,000 people to die each year due to dysentery.

Two billion people on our planet suffer serious water deprivation. More than 600 million lack a basic water system. People draw water from wells nearby and distant, often walking for hours each way carrying jugs. Even worse, some families rely on surface water that is subject to varying deleterious influences; the number who take their water from ditches and ponds is estimated to be 159 million.

"A Water Carrier," photo illustration from *Madeira, Old and New* by William Henry Koebel, 1909.

Attribution: see p. 160

Women and children are often water-gatherers. In seven out of ten households across 45 countries, women and girls fetch water. Time spent carrying water means no income-producing job for mother and no school for children. If families were freed from the burden of carrying water, the economic and educational improvements would be world-changing.

When water comes directly into a household, one of the most significant improvements may be economic. Dina Q. of Peru buys water from a delivery truck, then walks up a mountain path to bring the heavy jugs to her family. Not only does she lose money by not working due to the constant requirement to obtain household water, but she also loses money because the delivered water costs ten times more than water she could obtain if there were a nearby community system. In addition, jugs and plastic containers carrying water are heavy, some weighing 40 to 70 pounds, and the result is skeletal and medical problems among those straining to carry the jugs. When some of these water problems are solved, it may be possible to save 200 million hours—daily.

WINDOW ON THE ECONOMY

Clean Water and Sanitation

- For a family of six, collecting enough water for drinking, cooking, and basic hygiene means hauling water for an average of three hours per day.

- Over $30 billion in economic benefits each year could be realized from reducing health care costs if there were universal access to basic water and sanitation.

Sources:
Water.org. "An Economic Crisis." https://water.org/our-impact/water-crisis/economic-crisis/

VIDEO: "2030—SDG 6—Clean Water and Sanitation." TEDxKish. https://www.youtube.com/watch?v=U5TxygvcmU8

It is not just families and households that lack water systems. In some areas of the world, 35% of local health care clinics and facilities lack water and soap to wash their hands. Schools also suffer a dearth of drinking water; more than one-third lack potable water and sanitation facilities.

What can be done? The United Nations called for "universal and equitable access to safe and affordable drinking water" as Sustainable Development Goal #6. According to the UN, even making water available nearby, within 30 minutes round-trip, would change the world. Time is running short; by 2025, half of the world will live in a water-stressed area.

"Sustainable Development Goals" by UN, 2019.

Attribution: see p. 160

Water and Climate Change

"Water use has increased six-fold over the past century and is rising by about 1% a year. However, it is estimated that climate change, along with the increasing frequency and intensity of extreme events—storms, floods, droughts—will aggravate the situation in countries already currently experiencing 'water stress' and generate similar problems in areas that have not been severely affected" (UN, 21 March 2020). The World Meteorological Organization warned that 60% of national weather and hydrological services lack full capacity to provide needed climate services for water sustainability. Here are some reasons why climate change will necessitate rebuilding our water systems:

- Drinking water will become even more scarce. Globally, four in ten people suffer water scarcity; by 2025, 1.8 billion people will live in absolute water scarcity and two-thirds of the world may be in water-stress conditions.
- Droughts will increase, affecting agriculture, livestock, people, and wildlife. Land suitable for agriculture will lessen; 74.1 million acres (30 million hectares) are affected now, and by 2080 that figure could double.
- Migrants will be forced to leave their homelands. By 2030, if current climate change conditions continue, water problems in arid and semi-arid areas will force people to depart. Numbers of migrants are estimated at 24 million on the low end to 700 million in worst-case scenarios.
- Climate change resulting in CO_2 absorbed by oceans causes acidification, compromising the health of oceans and marine life.

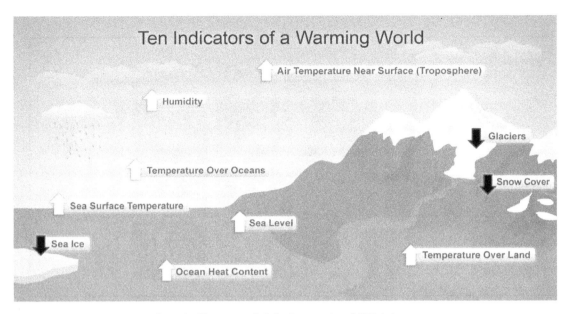

"Ten indicators of global warming." NOAA, 2010.

Attribution: see p. 161

- Warming oceans lead to sea rise, which destroys island nations, coastal environments and cities, and increases the frequency and intensity of storms and hurricanes. In the United States, 25 million people live in areas vulnerable to coastal flooding. Coastal economic activities generate 58% of the U.S. gross national product.
- As Arctic and Antarctic icecaps melt, tremendous amounts of water are being added to the world's oceans with predictable (and some unpredicted) impact (*Science*, 2020). Sea levels could rise between 7 and 23 inches (18 and 59 centimeters) by the end of the 21st century.
- Precipitation (both rain and snow) increased globally. Since 1901, global precipitation has increased 0.10 inches (0.25 centimeters). Floods killed 920 people in 20 countries just during the month of July 2021.
- Drought-related wildfires like California's Dixie Fire burned an area twice the size of New York City, while Siberia lost 3.7 million acres (1.5 million hectares) in 2021.
- Species that depend on one another may become out of sync. For example, plants might bloom earlier, before their pollinating insects become active.
- Floods may occur more frequently. In general, each degree rise can produce a 5-10% change in precipitation, a 3-10% increase in the amount of rainfall during the heaviest precipitation, and a 5-10% change in stream flow across many river basins.
- In Ethiopia, where drought is already a problem, rainfall could decline by 10% over the next 50 years.

> ### *WINDOW ON THE ECONOMY*
>
> "Since 1970, 44% of disasters and 31% of economic losses have been linked to floods."
>
> — World Meteorological Organization, 2021.
>
> Sources:
> World Meteorological Organization (WMO). https://public.wmo.int/en
>
> VIDEO: "State of Climate Services Report 2021: Water."
> https://youtube.com/watch?v=QlwukZtT3pU&feature=share
> Also available in Spanish

- Allocation of water will become more contentious as agriculture, cities, energy, and industry fight for their desired portion. The Colorado River Compact remains an example of water geopolitics. Future national and regional decisions about who gets water will continue, through negotiation or conflict. Organizations like Deltares and Water, Peace and Security may offer predictive methodologies to anticipate needs and avert conflict.
- Innovations will increase as water availability decreases. Agriculture will seek more ways to use less water. Cities may recycle water once thought impotable—and impossible. Filtering for impurities of minerals, bacteria, and microplastics will lead innovation. Desalination may become one of the most promising technologies, with Israel and others leading the way.

Sources:
Adusumilli, Susheel, et al. "Interannual variations in meltwater input to the Southern Ocean from Antarctic ice shelves." 10 August 2020. *Nature Geoscience* 13, 616-620 (2020). https://www.nature.com/articles/s41561-020-0616-z?proof=t%3B

Amos, Jonathan. "Climate change: Satellites record history of Antarctic melting." 10 August 2020. *BBC.com*. https://www.bbc.com/news/science-environment-53725288

"Antarctic ice sheet collapse could add 3 meters to sea-level rise." 23 July 2020. *Science.* www.antarcticglaciers.org/antarctica-2/east-antarctic-ice-sheet/

Davies, Bethan. "East Antarctic Ice Sheet." 22 June 2020. Antarctic Glaciers.org. http://www.antarcticglaciers.org/antarctica-2/east-antarctic-ice-sheet/

Deltares. Institute for Applied Research in the Field of Water and Subsurface: Flood Risk, Adoptive Delta Planning, Infrastructure, Water and Subsurface Resources, Environmental. https://www.deltares.nl/en/topdossiers/clean-water-is-vital/

Givetash, Linda. "Early-Warning Tools Aim to Prevent 'Water Wars', Curb Droughts." 25 December 2018. NBC News/World. https://www.nbcnews.com/news/world/early-warning-tools-aim-prevent-water-wars-curb-droughts-n917001

Hartley, Charlotte. "Antarctic ice sheet collapse could add 3 meters to sea-level rise." 23 July 2020. *Science.* https://www.sciencemag.org/news/2020/07/antarctic-ice-sheet-collapse-could-add-3-metres-sea-level-rise

IHE Delft. "Water, Peace, and Security Partnership. "Identifying and Addressing Developing Water-Related Security Risks, Linking Short-Term Water Shortage to Social, Political, Economic, and Hydrological Factors." n.d. https://www.un-ihe.org/water-peace-and-security-partnership

Jacobsen, Rowan. "Israel Proves the Desalination Era is Here: One of the Driest Countries on Earth Now Makes More Fresh Water Than it Needs." *Scientific American,* 9 July 2016. https://www.scientificamerican.com/article/israel-proves-the-desalination-era-is-here/

Kounang, Nadia. "El Paso to Drink Treated Sewage Water Due to Climate Change Drought." CNN, 5 December 2018. https://www.cnn.com/2018/11/30/health/water-climate-change-el-paso/index.html

United Nations. Food and Agriculture Organization (FAO). "Pacific leaders alarmed over climate change's negative impact of food systems and food security: call to action at COP23." http://www.fao.org/family-farming/detail/en/c/1068343/

United Nations. "The State of Climate Services 2021: Water." https://www.unwater.org/state-of-climate-services-water

United Nations. "Water and Climate Change." https://www.unwater.org/water-facts/climate-change/

United Nations. "World Water Development Report : Water and Climate Change." 21 March 2020. https://www.unwater.org/world-water-development-report-2020-water-and-climate-change/

UNESCO. "World Water Day 2014: Water and Energy." http://www.unesco.org/new/en/natural-sciences/environment/water/wwap/wwdr/2014-water-and-energy/

UNICEF. "Collecting water is often a colossal waste of time for women and girls." 29 August 2017. https://www.unicef.org/media/media_92690.html.

World Health Organization (WHO). "Drinking-water," 14 June 2019. https://www.who.int/news/item/ 01-07-2021-billions-of-people-will-lack-access-to-safe-water-sanitation-and-hygiene-in-2030-unless-progress-quadruples-warn-who-unicef

World Meteorological Organization (WMO). "2021 State of Climate Services —WMO No. 1278." https://library.wmo.int/index.php

Icebergs and Endangered Islands

What happens to ice once it breaks away from a polar shelf? In 2017, a massive section of the Larsen C Ice Shelf in Antarctica broke away and started drifting. By 2020 that iceberg, known as A-68A, had reached the southern Atlantic Ocean, threatening South Georgia and the South Sandwich Islands, located about 800 miles (1,300 km) southeast of the Falkland Islands. It is suspected that the breakup of the huge ice sheet occurred because of climate change. The islands are home to numerous colonies of penguins and seals. The area is a marvel of biodiversity: the number and variety of South Georgia's marine inhabitants may surpass even those of the Galápagos Islands. The areas received protection in 2012 with the creation of the South Georgia and South Sandwich Islands Marine Protected Area.

"Operation IceBridge View of Larsen C."
by NASA Goddard Space Flight Center, 2017.

Attribution: see p. 161

The size of A-68A, 93 miles (150 kms) long by 30 miles (48 km) wide, meant it would not melt quickly. Would it hit South Georgia and lodge there, endangering wildlife? Scientists held their collective breath. In 2021, European Space Agency (ESA) satellite images revealed the iceberg had broken into pieces, the largest measuring 37 miles (60 km) long and 14 miles (22 km) wide. South Georgia Island averted catastrophic danger that time, but A-68A is a warning that melting ice will continue to be problematic. Satellite data will help anticipate impending disasters—another instance of the importance of space in responding to climate change on Earth.

Of equal concern is the so-called "Doomsday Glacier," also known as Thwaites. The size of the United Kingdom, it releases 80 billion tons of water per year as it melts (in 1990, it was just 10 billion tons). If Thwaites melts, it will increase sea level worldwide by 1.64 feet (0.5 meters). But it gets worse: Thwaites sits on the West Antarctic Ice Sheet, so if Thwaites melts, the West Antarctic will be affected (Amos, 2020; Hogan, 2020; Jordan, et al., 2020).

If the Quelccaya ice cap in Peru continues to melt at its current rate, it will be gone by 2100, leaving thousands of people without a source for drinking water or for generating electricity.

If all the ice in Antarctica melted, seas would rise by 190.29 feet (58 meters). The Antarctic is described by scientists in three areas of ice: Antarctic Peninsula Ice Sheet, West Antarctic Ice Sheet, and East Antarctic Ice Sheet, the world's largest. If the East Antarctic Ice Sheet melts, seas will rise by 9 feet (2.7 meters) (*Science*, 2020).

Sources:

Amos, Jonathan. "A68 iceberg on collision path with South Georgia." 4 November 2020. BBC.com.

Amos, Jonathan. "A68: Iceberg that became a social media star melts away." 18 April 2021. BBC.com.

Amos, Jonathan. "Thwaites: 'Doomsday Glacier' vulnerability seen in new maps. " 9 September 2020. *BBC.com.*

"Antarctic ice sheet collapse could add 3 meters to sea-level rise." 23 July 2020. *Science.* www.antarcticglaciers.org/antarctica-2/east-antarctic-ice-sheet/

European Space Agency (ESA). "South Georgia Island." 21 December 2018. https://www.esa.int/ESA_Multimedia/Images/2018/12/South_Georgia_Island

Government of South Georgia and the South Sandwich Islands. "South Georgia and the South Sandwich Islands: Marine Protected Area Management Plan." 31 August 2013. https://www.gov.gs/docsarchive/Environment/Marine%20%Protected%Area/MPA%20Management%20Plan%20v2.0.pdf.

Hogan, Kelly A., et al. "Revealing the former bed of Thwaites Glacier using sea-floor bathymetry: Implications for warm-water routing and bed controls on ice flow and buttressing." 9 September 2020. *Cryosphere,* 14 (9). https://doi.org/10.5194/tc-14-2883-2020

Imster, Eleanor. "Is this the end of the A-68A iceberg?" 10 February 2021. *EarthSky.* https://earthsky.org/earth/end-of-the-a68a-iceberg-feb2021

Jordan, Tom A., et al. "New gravity-derived bathymetry for the Thwaites, Crosson, and Dotson ice shelves revealing two ice shelf populations." *Cryosphere*, vol. 14, no. 9 (9 September 2020). https://ui.adsabs.harvard.edu/abs/2020TCry...14.2869J/abstract

Readfearn, Graham. "Giant Antarctic iceberg on collision course with British territory of South Georgia: Fears the 150km long A-68A iceberg, which broke away from Larsen C ice shelf in 2017, could disrupt wildlife and shipping routes." 4 November 2020. *Guardian.* https://www.theguardian.com/environment/2020/nov/04/giant-antarctic-iceberg-on-collision-course-with-british-territory-of-south-georgia

Schwarz, Jill and M.P. Schodlok. "Impact of drifting icebergs on surface phytoplankton biomass in the Southern Ocean color remote sensing and *in situ* iceberg tracking." October 2009. *Deep Sea Research* Part 1, Oceanographic Research Papers 56 (10): 1727-1741. doi: 10.1016/j.dsr.2009.05.003.

More People Have Cellphones Than Toilets

World Water Day 2013 revealed a troubling statistic: more people have a cellphone than a toilet—perhaps because phones and their related technologies may be easier to acquire. In places where technology infrastructure is growing rapidly, the discrepancy is even sharper. In one country, half the population has mobile phone subscriptions while only one-third have a toilet. Less than half the people on Earth have access to their own toilet linked to a plumbing system that treats fecal matter. Some people can walk to a shared sanitation facility, but two billion people do not even have access to a toilet or latrine. About 892 million must defecate either in the street or directly into rivers and lakes. It is estimated that 10% of the world's people eat food that is grown using unfiltered wastewater for irrigation.

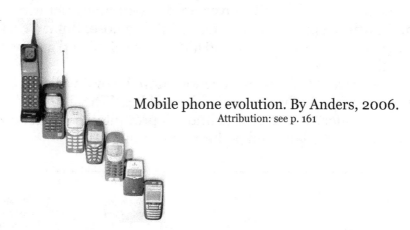

Mobile phone evolution. By Anders, 2006.
Attribution: see p. 161

Poor or no sanitation results in disease. Areas with no sanitation and open defecation suffer the largest number of infant and child deaths. Sanitation problems are estimated to be a critical factor in 58% of deaths from diarrhea. Scourges such as intestinal worms and other digestive diseases are also present.

What can be done? Since 1990, encouraging progress has occurred in the percentage of people who have access to sanitation—an increase from 54% to 68%. In 2010, the United Nations declared access to safe and clean drinking water and sanitation a human right. According to the World Health Organization, for every US$1.00 spent on sanitation improvements, the resulting benefit is worth US$5.00.

Sources:
Silver, Laura. "Smartphone ownership is growing rapidly around the world, but not always equally." 5 Feb. 2019. Pew Research Center. https://www.pewresearch.org/global/2019/02/05/smartphone-ownership-is-growing-rapidly-around-the-world-but-not-always-equally/

Telegraph. "India has more mobile phones than toilets: UN report." 15 April 2010. https://www.telegraph.co.uk/news/worldnews/asia/india/7593567/India-has-more-mobile-phones-than-toilets-UN-report.html

United Nations. World Toilet Day. https://www.un.org/en/observances/toilet-day

Wang, Yue. "More people have cell phones than toilets, U.N. study shows: Out of the world's estimated 7 billion people, 6 billion have access to mobile phones, but only 4.5 billion have access to working toilets," 25 March 2013. Time Magazine. https://newsfeed.time.com/2013/03/25/more-people-have-cell-phones-than-toilets-u-n-study-shows/

Wells and Aquifers: Fracking the Future

The well is an ancient symbol, a sacred source of clean water, a village gathering place. Wells often determine where to locate and build a settlement. But consider this: from 2003 to 2013, 21 of the world's 37 major aquifers lost volume. Thus, how underground water resources are protected and sustained is critically important. Every well drilled changes the future.

Shale oil and gas deposits—fossil fuel energy locked underground—were previously known but inaccessible. Recent innovations in specialized drilling have released some of these energy deposits. However, drilling has some associated problems, one of which involves water. Hydraulic fracturing (also called fracking) entails drilling powered by water: think fire hose. But if a cocktail of chemicals were added to dissolve rock and aid release of oil and gas, would you want that in your drinking water?

The process of fracking depends on wells—not wells for drinking, but nearby wells as a source of water to enable fracking. What if there were a water leak into a nearby aquifer? It's possible, although preventable. What about chemically tainted water going into land and perhaps poisoning soil?

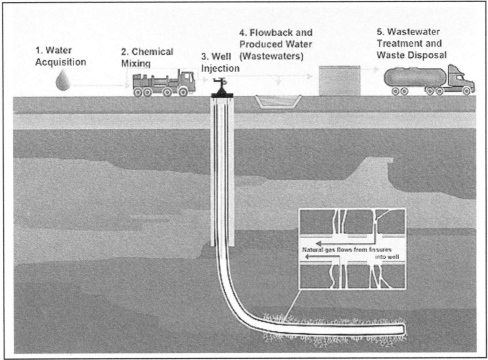

"Hydraulic Fracturing-Related Activity," by U.S. EPA, 2012.

Attribution: see p. 161

Global warming is linked to emissions released by burning fossil fuels. While carbon dioxide (CO_2) emissions last longer, methane (CH_4) is stronger, with 80 times more warming power in the first 20 years in the atmosphere. Methane emissions come from several sources, but the largest percentage is from fossil fuels, especially natural gas.

Recent spikes in methane levels can be traced to fracking. In November 2021, national leaders gathered in Glasgow for COP26 to sign a Global Methane Pledge to reduce methane emissions by 30% by 2030. The Pledge, initiated by the EU and U.S., will change hydraulic fracturing worldwide. That should result in a reduction of 41 million tons of methane emissions by 2023 to 2035—more than all the carbon dioxide from American cars and commercial aircraft in the entirety of 2019. In addition to countries signing the pledge, philanthropies contributed $328 million in funding, and the European Bank for Reconstruction and

Development, the European Investment Bank, and the Green Climate Fund joined as partners.

Methane is most likely to leak from abandoned wells. There are 3.2 million abandoned oil and gas wells in the U.S., which emitted more than 281 kilotons of methane in 2018: more than two million were never completely plugged. Globally, there may be 29 million abandoned wells, with emissions of 2.5 million tons of methane each year. While the Global Methane Pledge includes 100 countries that emit half of the world's methane, the major contributors of methane—China, India, and Russia—are not signatories.

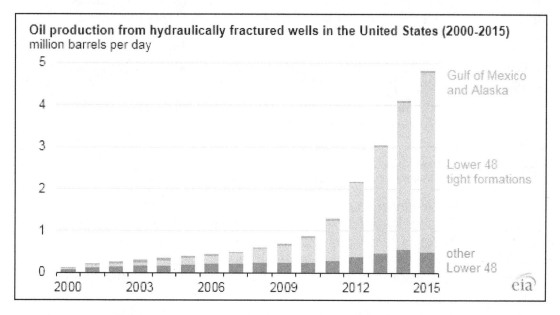

Oil production from hydraulically fractured wells in the U.S. (2000-2015).
Attribution: see p. 161

The past chair of the Railroad Commission of Texas, the agency in charge of fracking regulations in that state, once claimed Texans would know more about what is going into the ground for fracturing than what goes into a can of soda. But rules for disclosing formulations used vary by state. Texas allows companies to maintain chemical trade secrets; fewer trade secrets are allowed in North Dakota, location of one of the biggest shale energy resources in the United States, the Bakken deposit. In North Dakota, chemicals used in hydraulic fracturing are reported to FracFocus, a trade association. That group may, however, be funded by the industry it regulates; bylaws that allow participating energy companies to decide what constitutes a trade secret are so proprietary that it may be kept unreported.

There is big money in fracking, and jobs, too. North Dakota's Bakken fields added 40,000 jobs between 2008 and 2012. Along with the gold rush mentality, real estate prices skyrocketed and motels sprang up to house people already working while looking for a permanent place. Gas stations, restaurants, and especially hospitals expanded their capacities. McKenzie County Hospital in

Watford City, North Dakota, enlarged its facilities to treat wounded and injured workers. Traumatic injuries increased 200% from 2007 to 2012; ambulance calls doubled; emergency room visits shot up from 100 to 400 per month.

WINDOW ON THE ECONOMY

Hydraulic fracturing in the US

Fracking wells since 2005	137,000
Water used since 2005	239 billion gallons
Toxic wastewater produced in 2014, selected states	14 billion gallons
Land directly damaged since 2005	679,000 acres

Sources:

Elizabeth Ridlington and Kim Norman, Frontier Group and Rachel Richardson, Environment America Research & Policy Center. "Fracking by the Numbers," Table ES-1.

Environment America Research & Policy Center, 14 April 2016. "Fracking by the Numbers." htt;s://environmentamerica.org/reports/ame/fracking-numbers-0.

VIDEO: Mia Nacamulli. "How does fracking work?" 13 July 2017. https://ed.ted/com/lessons/how-does-fracking-work-mia-nacamulli.

Another danger, besides water and health, may be environment and air quality threats due to methane released during fracking. Methane can also seep into groundwater. Methane has a shorter half-life than carbon dioxide. CO_2 emitted during the building of ancient Sumer is still with us in the atmosphere; methane released by fracking Barnett shale in 1997 is almost gone. Still, methane is of concern.

There will be more on hydraulic fracturing in the Energy volume. Here, the impact of fracking on drinking water shows that contamination occurs, caused by blowouts, spills, and disposal of toxic fluids. Texas placed used chemicals in old abandoned oil wells, but not every site has such receptacles. Pennsylvania utilized sewage plants, but the facilities were not equipped to properly treat used chemicals. As a result, the Ohio River now has barium, strontium, and bromides that form brominated hydrocarbons in the drinking water of some cities and towns it passes through.

It has been proposed by Michael B. McElroy and Xi Lu of Harvard University that fracking could be used to transition toward a new standard of renewable energy. However, regions and nations continue to outlaw fracking: France so ruled in 2011; Bulgaria, Germany, and Scotland followed suit. Stopping just short of a ban, some countries have placed a moratorium on hydraulic fracturing: Czech Republic, Denmark, Ireland, Romania, South Africa, and the United Kingdom. Uruguay banned fracking for four years in 2017 with Law 19585, at the same time forming a commission to evaluate global fracking. Argentina's Province of Entre Rios banned fracking with Law 10477 in 2017, protecting rain, surface, underground water, but still continues fracking in other regions. In the United States, both New York State and Vermont have forbidden fracking; New York's decision was influenced in part by Artists Against Fracking, founded by Yoko Ono. "Because of our wealth of natural resources," declared the then-governor of the State of Maryland, "our administration has concluded that possible environmental risks of fracking outweigh any potential benefits." In 2017, Maryland joined New York and Vermont in outlawing fracking. This was not welcome news for those wishing to exploit Marcellus Shale, a deposit lying under Pennsylvania, West Virginia, and western Maryland. The deposit is over a million years old and packed with organic matter evolving to fossil fuels.

Fracking shows how a new technology can change a market when resources become newly accessible:

- In 2000, energy obtained by hydraulic fracturing comprised just 2% of U.S. oil production; by 2016, it was 50%, and 56% by 2019.
- In 2000, yield was 102,000 barrels per day; in 2016, 4.3 million.
- In 2000, there were just 23,000 fracking wells; in 2016, 300,000 wells; in 2021, 1.7 million wells.

Sources:

Elgin, Ben, Benjamin Hass, Phil Kuntz. "Fracking secrets by thousands keep US clueless on wells." 1 December 2012, Bloomberg.net. https://www.bloomberg.com/news/articles/2012-11-30/frack-secrets-by-thousands-keep-u-s-clueless-on-wells

FracFocus. https://fracfocus.org

Freedman, Andrew. "Methane limits could be COP26's real legacy." 2 November 2021. Axios.com. https://www.axios.com/methane-limits-cop26-legacy-57b0cad6-0beb-4dad-aee6-da8119d01fb0.html

Groom, Nichola. "Special Report: Millions of abandoned oil wells are leaking methane, a climate menace." 16 June 2020. https://www.reuters.com/article/us-usa-drilling-abandoned-specialreport-idUSKBN23N1NL

Herrara, Hector. "The legal status of fracking worldwide: An environmental law and human rights perspective." January 20219. https://www.researchgate.net/publication/341625371. The_legal_status_of_fracking_worldwide_An_ environmental_law_and_human_rights_perspective

Howarth, Robert W., Anthony Ingraffea, Terry Engelder. "Should fracking stop? Yes, it's too high risk." 15 September 2011. Nature, 477, 271-275. https://www.nature.com/articles/477271a

Kang, Mary. "Reducing methane emissions from abandoned oil and gas wells." 20 October 2020. Preventing or Abating Anthropogenic Methane Emissions Workshop, ARPA-E Remedy 2020. https://arpa-e.energy.gov/sites/default/files/Session%201.3%20-%20Kang_0.pdf

Levi, Michael. The Power Surge. Oxford: Oxford University Press, 2013. ISBN: 9780199986163.

Nacamulli, Mia. Video. "How does fracking work?" 13 July 2017. https://ed.ted.com/lessons/how-does-fracking-work-mia-nacamulli

Townsend, Dina. "The legal status of fracking worldwide: An environmental law and human rights perspective." Global Network for Human Rights and the Environment. 6 January 2020. https://gnhre.org/2020/01/06/the-legal-status-of-fracking-worldwide-an-environmental-law-and-human-rights-perspective/

United Nations Economic Commission for Europe. "Sustainable energy: The challenge—Methane management." http://unece.org/challenge

United Nations Environment Programme. Climate & Clean Air Coalition. "Global Methane Assessment: Benefits and Costs of Mitigating Methane Emissions." 2021. https://www.ccacoalition.org/en/resources/global-methane-assessment-full-report

Vuleta, Branka. "25+ astonishing fracking statistics everyone should know (2021 update)." 29 January 2021. Seed Scientific. https://seedscientific.com/fracking-statistics

Shrinking Lakes

Stacy Ginsberg just wanted to do her laundry. A casino dealer, Ginsberg had recently moved to Las Vegas, landed a job, and a bought a home in the Summerlin neighborhood. Ginsberg hoped there would be enough water to wash at least a few work outfits as she readied for another week at the casino. Water service in Summerlin depended on pipes stretching 50 miles and scaling heights over 2,000 vertical feet. Sometimes there was plenty of water, other times not. Ginsberg turned on the washing machine and was pleased to hear the sound of water.

In the casino where Stacy dealt blackjack later that night, Jody Jones won at the table, to a chorus of cheering friends. Jones had traveled to Las Vegas with her two sisters and a few close friends to celebrate her 40th birthday. As the group frequented casinos, hotels, shows, and restaurants, they gave little thought to water. Indeed, after a night of festivities, Jones enjoyed a bubble bath in her hotel suite.

The water used by Ginsberg and Jones came from Lake Mead in Arizona. This water reservoir was created during development of the Hoover Dam, harnessing and directing the Colorado River. Residents use 40% of Lake Mead's water, while 60% goes into lawns and landscaping. Household wastewater is recycled: some irrigates golf courses and powers water attractions that draw tourists; most returns to the Colorado River and, via the Las Vegas Wash, finds its way back into Lake Mead.

Lake Mead faces two problems: (1) It is shrinking as a result of climate change, and (2) its water delivery is deteriorating due to aging infrastructure that continues to degrade. Newer parts of the water system benefit from funding by developers, but depend on district authorities for maintenance.

In 2021, Lake Mead, water reservoir for the Colorado River, registered the lowest level on record since its inception. Even without climate change, depletion has become a problem: population growth in the area places demands that exceed replenishment flows even in normal climate conditions. But with climate change and accompanying drought, Lake Mead reached a new low of 143 feet (43.6 meters)—about the height of the Statue of Liberty (Ramirez, et al., 2021). Low water levels leave a "bathtub ring" of minerals, forming a visible warning. If water levels drop another 20 feet (6.1 meters) in 2022 as predicted, supply levels for agriculture, drinking water, and other needs will face severe cuts.

But there is another ominous danger: loss of hydroelectric power. Lake Mead was created as the reservoir for the Hoover Dam on the Colorado River, reduced electricity to eight million people. In 2021, lower water levels dropped the dam's hydroelectric capacity by 25%. If Lake Mead loses another 175 feet (53 meters), it will reach the grim milestone at which there will not be enough water to flow through the Hoover Dam.

Lake Mead.
Photograph by Michael Rosen, USGS, 2016.

Note: At the edges of Lake Mead, the nation's largest reservoir, a 'bathtub ring' of mineral deposits approximately 100 ft. high shows the drop in water level after years of drought along the Colorado River.
Attribution: see p. 161

Lake Powell, the second largest water reservoir by capacity in the U.S., also dropped to its lowest water levels since 1969. In September 2021, Lake Powell was at 30% of capacity, and its Glen Canyon Dam was 153 feet (46.63 meters) below full level.

Declining water levels in Lake Mead and Lake Powell are indicators of the decrease in the Lower Colorado River storage system which dropped to 39% capacity in 2021, prompting the Bureau of Reclamation to cut water allocations, with further cuts anticipated in 2022.

These are the first official declarations of shortage since the Colorado River Compact was formed in 1922, and are the initial enactments of a drought emergency plan established in 2007 under the Colorado River Interim Guidelines for Lower Basin Shortages and Coordinated Operations of Lake Powell and Lake Mead, the 2019 Lower Basin Drought Contingency Plan, and Minute 323 to the 1944 Water Treaty with Mexico. The Level 1 Shortage declaration affects partners in the Compact including basin states, original Native American nations like the Navajo, and Mexico.

If Lake Mead continues to shrink, it will have a much greater impact than just on the local laundry. Canals deliver water from the Colorado River to Arizona cities of Phoenix and Tucson. Realizing this, Arizona, California, and Nevada negotiated a drought plan and a policy of reduced use. Beyond that, talks between Mexico and the United States over water from the Colorado River, as well as its international boundary, must be further considered. The Colorado River Compact and subsequent legislation has already determined the share for Mexico.

In 1944, an agreement allowed Mexico to store its designated share in Lake Mead: "Under the 2022 Level 1 Shortage Condition, Mexico will lose 5% of its annual water allotment, while Nevada will lose 7% and Arizona 18% of water allocation." Mexico's partnership is also affected by an agreement named Minute 319 which permits international water banking and dedicates in-stream flows for environmental use (Stanger, 2013).

Minute 319 was amended to Minute 323 in 2017, and continued the shared plan that also affects a nature habitat on the Colorado River Delta. In 2021, the U.S. and Mexico cooperated to allow a release of water through the gates of the Morelos Dam on the Arizona/Mexico border to supply 35,000 acre-feet of water to nurture the Delta environment for plants and wildlife (Water Education Foundation, 2021).

Lake Mead is just one example of numerous lakes shrinking due to climate change, diversions of water by industry and agriculture, drought, irrigation, and residential use. In other global locations, lakes are also shrinking:

- China's Poyang Lake, an enormous freshwater lake that once covered 1,737 sq. mi. (4,500 sq. km.) but has measured as low as 77 sq. mi. (200 sq. km.).
- Iran's Lake Urmia, once the world's second-largest saltwater lake covering more than 2,000 sq. mi. (5170 sq. km.) during the 1990s when it was at its deepest. Since then, agriculture, irrigation, dams, declining rainfall, climate change, and a bridge spanning the lake, have wrought significant changes to the region bordering the lake's basin. Efforts to renew Lake Urmia include releasing water from the dams, desilting feeder rivers, and water-conserving agricultural practices.
- Lake Chapala in Mexico, now on the UN's list of ecological places critically endangered.
- Lake Poopó, Bolivia's second-largest lake, declined dramatically from 1986 to 2016. Glacial melting due to climate warming appears to be the reason, and it is expected to continue. According to the 2015 Fulbright Water Act, mountain glaciers supplying Lake Poopó diminished considerably, resulting in a further decline of the lake's water level. Other factors are drought caused by periodic *El Niño* fluctuations, and diversion of the lake's tributaries to serve agricultural and mining interests.
- Lake Chad: One of the most serious losses can be found in this lake, which at one time provided 30% of the fresh water in Africa. From 1975 to 2015, Lake Chad lost one-twentieth of its original size. As a result, people in lakeside fishing villages migrated, and local economies have morphed from aquaculture to agriculture—the latter made even more difficult due to reduced supplies of water for irrigation. Around Lake Chad, rivers are increasingly tapped causing many more to suffer the impacts of vanishing water.

The Lake Chad Basin Commission, comprised of members from Algeria, Cameroon, Central African Republic, Libya, Niger, Nigeria, and Sudan, endeavors to remedy the condition. The United Nations hosted conferences to help the Lake Chad Basin region: Oslo's 2017 meeting raised $672 million, followed by a 2018 Berlin gathering resulting in $2.17 billion in assistance.

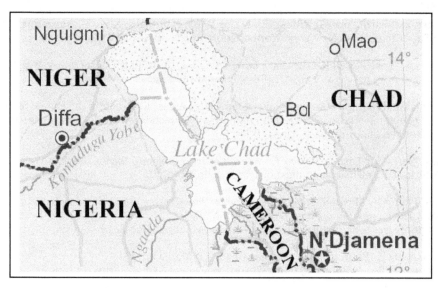

Lake Chad map, by United Nations, 2006.

WINDOW ON THE ECONOMY

- Lake Chad serves the water needs of the African nations of Cameroon, Chad, Niger, and Nigeria. Over 50 million people are threatened as water levels decline.

- The cost of "recharging" Lake Chad: $50 billion.

Source:
Pope, Cody T. "Vanishing Lake Chad – A Water Crisis in Central Africa." Circle of Blue. https://www.circleofblue.org/2008/world/vanishing-lake-chad-a-water-crisis-in-central-africa/

VIDEO: European Space Agency (ESA), "Earth from Space: Lake Chad," 22 March 2019. https://www.esa.int/ESA_Multimedia/Images/2019/03/Lake_Chad_s_shrinking_waters

---

Sources:
Allison, Edward H, et al. "Vulnerability of national economies to the impacts of climate change on fisheries." *Fish and Fisheries.* https://www.researchgate.net/publication/257257562_Vulnerability_of_National_Economies_to_Potential_Impacts_of_Climate_Change_on_Fisheries/

Brean, Henry. "Follow a gallon of water from Lake Mead to a Las Vegas tap." 15 April 2017, *Las Vegas Review-Journal.* https://www.reviewjournal.com/local/local-las-vegas/follow-a-gallon-of-water-from-lake-mead-to-a-las-vegas-tap/

Brean, Henry. "War of words flares in Arizona over Lake Mead water.' 3 May 2017. *Las Vegas Review-Journal.* https://www.reviewjournal.com/local/local-nevada/war-of-words-flares-in-arizona-over-lake-mead-water/

Brown, R. Lester, and Earth Policy Institute. "Emerging Water Shortages: Lakes Disappearing," *Plan B 3.0: Mobilizing to Save Civilization.* New York: Norton, 2008, pp. 75-78. ISBN: 9780393065893.

Carlowicz, Michael. "Lake Powell Reaches New Low.' 27 August 2021. Earth Observatory, NASA. https://earthobservatory.nasa.gov/images/148861/lake-powell-reaches-new-low

Carlowicz, Michael and Kathryn Hansen. "Lake Mead - The Largest Reservoir in the United States - Drops to a Record Low." 4 September 2021, Scitechdaily.com. https://scitechdaily.com/lake-mead-the-largest-reservoir-in-the-united-states-drops-to-a-record-low/

Carlton, James. "Shrinking Lake in Mexico Threatens Future of Region." Baylor University. https://www.baylor.edu/mediacommunications/index.php?id=9232

Doubek, James. Photos by Maximilian Mann featured in "The Death and Life of Iran's Lake Urmia." 12 November 2019. *The Picture Show Photo Stories from NPR.* https://www.npr.org/sections/pictureshow/2019/11/12/751360322/the-death-and-life-of-irans-lake-urmia/

European Space Agency, "Earth from Space: Lake Chad," 22 March 2019. https://www.esa.int/ESA_Multimedia/Images/2019/03/Lake_Chad_s_shrinking_waters

Ighobor, Kingsley. "Address development issues in the Lake Chad basin." https://www.un.org/africarenewal/magazine/december-2019-march-2020/address-development-issues-lake-chad-basin

Lake Mead website. "Lake Mead Water Level." http://mead.uslakes.info/level.asp

Purvis, Katherine and Catalin Trif. "The lakes of the world are disappearing – in pictures. Climate change and human activity are threatening the existence of some of the world's largest lakes." *Guardian,* 9 December 2016. https://www.theguardian.com/global-development-professionals-network/gallery/2016/dec/09/the-lakes-of-the-world-are-disappearing-in-pictures

Ramirez, Rachel, Pedram Javaheri, and Drew Kann. "The shocking numbers behind the Lake Mead drought crisis." 17 June 2021, CNN.com. https://www.cnn.com/2021/06/17/us/lake-mead-drought-water-shortage-climate/index.html

Sow, Mariama. "Figure of the week: The shrinking Lake Chad" 9 February 2017. https://www.brookings.edu/blog/africa-in-focus/2017/02/09/figure-of-the-week-the-shrinking-lake-chad/

Stanger, William F. The Colorado River Delta and Minute 319: A Transboundary Water Law Analysis. Masters Thesis. 2013. https://environs.law.ucdavis.edu/volumes/37/1/stanger.pdf

United States Bureau of Reclamation. Colorado River Basin Drought Contingency Plans. 2019. https://www.usbr.gov/dcp/

United States Bureau of Reclamation. Companion Agreement. https://www.usbr.gov/dcp/docs/final/Companion-Agreement-Final.pdf

United States Bureau of Reclamation. "Reclamation announces 2022 operating conditions for Lake Powell and Lake Mead: Historic Drought Impacting Entire Colorado River Basin." 16 August 2021. https://www.usbr.gov/newsroom/#/news-release/3950

United States Congress. H.R. 2030 - 116th Congress (2019-2020). Colorado River Drought Contingency Plan Authorization Act. https://www.congress.gov/bill/116th-congress/house-bill/2030

Usigbe, Leon. "Drying Lake Chad Basin gives rise to crisis: Food insecurity, conflicts, terrorism, displacement, and climate change effects compound changes," *United Nations.* https://www.un.org/africarenewal/magazine/december-2019-march-2020/drying-lake-chad-basin-gives-rise-crisis

Water Education Foundation. "Colorado River Water and Mexico." 2021. https://www.watereducation.org/aquapedia/mexico-and-colorado-river-water

Oceans of Plastic and Garbage Gyres

Earth's oceans are filled with plastic, resulting in one prediction that by 2050 the weight of plastic trash in the water will exceed the weight of marine life—if, indeed, there is any marine life left. Today, sea creatures are routinely found with bellies full of indigestible plastic. Considerable evidence points to plastic sinking so deep into the ocean that it is virtually impossible to remove.

Captain Charles Moore, sailing home from Hawaii to California after a 1997 yacht race, discovered what is now known as the Great Pacific Garbage Patch. When warm air in the South Pacific meets its cooler northern cousin, a strong current, or gyre, forms which causes a churning rotation that draws garbage into its vortex. Trash from California drifts for years before being drawn into the circle; detritus from Japan eventually arrives. In fact, some scientists have now identified two patches: the Eastern Garbage Patch between Hawaii and California, and the Western Garbage Patch between Hawaii and Japan. Most of the trash is visible, but over time sunlight degrades plastic into micro-particles that appear as cloudy water.

Responsibility for cleanup is equally murky because the Great Pacific Garbage Patch (also called the Trash Vortex) is offshore in international waters. The U.S. National Oceanic and Atmospheric Administration (NOAA) estimates it would take 67 ships one year to clean up just one percent of the North Pacific. Even more discouraging is the fact that most of the marine debris is not caught in the gyre; 70% sinks to the ocean floor.

Plastic never goes away, but it could be used as a building material. David de Rothschild and team built a catamaran constructed of discarded plastic water bottles, and the prototype vessel successfully sailed from San Francisco, California to Sydney, Australia. The catamaran was named "Plastiki" with a hull made of frames filled with 12,000 plastic bottles.

The Great Pacific Garbage Gyre might find a solution in ocean cleanup System 001, a floating barrier with a catch mechanism below, towed from California 240 miles offshore in 2018 and updated to System 001/B in 2019. The system is designed to gather floating plastic while allowing fish to swim underneath the mechanism. As plastic accumulates, small boats meet the device and take the plastic back to shore for recycling. It is a careful development process: 273 scale models, 6 at-sea test prototypes, and a mapping of the Great Pacific Garbage Patch with 30 ships and one airplane. If initial tests prove successful, the design process for System 002, the first full-scale operational system, will be deployed. Some critics worry that the sizable device might itself create an environmental hazard. However, if successful, the system could recover up to 50 tons of plastic from the ocean each year.

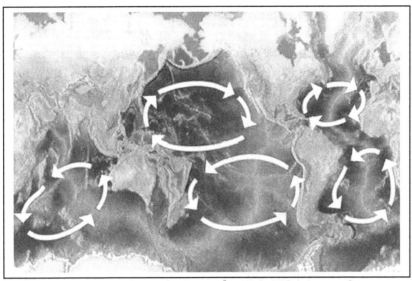

Oceanic Gyres, by U.S. NOAA, 2008.

Attribution: see p. 162

There are more garbage patches and gyres than the Great Pacific Garbage Gyre. If you would like to do something to help the marine plastic problem, consider the Marine Debris Tracker App, a joint initiative between NOAA and the Southeast Atlantic Marine Debris Initiative (SEA-MDI) from the University of Georgia College of Engineering, which allows people to get involved locally. The Marine Debris Tracker is an open-data, citizen science tool that enables users to log their findings on litter and debris. For more on the two million pieces of litter reported and logged in by citizen scientists, see the Marine Debris Tracker at https://debristracker.org/.

WINDOW ON THE ECONOMY

<u>Cleaning Up Plastic in Oceans</u>

It would take 67 ships one year to clean up
just 1% of the North Pacific Ocean.

Sources:
Cirino, Erica. "Charles Moore is now a two-time Garbage Patch discoverer." 20 July 2017, *National Geographic*. https://www.safinacenter.org/blog/charles-moore-is-now-a-two-time-garbage-patch-discoverer-and-i-can-tell-you-what-a-garbage-patch-looks-like

VIDEO: "What is the Great Pacific Garbage Patch?" NOAA.
https://marinedebris.noaa.gov/videos/trash-talk-what-great-pacific-garbage-patch-0.

Sources:
Marine Debris Tracker. http://www.marinedebris.engr.uga.edu/

McKie, Robin. "Eco-Warrior sets sail to save oceans from 'plastic death'." 11 April 2009. *Guardian.*
https://www.theguardian.com/environment/2009/apr/12/david-de-rothschild-plastiki-pacific.

NOAA. Marine Debris Program. Office of Response and Restoration. "TRASH TALK: What is the Great Pacific
Garbage Patch?" 29 September 2020. https://marinedebris.noaa.gov/videos/trash-talk-what-great-pacific-
garbage-patch-0

The Ocean Cleanup.com. "System 001/B – The Mission Plan." 27 June 2019.
https://theoceancleanup.com/updates/system-001-b-the-mission-plan/

Williams, David. "Plan to clean up the Great Pacific Garbage Patch gets underway." CNN, 10 Sep 2018,
https://www.cnn.com/2018/09/10/health/ocean-cleanup-test-trnd/index.html.

Microbeads

Not all trash is big. Cosmetics and pharmaceuticals may be endangering water supplies with invisible but nevertheless lethal pollutants. Hair products—shampoos, conditioners, styling gels, colorings, highlighters—often contain nonbiodegradable elements. According to Catherine Carré of the Université Paris/Panthéon-Sorbonne, micro-pollutants in cosmetic products are rinsed from heads and hands, into sinks, and then into rivers. Cleaning products leave dangerous residues that enter the water supply. Household and industrial cleaning products are filled with microbeads—tiny particles that

---

WINDOW ON THE ECONOMY

Microbead pollutants are found in:
body lotion
conditioner
facial cleanser cosmetics
hand cream
household cleaning products
shampoo
styling gel
toothpaste

Sources:
Carré, Catherine, University of Paris. Fulbright Water Act, 2015.

VIDEO: University of Bath, "Biodegradable alternative to replace microplastics in cosmetics and toiletries." 12 August 2019.
https://www.youtube.com/watch?v=iaUf2gzV7Wc

---

enhance the cleaning power of consumer products but have been banned recently in some countries. In the U.S., in 2015, over eight trillion microbeads entered the aquatic supply—daily. Passage of the Microbead-Free Waters Act of 2015 in the United States prevented manufacturers from putting microbeads into products beginning July 2017. Canada passed the Microbead Elimination and Monitoring

Act of 2015. The Plastic Soup Foundation, pioneered in the Netherlands, may help protect and sustain safe water. Filtration efforts could help to screen out micro-pollutants, but broad-based action is needed.

What are microbeads? Why is there a problem with them? PE (polyethylene) or PP (polypropylene) or PET (polyethylene terephthalate) or even PMMA (polymethyl methacrylate) are the "DNA" of microbeads. These plastic particles are so tiny they can easily be incorporated into toothpaste and other products. Some cosmetics contain these tiny plastics, especially products aimed at facial rejuvenation. Of course, products with plastic so intimately applied may harm the body. Some small amount of toothpaste is swallowed when teeth are brushed; if that toothpaste contains microbeads, now they are in your system, likely coating your teeth and possibly seeping into your gums.

Moreover, after brushing your teeth, you expel used water and toothpaste into the sink. After applying facial creams and cosmetics, you wash your hands. Almost all of these products are rinsed down a drain. But that is not the end of the story; rather, it is just the beginning.

What happens when microbeads wash down the drain? First, they go to the wastewater treatment plant where unwanted detritus is filtered out. Unfortunately, microbeads are too tiny to be filtered, so most wastewater treatment facilities can't capture this plastic dust. It slips through and washes out to the river, the lake, the canal, the bay, the ocean. In such manner, microbeads enter the world water supply—and marine life. Fish eat the stuff, and their entire body absorbs these plastic toxins.

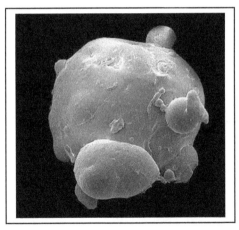

"Plastic microbead," by Andrew Watts, 2016.

Note: Image of a plastic microbead from a facewash, taken via scanning electron microscopy.
Attribution: see p. 162

Microbeads appear almost everywhere. According to a recent study in *Nature* by scientists from the Aquatic Health Program at the University of California, Davis, and the Graduate School of Public Health at San Diego State University, small plastic debris is ubiquitous in the aquatic environment, contaminating coastal, deep-sea, near-shore, and open ocean habitats. The production of plastic has increased 200-fold in just 60 years.

Plastic shopping bags were once the conveyance of choice at grocery stores. Water bottles, made of plastic, are also in the hands of many walkers and runners. Plastic bags and bottles degrade over time, but the bad news is they break down into tiny bits of plastic that enter rivers, lakes, and oceans. We can recycle bottles and ban plastic bags, but what about microbeads? Unfortunately, removing microbeads and microplastics is challenging. The best solution is to reduce the source, warned Austin Baldwin of the United States Geological Survey.

Some municipal authorities are taking action, and some states are banning microbeads. New York State introduced the Microbead-Free Waters Act. Those who still crave the skin cleansing effects of an exfoliant might turn to natural products made from walnut shells or apricot seeds. Noting the trend, and responding to an increased prevalence of bans, some large consumer product manufacturers like Colgate-Palmolive and L'Oréal are phasing out microbeads.

Making it easier to determine if a product contains microbeads, there are apps like "Ban the Microbead," developed by the Plastic Soup Foundation, to enable shoppers to scan potential purchases before deciding selection.

Sources:
Baldwin, Austin K., et al. "Plastic debris in 29 Great Lakes tributaries: Relations to watershed attributes and hydrology." *Environmental Science and Technology*, 2016, 50 (19), pp. 10377-10385. DOI: 10.1021/acs.est.6b02917. http://pubs.acs.org/doi/abs/10.1021/acs.est.6b02917

"Beat the Microbead: Scientific evidence about microplastic ingredients." https://www.beatthemicrobead.org/faq/

Bressy, Adèle, Catherine Carré, José-Frédéric Deroubaix, Bernard de Gouvello, Mathilde Soyer, et al. "Domestic micropollutants, a diffuse industrial pollution -Part 2: Source reduction by changing personal consumption practices." 16th international conference on Chemistry and the Environment (ICCE 2017). June 2017, Oslo, Norway. https://hal.archives-ouvertes.fr/hal-01699801

Eriksen, Marcus, et al. "Microplastic pollution in the surface waters of the Laurentian Great Lakes." *Marine Pollution Bulletin*, 77, Issues 1-2, 15 December 2013, pp. 177-182. http://www.sciencedirect.com/science/article/pii/S0025326X13006097

Gall, S. C. and R.C. Thompson. "The Impact of debris on marine life." *Marine Pollution Bulletin* 92, 170-179. http://dx.doi.org/10.1016/j.marpolbul.2014.12.041

Matsangou, Elizabeth. "Counting the cost of plastic pollution." World Finance.com . 2 July 2018. https://www.worldfinance.com/markets/counting-the-cost-of-plastic-pollution

Microbead-Free Waters Act of 2015. https://www.congress.gov/bill/114th-congress/house-bill/1321

Plastic Soup Foundation. https://www.plasticsoupfoundation.org/en/

Teh, J. "Ingested plastic transfers hazardous chemicals to fish and induces hepatic stress." *Nature,* Scientific Reports 3, Article number 3263. http://www.nature.com/articles/srep03263

University of Plymouth. Video. "Plastic microbeads," 30 September 2016. https://www.youtube.com/watch?v=AOWrHQ8IWX4

WINDOW ON THE ECONOMY

Microbeads, which are harmful to human health,
accumulate in all kinds of fish and shellfish,
such as anchovies, mussels, oysters, salmon, and tuna.
Environmental damage to marine ecosystems: $13 billion per year.

Sources:
"Beat the Microbead: Scientific evidence about microplastic ingredients."
www.beatthemicrobead.org/science

Matsangou, Elizabeth. "Counting the cost of plastic pollution." World Finance.com . 2 July
2018. https://www.worldfinance.com/markets/counting-the-cost-of-plastic-pollution

VIDEO: University of Plymouth, "Plastic microbeads," 30 September 2016.
https://www.youtube.com/watch?v=AOWrHQ8IWX4

Medicines and Pharmaceuticals in Water

Medicines may heal the body, but improperly discarded pharmaceuticals can poison water systems. Many people flush unused medicine down a sink or toilet. But that action does not get rid of the chemicals. Rather, flushed medicine "treats" the whole water system; now your neighbor is taking your blood pressure medication and you are imbibing another neighbor's contraceptive.

It is widely recognized that people tend to flush medications, either intentionally to dispose of unwanted or expired drugs or unintentionally by excreting drugs when using the bathroom on a normal basis. What may not be known is that most sewage treatment facilities are not required to filter out those medicines. Rural households that use a septic system must pass a certification inspection, but there may not be enough rules to govern filtering of pharmaceuticals.

"Medicine Drugs," clipart by ernes, 2009.
Attribution: see p. 162

In the first large-scale systematic assessment of hormone and pharmaceutical occurrences in groundwater used for drinking in the United States, findings revealed 21 hormones and 103 pharmaceuticals (Bexfield, et al., 2019). During 1999–2000, the U.S. Geological Survey conducted a test of water from numerous U.S. rivers and streams. It found that 80% of the water tested contained a cocktail of antibiotics, hormones, and other pharmaceuticals. If you take Prozac, you may be surprised to learn that antidepressants not only impact humans but also fish and shellfish that live in affected waters. In the United States, recognition of the problem and the requirement for a solution resulted in "Take Back Days," held periodically to enable people to drop off unused or expired medicines safely. In other instances, local police stations have a collection box in the precinct lobby.

But there is no easy solution to the latest form of drugs entering the water supply. Nanomedicine is a new field that promises help for diseases such as cancer and respiratory conditions. Micro-size, balloon-shaped structures are filled with a drug and then delivered straight to a tumor, rather than systemically as in chemotherapy. Nanomedicines travel quickly and smoothly through the body, and through water. What about veterinary drugs or animal feeds? According to a seminal study by the World Health Organization (WHO, 2012), drugs intended both for people and for animals are entering the water supply.

Water filtration with natural materials may be enjoying renewed interested. Ancient Egyptians filtered water with sand; in classical Greece, Hippocrates (often called the parent of medicine) devised a cloth bag or "Hippocratic sleeve" to filter water used to treat patients. Recent filtration innovations include using branches from trees such as pine and ginko with internal conduit structures like gymnosperm xylem with options for a range of low-cost, biodegradable, xylem-based filtration devices that could be practical on a global scale.

Sources:
Bexfield, L. M, P. L. Toccalino, K. Belitz, W. T. Foreman, and E. T. Furlong. "Hormones and pharmaceuticals in groundwater used as a source of drinking water across the United States." *Environ Sci Technol*. 2019 Mar 19;53(6):2950-2960. https://pubs.acs.org/doi/10.1021/acs.est.8b05592

Borener, Leigh Krietsch. "The complicated question of drugs in the water." *NovaNext/PBS*. 14 May 2017. http://www.pbs.org/wgbh/nova/next/body/pharmaceuticals-in-the-water/

Chu, Jennifer. "MIT engineers make filters from tree branches to purify drinking water." 25 March 2021. *MIT News*. https://news.mit.edu/2021/filters-sapwood-purify-water-0325. Also: video https://youtu.be/RujY7JsSrVQ

Environmental Protection Agency (EPA). National Primary Drinking Water Regulations. 2020. https://www.epa.gov/ground-water-and-drinking-water/national-primary-drinking-water-regulations

Karnik, Rohit, K. Ramchander, M. Hegde, and K. Leith. "Xylem Water Filter." www.xylemwaterfilter.org

Pereira, André, L. Silva, C. Laranjeiro, A. Pena. "Assessment of human pharmaceuticals in drinking water catchments, tap and drinking fountain waters. 30 July 2021. Molecular Diversity Preservation International (MDPI). *Applied Sciences*, vol. 11 (2021): 7062. https://doi.org/10.3390/app11157062

Ramchander, Krithika, et al. "Engineering and characterization of gymnosperm sapwood toward enabling the design of water filtration devices. *Nature Communications*, vol. 12, no. 1 (March 2021). https://www.nature.com/articles/s41467-021-22055-w. DOI: 10.1038/s41467-021-22055-w

Scheer, Roddy, and Doug Moss. EarthTalk™. "External medicine: Discarded drugs may contaminate 40 million Americans' drinking water." *Scientific American*. https://www.scientificamerican.com/article/pharmaceuticals-in-the-water/

World Health Organization. "Pharmaceuticals in drinking-water." 2012. https://apps.who.int/iris/handle/10665/44630

Wu, Jishan, Miao Cao, Draco Tong, Zach Finkelstein, and Eric M. V. Hoek. "A critical review of point-of-use drinking water treatment in the United States." Review of point-of-use filtration technologies. 22 July 2021. *Clean Water*, Nature Partner Journals. Article: 40 (2021). https://www.nature.com/articles/s41545-021-00128-z#Sec26

Oceanic Buried Treasure

Oceans hold hidden treasure; we must now decide whether to leave it buried. There are perhaps 33,000 oceanic seamounts throughout 14 bioregions. Habitats have been studied in several mineral deposit areas in the Exclusive Economic Zone (EEZ) of Kiribati, Marshall Islands, Micronesia, Samoa, and Tuvalu. Deep-sea mining may disturb these habitats and cause other damage that should be evaluated before exploitation begins. "Deep-sea mining is a new ocean industry. In fact, it is so new that not even one kilogram of ore has been recovered from the ocean," stated Secretary-General of the International Seabed Authority (ISA), Michael W. Lodge, on 3 June 2020 in Norway during discussions on an action platform for sustainable ocean business.

While not one kilogram of ore had been recovered—taken—at that time, we know what kinds of ore have been discovered: cobalt, copper, manganese, nickel, platinum. Some ores or deposits occur within the EEZs of various coastal countries. These same countries are threatened by rising seas and may consider deep-sea mining as an economic strategy.

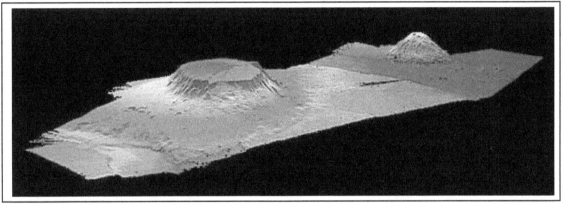

"Bear Seamount guyot," by NOAA, 2007.

Attribution, see page 162

In 2012, ISA adopted regulations for exploration of crusts in the territory of the High Seas, i.e., beyond 200 nautical miles. ISA has signed contracts for exploration with some countries that want to do deep-sea mining in the High Seas territory, not in anybody's EEZ; however, those proposals are pending.

Cobalt and other ore deposits are found in the crusts that form the bumps and humps of rocky undersea-rises called seamounts. It takes a long time to make these deposits: cobalt-rich crusts grow less than an inch per million years (World Ocean Review). Some experts estimate there may be three times more manganese in the Prime Crust Zone than would be mineable on land.

If (or when) mining occurs, various treasures will demand various approaches. Manganese is relatively easy to access and can be scooped up aboard a ship with the seafaring version of a backhoe. Manganese deposits are also easy to detect and document with video detailing the size of the nodule. Exploring cobalt is much trickier, and possibly more damaging, because "rock boulders have to be torn or drilled out. Local thickness differences are poorly constrained and the spot sampling is extremely time-consuming and expensive" (World Ocean Review, 2014). Other exploration technologies including gamma-ray detectors are under development.

Like mountains on land, each seamount terrain has unique inhabitants, both flora and fauna. Currents swirling around seamounts draw nutrients into a kind of circling salad bar where sharks and tuna graze. What will happen as the world runs out of land-based materials used so widely in modern life? We know there are ores we need in places we can reach. So far, it's been about exploration, not exploitation. Some scientists call for experimental mining projects as pilot studies to assess the environmental impact of seabed mining.

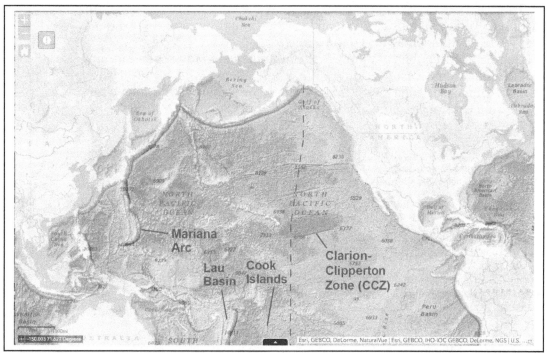

"Location of the Clarion-Clipperton Zone," by Coastal Marine Hazards and Resources Program, U.S. Geological Survey, 2018.

Attribution: see p. 162

Seabed exploration and mining has a long history. On 7 March 1873, the *HMS Challenger* expedition discovered manganese oxide in an exploration dredge. A century later, a consortium formed including many countries interested in assessment and potential extraction of polymetallic nodules in the Clarion-Clipperton Zone in the Pacific Ocean. When the United Nations established the Law of the Sea in 1982, and ISA entered into force in 1994, contracts for exploration began first by countries and then in 2010 by private enterprise. ISA grants 15-year contracts for exploration of "polymetallic nodules, polymetallic sulphides, and cobalt-rich ferromanganese crusts in the deep seabed" (ISA, 2020). In 2020, there were 30 contracts, allotted to 18 governments and enterprises. Located in Kingston, Jamaica, ISA holds workshops and webinars: in 2006 there were five events; in 2020, educational offerings expanded to 14. ISA's International Tribunal, for dispute resolution, is located in Hamburg, Germany. The 26th session of ISA announced a new president, Ambassador Denys Wibaux, Permanent Representative of the Republic of France to the International Seabed Authority on 29 October 2020.

WINDOW ON THE ECONOMY
Cobalt Mining

Ancient Egyptian tombs contain cobalt-glazed pottery crafted 2600 years ago. Today, cobalt is used in batteries for mobile phones and electric cars. Demand for cobalt use in electric vehicles may double by 2030.

There have been ethical concerns about some land-based cobalt mining. In 2018, the average spot price of cobalt was $37/pound; in 2019, $17/pound. Average use volume in 2016: 116,000 tons.

Democratic Republic of Congo is the dominant source of cobalt mining, with 50% of global cobalt reserves and production. Other mining locations are Canada, China, Australia, and Russia. Cobalt mining is also the subject of exploration contracts granted by the International Seabed Authority.

Sources:
Bochove, Danielle. "Rare metal used in electric cars causes cobalt rush." *Bloomberg*. 1 November 2017. *The Toronto Star*. https://www.thestar.com/news/canada/2017/11/01/rare-metal-used-in-electric-cars-causes-a-cobalt-rush-in-cobalt-ont.html

Cobalt Institute. "Cobalt Around the World." https://www.cobaltinstitute.org/about-cobalt/cobalt-around-the-world/

Garside, M. "Cobalt's average spot price in the US 2008-2019," 18 February 2020. *Statista*. https://www.statista.com/statistics/339743/average-spot-price-of-cobalt-in-the-us/

VIDEO: MIT Mechanical Engineering. "Visualizing Deep-sea Mining." 10 December 2019. https://www.youtube.com/watch?v=Lwq1j3nOODA

Sources:
International Seabed Authority. "ISA Strategic Directions: 2019-2023." 26 July 2018. https://www.isa.org.jm/index.php/strategic-plan.

International Seabed Authority. "Deep Sea Mineral Resources: Cobalt-Rich Ferromanganese." https://www.isa.org.jm/deep-sea-mineral-resources-cobalt-rich-ferromanganese.

International Tribunal for the Law of the Sea. https://www.itlos.org.

Langley, Winston E. "Lecture and discussion: International Seabed Authority," 18 October 2019, University of Massachusetts Boston.

World Ocean Review. "Metal-rich crusts," Marine Resources – Opportunities and Risks, 2014. https://www.worldoceanreview.com/en/wor-3/mineral-resources/cobalt-crusts/.

Almonds and Animals: The Future of Food

California ranks as one of the world's largest economies, with a Gross State Product (GSP) greater than the United Kingdom (California: $2.75 trillion versus UK: £2.03 trillion, as of January 2022). If California were a country, it would be the world's fifth-largest economy. The state is a leader in agriculture, economics, education, and technological innovation.

In 2020, California, Oregon, and Washington state suffered a season of fires resulting in loss of lives and homes. Many attribute the severity and scope of the fires to climate change. It will be important to observe the actions taken by these states in the decade 2020 to 2030. This area has suffered the worst extended drought in 1,200 years, along with devastating fires. Should water use be re-evaluated?

Agricultural production in California consumes 80% of the state's water supply, producing more broccoli, cauliflower, onions, peppers, spinach, tomatoes—and almonds—than any other state. By itself, almond farming accounts for 10% of California's water use, requiring 1.1 trillion gallons (4.163 trillion liters) of water each year. To estimate that amount, imagine taking a 10-minute shower each day—for 86 million years. Other crops are similarly thirsty, such as avocados, which require 220 gallons (757 liters).

Any drought causes farmers to tap into groundwater aquifers, thereby lowering resources for all, including urban areas. Recent innovations in pipes and tapping mean less leakage and more efficient agriculture—but problems remain. Drought and scarce water may lead to struggles over water rights. Farmers in California negotiated proposals in which they willingly lowered their water consumption by 25% (through reducing usage or even plowing under some fields) in exchange for a permanent guarantee of unrestricted access to the land they retain. Will actions California has taken and will need to take, set precedents for an increasingly thirsty world?

"Fresh-cut fruits and vegetables," by Peggy Greb, 2013.

Attribution: see p. 162

Almonds take 10% of California's agricultural water; animals raised for food demand another 30%. The full production cycle that results in one hamburger requires 621 gallons (2,350 liters) of water.

Livestock production causes 14% of greenhouse gas emissions, with some estimates as high as 51%. Some agricultural engineers are evaluating feed additives to inhibit microorganisms that result in methane (Curnow, 2019). The health of the planet could also enhance individual wellness: eating less meat might reduce deaths from heart disease and cancer. More than 800 million people endure hunger, but the cereal that could feed three times that number is instead fed to animals raised for food.

Agriculture and water management for transboundary water resources may find ways to balance agriculture production and conservation. In a 2020 study of the Mekong River, workshops in Cambodia, Laos, Thailand, and Vietnam consulted stakeholders on best practice for preserving the river that sustains so many.

Sources:
Bailey, Rob, Antony Froggatt, and Laura Wellesley. "Livestock—Climate change's forgotten sector: Global public opinion on meat and dairy consumption." 3 December 2014. Chatham House, Royal Institute of International Affairs. https://www.chathamhouse.org/2014/12/livestock-climate-changes-forgotten-sector-global-public-opinion-meat-and-dairy-consumption

"Best States for Business 2019: California." *Forbes*, 2019. https://www.forbes.com/places/ca/#5c37eeb93fef/

"California is now the world's fifth-largest economy, surpassing the United Kingdom." 4 May 2018. *Los Angeles Times.* https://www.latimes.com/business/la-fi-california-economy-gdp-20180504-story.html

Curnow, Mandy. "Carbon farming: reducing methane emissions from cattle using feed additives." 21 November 2019. Department of Primary Industries and Regional Development, Government of Western Australia. https://www.agric.wa.gov.au/climate-change/carbon-farming-reducing-methane-emissions-cattle-using-feed-additives

Datta, A., et al. "Study report on wetland agriculture and water management in the Mekong Region." 2020. Bangkok: FAO and Asian Institute of Technology. ISBN: 9789251330951. https://doi.org/10.4060/cb0378en

"Oregon warns of 'mass fatality incident;' nearly 5 million acres burned." *New York Times,* 11 September 2020. https://www.nytimes.com/2020/09/11/us/fires-oregon-california-washington.html

Poisoned Water and Aging Infrastructure

In what was at the time deemed a temporary cost-cutting measure, city authorities in Flint, Michigan, USA, made the decision in 2014 to begin taking the city's water supply from the nearby Flint River rather than from more distant Lake Huron via Detroit. That decision was an attempt to save city monies. The Flint River was well known for high levels of corrosive minerals, yet no filters or safeguards were applied. When the river began flowing through aged pipes, interior coatings dissolved, allowing lead to leach into city water. Residents quickly noticed the color change as they drew a glass of water; taste was altered as well. Soon, pediatrician Dr. Mona Hanna-Attisha began to observe increasing instances of lead poisoning among children who were drinking the water. Despite such evidence, and the urgent call by medical professionals and others for immediate action, it was more than a year later before any actions were taken. By then, a new generation already faced an uncertain future. The irony is that medical treatment is estimated to cost $100 million; fixing the pipes will cost $1.5 billion. The amount city authorities believed would be "saved" by switching from Lake Huron water to Flint River water? $5 million over two years.

In 2016, after considerable outrage and criticism, Flint residents began receiving water in plastic bottles as a temporary measure. Such an approach was not ideal, for several reasons. Large amounts of bottled water were needed; one family might use more than 150 bottles a day. That's a lot of plastic, which quickly caused a recycling crisis. In 2021, plastic bottles sold yearly worldwide may reach 583.3 billion. In 2017, the global population used one million plastic bottles— every minute. Most are discarded, to the detriment of the environment. Equally troubling is the quality of bottled water. Often it is not pure, as a plastic bottle can leach impurities and contaminants into the water it holds. Cost is also a factor: bottled water costs 600 times more than tap water (EPA, 2021; Livingston, 2021).

The situation in Flint was a wake-up call to the condition of local water infrastructures and their potential dangers. The Environmental Protection Agency (EPA) monitors lead levels in water and sets guidelines. Lead is measured in parts per billion (ppb); levels over 5ppb are cause for concern; over 15ppb is actionable. In nearby Troy, Michigan, drinking water measured 1ppb and in Detroit just over 2ppb. In contrast, Flint tallied 27ppb, 158ppb, 397ppb, 1,000ppb, 5,000ppb (the level that defines toxic waste), and even 13,000ppb (EPA, 2021).

"Water on Tap (Unsplash)," by Luis Tosta, 2017.

Attribution: see p. 162

What alternatives did Flint have? While residents were instructed to boil water and use supplied filters, there may be hope for Flint and many other areas in the world where water quality and safety are threatened. An innovation from FloWater, a California company specializing in water purification for businesses, hotels, fitness centers, and schools, developed units that filter tap water in seven cycles to remove contaminants including lead. FloWater's CEO Rich Razgaitis proposed bringing water purification stations to Flint. Such stations would reduce the number of accumulating plastic bottles. But more importantly, water quality might improve. In 2019, FloWater partnered with Bluewater Technologies, a company specializing in sustainable water technologies: the result was a $15 million series B investment. Another improvement: Flint high school and college students are joining chemists from the University of Michigan in the McKenzie Patrice Croom Flint Community Lab to evaluate the water in 20,000 Flint households (Smith, 2020). Can situations like Flint become test cases for supplying water during disasters?

Aging infrastructure leading to contaminated water is, unfortunately, not unique to Flint, Michigan. Benton Harbor, also in Michigan, found lead in its aging water lines in 2021; the cure would be replacement of 6,000 lines at a cost of $30 million (AP 2021; EPA, 2021). The town of Sebring, Ohio, found lead in its tap water after it stopped an anti-corrosion treatment of pipes carrying the local water supply. After a five-month delay, the town sent out official notices to its residents that Sebring's water should not be consumed, especially by children or pregnant mothers. Fountains and taps at all schools were turned off.

Remote areas are frequently presumed to be more vulnerable to water contamination because there may be little political influence. Yet, the capital of the United States—Washington, DC—found lead in its drinking water in 2001. Like Sebring, the problem occurred after a change in water treatment protocols. Tests revealed contamination up to 20 times national guidelines, yet the problem was not fully disclosed to residents for five years.

Occasioned by discoveries in Flint, Sebring, and Washington D.C., additional investigations revealed other problems. More than 2,000 U.S. water systems were found to contain levels of lead higher than regulated. More than 350 such systems served schools or daycare centers. There are more than 155,000 different water systems in the U.S., so testing is not easy. More than 75 million houses and apartment buildings in the United States were built before 1980 when lead-pipe legislation was enacted. The oldest pipes, and the most problematic, are in some of the earliest settled states. EPA regulations allow testing intervals of up to three years, and sampling rather than complete evaluation. As a result, home testing and use of filters beyond those provided by the community are sometimes viewed as proactive prevention.

In 2021, the United States proposed the Drinking Water and Wastewater Infrastructure Act, following on a 2020 revision of the Lead and Copper Rule. If all nations' lead water pipes were removed and replaced, it would mean significant upgrades to public health. Estimates indicate there are 6 to 10 million lead service lines still in use, reaching some 400,000 schools and childcare centers. Proposals to remove existing lead lines and pipes could cost $15 billion; replacements, at an average of $4,700 per line, would cost $45 billion (Campbell & Wessel, 2021). Lead in drinking water is a global problem that requires updated assessments by the World Health Organization in order to meet Sustainable Development Goal #6 for clean water and sanitation.

Even if water is clean, aging infrastructure remains a serious concern. In Chicago, Illinois, the Jardine Water Purification Plant, world's largest by volume, draws water from the Great Lakes for distribution to 390 million city dwellers. But an estimated 6 billion gallons per day may be lost due to old leaky pipes in the network. In fact, U.S. water leakage tops 2.1 trillion gallons per year—enough to put Manhattan under 300 feet of water.

Similar problems may be present in aging water systems worldwide. Western Europe's water serves 390 million people in 17 countries where water networks last about 100 years. In 2001, the European Union sent warnings to Austria, Belgium, Denmark, France, Greece, Luxembourg, Portugal, Spain, Sweden, and the United Kingdom regarding their failure to file updates on safety and purity of national drinking water. Warnings called particular attention to France and Spain which were already in receipt of second notices.

VOICE OF THE FUTURE
—Upmanu Lall

"Much of our water infrastructure isn't working. In America, the land which we talk about as being from sea to shining sea, from water to water, we don't seem to nearly have a sense of the national issues on water that we should."

—Upmanu Lall, Director, Columbia Water Center, Columbia University, NY

Source:
VIDEO: Columbia Water Center, "Building America's Water Initiative," 15 April 2016.
https://www.youtube.com/watch?v=a-5fLkhfScQ&feature=emb_logo

Europe spends a considerable amount of its water infrastructure budget on rehabilitation. For instance, in the past two decades, Germany has invested more than €100 billion to improve its water, wastewater collection, and treatment systems. The European Union gave direction regarding the safety of drinking water in Council Directive 98/83/EC on 3 November 1998, which set guidelines for the future. When the European Water Framework Directive (WFD) began in 2000, it set 2027 as the year to attain a rating of "good" or higher. Now, WFD legislation to protect water ecosystems and preserve sustainable water across Europe estimates that achievement of the 2027 goal is uncertain. A 2018 assessment by the European Environment Agency revealed that "60% of surface water bodies were failing to achieve good ecological status" (Carvalho, 2019).

Sources:
Building the World blog. "Skin-Flint." http://blogs.umb.edu/buildingtheworld/2016/01/23/skin-flint

Campbell, Sophia and David Wessel. "What would it cost to replace all the nation's lead water pipes?" 13 May 2021. https://www.brookings.edu/blog/up-front/2021/05/13/what-would-it-cost-to-replace-all-the-nations-lead-water-pipes/

Carvalho, Laurence, et al. "Protecting and restoring Europe's waters: An analysis of the future development needs of the Water Framework Directive." *Science of the Total Environment,* vol. 658, 29 March 2019, 1228-1238. https://www.sciencedirect.com/science/article/pii/S004896971835126X

CBS Interactive Inc. "Ohio town may be the next Flint with its water crisis." 25 January 2016. https://www.cbsnews.com/news/sebring-ohio-next-flint-water-crisis-lead-copper/

Dickinson, Tim. "WTF is happening in the Flint water crisis explained." 22 January 2016. *Rolling Stone Magazine.* https://www.rollingstone.com/politics/politics-news/wtf-is-happening-in-the-flint-water-crisis-explained-227776/

Euronews. "Bottled water is 3,500 times worse for the environment than tap water, say scientists." 8 August 2021. https://www.euronews.com/green/2021/08/05/bottled-water-is-3-500-times-worse-for-the-environment-than-tap-water-say-scientists

European Commission. "EU Water Legislation – Fitness Check" 26 July 2021. https://ec.europa.eu/environment/water/fitness_check_of_the_eu_water_legislation/index_en.htm

FloWater. https://www.drinkflowater.com

Livingston, Amy. "Ways to Save Money by Conserving Water (Indoors & Outdoors)." 11 Aug 2021. Money Crashers. https://www.moneycrashers.com/ways-conserve-water/

Lusk, Tina, RN. "Missouri Water at Risk for Contaminants Detrimental to the Health of Its Inhabitants." University of Missouri, St. Louis. 10 May 2020.

National Public Radio (NPR). "This city will rely on bottled water for weeks because of high lead levels." 22 October 2021. Includes audio link. https://www.npr.org/2021/10/22/1048605644/benton-harbor-michigan-lead-water-crisis

Official Journal of the European Communities. "Directive 2000/60/EC of the European Parliament and of the Council of 23 October 2000 Establishing a Framework For Community Action in the Field of Water Policy." https://eur-lex.europa.eu/resource.html?uri=cellar:5c835afb-2ec6-4577-bdf8-756d3d694eeb.0004.02/DOC_1&format=PDF

Pianin, Eric. "Flint is One of Many Lead-Polluted Water Systems in the US." 26 February 2016. *Fiscal Times.* https://www.thefiscaltimes.com/2016/02/28/Flint-One-Many-Lead-Polluted-Water-Systems-US

Plastic Soup Foundation. "The world's population consumes 1 million plastic bottles every minute." July 2017. https://www.plasticsoupfoundation.org/2017/07/the-worlds-population-consumes-1-million-plastic-bottles-every-minute/

Ras, Bonnie Riva. "Flowater Raised $15 Million to Help Eradicate Plastic Water Bottles." 23 January 2019. Goodnet. https://www.goodnet.org/articles/flowater-raised-15-million-to-help-eradicate-plastic-water-bottles/

Schaper, David. "As infrastructure crumbles, trillions of gallons of water lost." *All Things Considered/National Public Radio.* 29 October 2014. http://www.npr.org/2014/10/29/359875321/as-infrastructure-crumbles-trillions-of-gallons-of-water-lost

Smith, Amanda. "One year later: Are Sebring's water issues solved?" January 24, 2017; updated: April 3, 2017. WKBN.com. https://www.wkbn.com/news/one-year-later-are-sebrings-water-issues-solved/

U.S. Environmental Protection Agency (EPA). "Benton Harbor Drinking Water" 5 November 2021. https://www.epa.gov/mi/benton-harbor-drinking-water

World Health Organization (WHO). "Lead in Drinking Water." WHO/SDE/WSH/03.04/09/Rev/1. https://www.who.int/water_sanitation_health//dwq/chemicals/lead.pdf

WINDOW ON THE ECONOMY

- Earth receives 39 inches (100 cm) of rainfall: 36% runs into rivers and lakes, 64% evaporates.
- Higher evaporation rates can cause drought.
- Rainwater is unique: it is sodium-free.
- Water demand will increase in some areas of the world by over 40%.
- An integrated water cycle using rainwater harvesting in Australia would save $2.5 billion on household water bills by 2050.

Sources:
Earth Observatory. https://earthobservatory.nasa.gov/global-maps/TRMM_3B43M.

"Global Water Security: A plan to ensure that all nations have access to clean water"
Solving Complex Problems. Massachusetts Institute of Technology (MIT).
https://terrascope.mit.edu/portfolio_page/mission-2017/

Radcliffe, John C., and Declan Page. "Water re-use and recycling in Australia—History, current situation and future perspectives. *Water Cycle*, vol. 1, 2020, 19-40.
https://doi.org/10.1016/j.watcyc.2020.05.005 and
https://www.sciencedirect.com/science/article/pii/S2666445320300064

"Rainwater Harvesting: Water for All Mission 2017." MIT: Global Water Security.
http://12.000.scripts.mit.edu/mission2017/solutions/engineering-solutions/rainwater-harvesting-techniques/

VIDEO: NASA, "20 Years of Global Rain," 16 October 2019.
https://gpm.nasa.gov/resources/videos/nasa-remasters-nearly-20-years-global-rain

SOLUTIONS and INNOVATIONS

It is true that there are water problems, and they are increasing. But problems lead to solutions, resulting in innovation and opportunity. Solving water problems will bring great benefit to all, from those whose health will improve with access to clean drinking water and safe sanitation, to industries that will prosper due to wise use of Earth's most important shared resource. Looking at problems from the vantage point of solutions is the purpose of this book. The opportunities are significant, and call a new generation to action and vision. How can we rebuild, and renew, water?

Waterscapes: What to Do When It Rains

In a world where some regions don't have sufficient water while other regions face the prospect of flooding, certain landscapes could become waterscapes by creating an environment that welcomes water. Waterscapes are already changing the landscape in many areas.

Waterscapes, such as the New River and the River Lea (both in England), incorporate water-cleansing natural elements that provide several benefits. One might be their ability to respond to flooding, a problem many believe will increase. Waterscapes create new wetlands that provide places for flood water to go. New channels or small canals are lined with reeds, offering a welcome habitat for bird and animal life waterside.

"Reed Bed," by Pixella, 2016.

Attribution: see p. 163

Equally important, reeds act as a natural filtration system cleansing water. Another bonus: oxygenation of water. It's like the bubbler in a fish tank. Why are reeds so effective? They convert ammonia into nitrate, a less toxic substance. Two types of reed beds have been found effective in different conditions. Where it is possible to plant directly along a river bed, *phragmites* or common reeds are used. But in some places where establishing such colonies may be impossible—for example, a wall or lined surface—a floating reed bed can be established with its roots dangling down to filter the water.

Stretches of new reed beds helped revive the River Lea in East London. In an innovative outreach, the "Love the Lea Programme" invited area citizens and businesses to fund a reed bed. The goal of Thames21 is to establish a reed bed every 984 feet (300 meters) down the entire length of the Thames River. In 2020, with funding from City Bridge Trust, Thames21 began a new project called "Thames Connections" to provide all London residents more access to the Thames River. The program invites people living within 10 minutes' walking distance to discuss needs and interests.

"Rainwater collector" by Jonathan Wilkins, 2009.
Note: This one has a porous wall as well as a collecting apron, so it should collect mist, dew, and wind-driven rainfall.

Attribution: see p. 163

Another kind of waterscape is one that conserves water. In Montgomery County, Maryland (U.S.), a program called RainScapes offered a "RainScapes Rewards Rebate" to property owners who installed rain barrels or created rain gardens and other conservation landscaping to control flooding and loss of water during storms. Residential property owners could claim a rebate of $2,500; multifamily, commercial, or institutional properties could get $10,000. A website suggested potential landscapes in a range of options:

- Conservation landscaping: plants that slow absorption of rain by soaking it up.
- Dry well: a hole in the ground with a beautiful rock bed to receive and filter rain water.
- Green roof: plants atop a roof receive rain and soak it up, offering insulating qualities as well.
- Permeable pavement or pavers: place bricks some distance apart to drain and store rainwater. Pavers could be inscribed with names, with donations going to the community.
- Pavement restoration: remove old paved areas and plant a conservation landscape or a rain garden.
- Rain garden: surface land, depressed six inches (15 centimeters), to encourage formation of a pond for 24 to 48 hours during and after a rain storm, with the water draining slowly into the surrounding land.
- Rain barrels and cisterns connected to a roof downspout: on dry days, there will be water. Cisterns (the larger cousins of barrels) hold 250 gallons (946 liters) and can supply a school or apartment building.

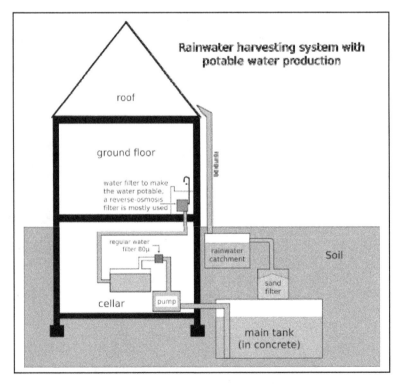

"Rainwater harvesting system," by Genetics4good and Fred the Oyster, 2010.
Attribution: see p. 163

Waterscapes offer water conservation and filtering systems. Massachusetts Audubon Broad Meadow Brook Wildlife Sanctuary in Worcester, Massachusetts, built a waterscape as part of an education program that invited summer campers to learn about sustaining water supply. MIT's Rainwater Harvesting Mission 2017 proposed tariffs on water as incentives to conserve water use and reduce waste. Water was segmented according to purpose: a VMQ (Vital Minimum Quantity) sustains life; real living requires EMQ (Essential Minimum Quantity) for washing and cooking.

Cisterns and storage tanks can be prohibitively expensive. In 2020, MIT's D-Lab (D stands for development through dialogue, design, and dissemination) initiated a project for low-cost rainwater harvesting using storage bags instead of cisterns. An added advantage, besides cost, is adaptability: different kinds of attachments can facilitate hand-washing, pumping, or spraying. Waterscapes will likely be part of the future, adding to ways we receive and return water.

Sources:
Adkins, Adele. "River Lea." Music and lyrics. 24 June 2016 Release. LISTEN: https://www.facebook.com/IndonesianAdele/videos/river-lea-live-at-the-glastonbury-festival/1009159952486016/

Coombes, Peter J., Michael Smit, and Garth MacDonald. "A Case Study: Resolving boundary conditions in economic analysis of distributed solutions for water cycle management." *Australian Journal of Water Resources*, Volume 20, 2016, Issue 1. ISBN: 9781922107671. https://www.tandfonline.com/doi/full/10.1080/13241583.2016.1162762

Department of Environmental Protection, Montgomery County, Maryland, USA. "About RainScapes." https://www.montgomerycountymd.gov/water/rainscapes/about.html#types

Hoering, Thomas. "The isotopic composition of the ammonia and the nitrate ion in rain." *Geochimica et Cosmochimica Acta*. Vol. 12, issues 1-2, 1957, 97-102. https://www.sciencedirect.com/science/article/abs/pii/0016703757900212

Johnston, K. "Youths create new rain garden at Broad Meadow Brook in Worcester." 6 September 2017. Worcester Youth Center. https://worcesteryouthcenter.org/2017/09/06/youths-create-new-rain-garden-at-broad-meadow-brook-in-worcester/

Smith, Amy. "Design: Mini-Project: Low-Cost Rainwater Harvesting." 18 February 2020. https://d-lab.mit.edu/news-blog/blog/design-mini-project-low-cost-rainwater-harvesting

Thames21. "Reedbeds." https://www.thames21.org.uk/project-reedbed-2/

Verma, Piyush, "Rainwater harvesting in western Ghats of Maharastra, India: The case of Velhe Block, Pune District: A comprehensive multi-scalar approach." May 2020. https://dspace.mit.edu/handle/1721.1/127557

World Bank. 2013. World Bank Open Data. http://data.worldbank.org/

River From the Sky

Bhagwati Agrawal, Executive Director of Sustainable Innovations, incorporated traditional Indian customs in a project in Rajasthan to collect and distribute rainwater. Agrawal calls the program *Aakash Ganga,* or "River from the Sky." The system collects monsoon rains, thereby channeling potential floods into treasured reservoirs. Catch basins are installed on every available roof in a village; some homes have strong tops suitable for holding a tank, while others may have only a thatched roof. Homes with a tank on top can keep half of the stored water; the other half goes to a communal village cistern to be shared with nearby families. Once-dreaded monsoons are now regarded as a blessing, a veritable "river from the sky."

Rainwater catchment and distribution is a worldwide problem, and opportunity. For example, after the Berlin Wall opened, the city embarked on renovations to Potsdamer Platz, including a 19-building system to catch rainwater, later stored below ground in tanks, to power sanitation and irrigate gardens. Singapore, where 86% of the population resides in high-rise apartments, rooftop catchment is used to save up to 40% of water that would otherwise have to be pumped upward to residential units. The cost of rooftop rainwater is S$0.96 as contrasted to S$1.17. Japan may boast one of the world's most massive rooftop catchment achievements. Dr. "Skywater" Makoto initiated the Skywater Harvesting system now in use at Ryōgoku Kokugikan Sumo Wrestling Arena. Built in 1985, it saves rain on the roof and pipes it to underground storage. The captured and retained water provides sanitation and air conditioning for the stadium, which holds 13,000 people. The arena hosted the boxing competition in the 2020 Summer Olympics.

"Former Ryōgoku Kokugikan Sumo Hall Interior, c. 1910,"
by unknown photographer.

Attribution: see p. 163

Sources:
Ghimire, Santosh R. and John M. Johnston. "Holistic impact assessment and cost savings of rainwater harvesting at the watershed level." 18 July 2017. Environmental Protection Agency. https://www.ncbi.nlm.nih.gov/pmc/articles/PMC6638562/

Global Rain Harvesting Collective (GRWHC). United Nations Partnerships for SDGs Platform. https://sustainabledevelopment.un.org/partnership/?p=1646

"Harvesting Innovations for People," Sustainable Innovations. https://www.si-usa.org

Skywater Harvesting. http://dr-skywater.com

Thames21. "New project to open up access to the Thames." 17 August 2020. Thames21.org.https://www.thames21.org.uk/2020/08/thames21-receives-funding-for-thames-connections-project/

UNEP. "Rainwater Harvesting and Utilisation: An Environmentally Sound Approach for Sustainable Urban Water Management. An Introductory Guide for Decision-makers." IETC Urban Environment Series (2). 2002. https://www.ircwash.org/sites/default/files/213.1-01RA-17421.pdf

Filter of the Future

Local clay from nature's ancient *terra firma* makes new nano filters. Pioneering professors and scientists Ebenezer Annan, Kwabena Kan-Dapaah, Salifu T. Azeko, Kabiru Mustapha, Joseph Asare, M. G. Zebaze Kana, and Wole Soboyejo describe what may be the microporous and nanoporous filter of the future:

> The results of an experimental study of the effects of clay mixtures on the mechanical properties of mixed clays with controlled levels of plasticity, prior to the firing of porous ceramic water filters for water filtration. Two clays with well-characterized initial compositions (Iro and Ewuya clays) are mixed with varying proportions to control their plasticity. The mechanical properties of the mixed and fired clays are then studied using a combination of experiments and theoretical models. These include the flexural strength, fracture toughness, Young's modulus, and thermal shock resistance of fire clay mixtures. The results show that clay mixtures with 45-60 vol.% of Iro clay and 40-55 vol.% Ewuya clay can be used to produce clay composite filters with robust mechanical properties. The thermal shock resistance of a mixed clay filter (containing 50% Iro clay and 50% Ewuya clay) is also explained using a combination of elastic and visco-elastic crack-bridging models. The regimes for effective visco-elastic crack-bridging are identified by comparing the relaxation times to the thermal shock durations. The implications of the results are then discussed for the mixing of locally available clays into robust micro- and nanoporous materials for applications in clay ceramic water filters.

Source:
Annan, Ebenezer, Kwabena Kan-Dapaah, Salifu T. Azeko, Kabiru Mustapha, Joseph Asare, M. G. Zebaze Kana, Wole Soboyejo. "Clay Mixtures and the Mechanical Properties of Microporous and Nanoporous Ceramic Water Filters." *Journal of Materials in Civil Engineering* 28 (10):04016105. May 2016. https://ascelibrary.org/doi/abs/10.1061/%28ASCE%29MT.1943-5533.0001596.

Sift for Success

Askwar Hilonga, chemical engineer from Tanzania, won the inaugural Africa Prize for Engineering Innovation, awarded in 2015 by Britain's Royal Academy of Engineering. His invention married something old (sand) with something new (nanotechnology) to create a water filter. The sifter removes copper, fluoride, bacteria, and even pesticides from water. It is estimated that 70% of Tanzanians lack clean drinking water, so this filter could go a long way toward changing that. Worldwide, the application is equally significant: 660-700 million people (1 in 10) lack safe water, a figure predicted to expand to 1.8 billion.

Even cities with established plumbing lines must examine aging infrastructure to avoid tragedies. In some areas of the world, the fortunate may have clean wells nearby, but these aquifers are also subject to contamination by industries including hydraulic fracturing. Finally, there are millions who must use surface water for both drinking and sanitation. Water filtering is essential for those who await improvement. Filtering, already practiced on the International Space Station where astronauts quaff thirst via purified body fluids, including breath, may be one of the keys to utilizing water in space.

In 2021 the Space Station's Environmental Control and Life Support System (ECLSS) received a new technology, a Brine Processor Assembly (BPA) to increase fluid yields, with a goal of future systems for moon and Mars missions and habitats.

Sources:
Doty, Reiley. "New Brine Processor Increases Water Recycling on International Space Station." 26 February 2021. Johnson Space Center, Houston, TX. https://www.nasa.gov/feature/new-brine-processor-increases-water-recycling-on-international-space-station

NASA. International Space Station Program Science Forum. "International Space Station: Benefits for Humanity," 87-91. NP-2018-06-013-JSC. https://www.nasa.gov/sites/default/files/atoms/files/benefits-for-humanity_third.pdf

Royal Academy of Engineering. "Tanzanian low-cost water filter wins innovation prize." 2 June 2015. BBC.com. https://www.bbc.com/news/world-africa-32973591

Water from Space

In 2009, Lawrence Taylor of the University of Tennessee at Knoxville, recalled that forty years earlier, when Apollo astronauts returned boxes of rocks brought back to Earth from the moon, the boxes were wet. However, Taylor and his colleagues might not have suspected what NASA later discovered: there *is* water on the moon. In 2009, the LCROSS (Lunar Crater Observation and Sensing Satellite) successfully uncovered water during the October 9, 2009 impacts fired into the moon's Cabeus crater.

Mars promises potential; hydrated salts have been confirmed in Hale Crater, according to the Mars Reconnaissance Orbiter. Asteroids may yield water: commercial enterprises, such as Planetary Resources Inc, have structured missions to find, mine, and refine water for many uses including rocket fuel.

Water found in space would change the future, making hydrogen (the H of H_2O) available for refueling rockets in space, for space construction, and industrial processes. Just as reusable booster rockets, like those developed by SpaceX, changed the economics of space transport, refueling in space could make carrying additional fuel obsolete. According to NASA, liquid hydrogen may be the fuel of choice for space exploration.

Enceladus, a Saturn moon, may be among the biggest water reservoirs in the known universe. Enceladus contains 140 trillion times all the water in Earth's oceans—but it is 12 billion light-years away.

Closer, in distance and in potential deployment, is water that NASA and the Taylor team detected. NASA began studying the moon's properties in 2009 via the Lunar Reconnaissance Orbiter, a telescope carried by a Boeing 747SP aircraft in a joint project with German Aerospace Center (DLR) and the Stratospheric Observatory for Infrared Astronomy (SOFIA) . In 2018, SOFIA discovered "widespread hydration" in sunlit lunar areas, in molecular forms and hydroxyl compounds (Honniball, 2020). In 2020, lunar water was confirmed. More water may be on the moon's shadowed areas where it could be in a frozen state (Strickland, 2020). Water means drinking accessibility on a potential lunar base, as well as options for a refueling station in space with hydrogen for rocket fuel.

"Water detected at high latitudes on the moon," by NASA, 2009.
Attribution: see page 163

Sources:
Bradford, C.M., A.D. Bolatto, P.R. Maloney, J.E. Aguirre, et al. "The water vapor spectrum of APM 08279+5255: X-Ray heating and infrared pumping over hundreds of parsecs." arXiv.1106.4301 (astro-ph.CO). DOI: 10.1088/2041-8205/741/2/L37. https://arxiv.org/abs/1106.4301

Asteroids
Voosen, Paul. "A NASA mission is about to capture carbon-rich dust from a former water world." Science Magazine. 8 October 2020. https://www.sciencemag.org/news/2020/10/nasa-mission-about-capture-carbon-rich-dust-former-water-world

Enceladus
Chang, Kenneth. "Under icy surface of a Saturn moon lies a sea of water, scientists say." 3 April 2014. *New York Times.* https://www.nytimes.com/2014/04/04/science/space/a-moon-of-saturn-has-a-sea-scientists-say.html

Hansen, Candice, J., L. Esposito, A.I.F. Steward, J. Colwell, A. Hendrix, W. Pryor, D. Shemansky, and R. West. "Enceladus' water plume." *Science* 311, no. 5766 (10 March 2006): 1422-1425. DOI:10.1126/science.1121254. https://science.sciencemag.org/content/311/5766/1422/tab-article-info

Lunar
Dino, Jonas, "LCROSS impact data indicates water on moon." 13 November 2009. NASA Ames Research Center. https://space.nss.org/lcross-impact-data-indicates-water-on-moon/

Honniball, C.I., P.G. Lucey, S. Li, et al. "Molecular water detected on the sunlit Moon by SOFIA." 26 October 2020. *Nat. Astron* (2020) https://doi.org/10.1038/s41550-020-01222-x

Strickland, Ashley. "NASA mission finds water on the sunlit surface of the moon." 26 October 2020. CNN.com. https://www.cnn.com/2020/10/26/world/moon-water-nasa-announcement-scn-trnd/index.html

Mars
NASA. "NASA confirms evidence that liquid water flows on today's Mars." 28 September 2015. https://www.nasa.gov/press-release/nasa-confirms-evidence-that-liquid-water-flows-on-today-s-mars

O'Callaghan, Jonathan. "Water on Mars: Discovery of three buried lakes intrigues scientists." 28 September 2020. *Nature.* https://www.nature.com/articles/d41586-020-02751-1

Worth Its Salt

Oceans surround us, yet most drinking water does not come from the sea. Advances in desalination may change that. Israel in 2004 derived all potable water from aquifers or rain; by 2010, 20% came from the sea. Israel Desalination Enterprises (IDE) Technologies spent $500 million on *Sorek,* a reverse osmosis facility producing 165,636 gallons (627 cubic meters) of water daily at a cost of $0.58 per person per day. Previous worldwide desalination typically yielded water for agriculture or other non-drinking use. But Israel advanced the field and now desalinates 80% of its drinking water.

A recent tally of desalination plants worldwide counts almost 20,000 facilities: 48% in North Africa and the Middle East (Jones, et al., 2019; Crawford, 2020). More than 300 million people rely on desalinated water. Siemens Austria built, in 2019, a macro-scale desalination plant powered by solar power: so much energy is generated that a surplus of electricity goes to the public grid (Crawford, 2020).

View of the Zarchin Desalination Plant on the Red Sea in Eilat.
by Moshe Pridan, 1964.

Attribution: see p. 164

Because desalination using seawater requires considerable energy resources, innovations include use of inland brackish water resources. Among these innovations: a co-axial composite membrane that filters 99.99% of salt monthly, and brine disposal options (Woo, et al., 2021). Kuwait, Qatar, Saudi Arabia, and the UAE produce over 50% of global brine.

Sources:
Crawford, Mark. "8 Engineering challenges for desalination technologies." 6 May 2020. American Society of Mechanical Engineers (ASME). https://www.asme.org/topics-resources/content/8-engineering-challenges-for-desalination-technologies?utm_source=facebook&utm_medium=social&utm_content=technology_and_society&utm_campaign=wk_050420

Jacobsen, Rowan. "Israel proves the desalination era is here: One of the driest countries on Earth now makes more freshwater than it needs." *Scientific American*, 29 July 2016. https://www.scientificamerican.com/article/israel-proves-the-desalination-era-is-here/

Jones, Edward, et al. "The state of desalination and brine production: A global outlook." April 2019. *Science of the Total Environment* 657 (2019) 1343-1356. https://pubmed.ncbi.nlm.nih.gov/30677901/

Kolyohin, Nick. "Feature: Israel aims to secure all of its water supply through desalination." 22 November 2019. *Xinhuanet* 22 November 2019. http://www.xinhuanet.com/english/20-19-11/c_138575940.htm

Siegel, Seth M. *Let There Be Water: Israel's Solution for a Water-Starved World*. New York: McMillan, 2015. ISBN: 9781466885448.

Siegel, Seth M. *Troubled Water: What's Wrong With What We Drink?* 2019. New York: Thomas Dunn Books. ISBN: 9781250132543.

Woo, Yun Chul, et al. "Co-axially electrospun superhydrophobic nanofiber membranes with 3D-hierarchically structured surface for desalination by long-term membrane distillation." *Journal of Membrane Science*, vol. 623 (2021). https://doi.org/10.1016/j.memsci.2020.119028. https://www.sciencedirect.com/science/article/pii/S0376738820316008

Ocean State's Lot

In a place known for its bridges and beaches, the waters of Rhode Island are of considerable interest, especially to those who live and work on its shores. Sheldon Whitehouse, U.S. Senator from Rhode Island, delivered the inaugural Macro Lecture in honor of Frank P. Davidson, on 31 March 2016, to students, faculty, and community gathered at Roger Williams University in Bristol, noting:

- 2015 was the hottest year on record, with December setting a record for any one month.
- 2016 saw that record broken: February took the honors.
- 2011-2016 was the warmest period on Earth.

Senator Whitehouse has continuing cause for concern: 2021 broke records for heat, with July the hottest month on record in history. Whitehouse gave his famous "Time to Wake Up" speech 279 times to policymakers in the United States, delivering a final warning in 2021. The message will continue to resonate: by 2050, the number of heat-wave days in Rhode Island may quadruple, from 10 to 40. Rainfall is increasing, with 27,000 people living in areas of inland flood risk. Sanitation systems may strain: during a recent hurricane, 18.4 million gallons (69.7 million liters) of sewage spilled due to inundation (States at Risk, 2021). Such rising numbers are ominous for a state that inscribes on its automobile license plates the phrase, "The Ocean State."

As temperatures rise, so do ocean levels. Whitehouse warned that 90% of heat generated by global warming goes into the oceans, as does 30% of CO_2. Students of the law of thermal expansion noted the inevitable conclusion: the hotter it gets, the more oceans will rise. Some observe that global warming does vary statistically according to cycles. But whatever the cause, it is undeniable that rising waters threaten coastal properties such as those of fabled Newport, where Cornelius Vanderbilt (1794–1877) built his "summer cottage" known as The Breakers, and where Jacqueline Bouvier married Senator John F. Kennedy. Disappearing coastlines mean trouble for all homes large and small, old and new, that dot Rhode Island's shores, and of course, coastal communities worldwide.

Lagos, Nigeria, may experience a sea level rise of around 35 inches (89 centimeters) in the next few decades if current warming trends continue. Lagos is home to millions of people; multitudes of houses, businesses, schools, and hospitals face flooding; streets and electrical lines may suffer the effects of inundation. Rising seas are a slow-moving disaster. Another example is Bangladesh, which is particularly susceptible to inundation along its extensive coastline. Island nations are even more vulnerable: whole countries could disappear.

Whitehouse praised Roger Williams University's tree planting program, and the Children's Arboretum of Newport, both of which convey what the senator called innovations resulting from "high-quality frustration." When a problem exists, frustration can develop into positive actions and solutions.

While trees are not the answer in all situations, they may help. Loren White, a student at Roger Williams University, initiated a tree-planting project as an independent study for her architecture degree. Soon, White's effort was joined by classmate Christian Johnson and university officials, which led to a proposal that the entire university campus become an arboretum (Rodrigues, 2015). With 30 species of trees digitally mapped for taxonomic labeling via technology from the U.S. Forest Service, the campus earned its arboreal credential from the Morton Arboretum's ArbNet Arboretum Accreditation Program, which sets world standards. Earth Day, the largest secular observance in the world, set a new direction in 2016: the goal of 7.8 billion trees to be planted in five years.

Trees, and their collective form of forests, hold water. They preserve underground sources and conserve rainwater. Over 30% of the world's watersheds are covered and protected by forests. But even when forests are part of a national program, access to their watersheds may vary. For example, in the United States, a forest may be protected nationally, but use of its water might be determined by the state where the forest is located. In California, water rights law is administered by the State Water Resources Control Board. Surface water, such as that in a lake or stream, is accessed through pipes; groundwater is accessed through wells.

Pōhutukawa trees, Cornwallis Beach, West Auckland, NZ, by Ed323.

Attribution: see p. 164

During drought, water use may be curtailed. In 2021, the system faced considerable challenges during a sustained dry period. On the California/ Oregon border, the Klamath River Basin was unable to provide enough water for fish, especially important to Native American Klamath tribe members who depend on the water for food and for drinking water in local wells. Migratory birds stopped visiting the area. Faced with predictions of continuing drought, residents are searching for their own water rights via the California Water Resources Control Board GIS System.

Worldwide, forest and water rights also vary. The United Nations Food and Agriculture Organization (FAO), and the Economic Commission for Europe (ECE), directed a study about ways in which payments for ecosystem services can be applied to forests, focusing on hydrological functions for the benefit of humans and the broader environment UNECE, 2018).

Trees have measurable economic value. Professor T. M. Das, University of Calcutta, states that a tree living for 50 years generates:

- $31,250 worth of oxygen
- $62,000 worth of air pollution control and soil erosion prevention
- $37,500 soil fertility increase
- $31,250 home shelter for animals.

Professor Das' figures do not include the value of fruit, lumber, or beauty. The U.S. Forest Service estimates homes increase in value if trees are on the property, with some prices rising as much as 20%. Soon, the Ocean State may become known for both waves and leaves. Can Rhode Island serve as an example for other areas of the world that must combat ocean rise?

Trees also help mitigate climate change by absorbing CO_2 emissions. In many areas of the world, deforestation—cutting and clearing trees to use land for other purposes—depletes forests that absorb the warming gas. During the 2021 meeting in Glasgow for COP26, in the "Global Forest Finance Pledge: Glasgow Leaders' Declaration on Forests and Land Use," world leaders pledged $19 billion to end and reverse deforestation by 2030. Notable among the signatories was Brazil, where Amazon forests have suffered significant deforestation. Canada, China, Russia, nations of the EU, the UK, and the United States also signed the declaration; these nations represent more than 85% of the world's forests. Equally important, 30 global financial organizations agreed to end investment in activities tied to cutting forests. Finally, a fund to protect the world's second largest rainforest, in the Congo Basin, completed the pact. Some observers noted that a similar pledge, the "New York Declaration on Forests" of 2014, promised hope but ended in disappointment: some key countries like Brazil, China, and Russia were not signatories. Brazil is home to the planet's biggest rainforest, and Russia has more than 20% of the world's trees. Optimists noted that the difference between 2014's declaration and 2021's is indicated in the title: the key commitment of financing.

Sources:
Beckham, Nancy. "Trees: finding their true value: pricing the environment." https://www.unep.org/news-and-stories/opinion/heatwaves-rising-seas-how-trees-defend-us

Kirkpatrick, Nick, et al. "Climate change fuels a water rights conflict built on over a century of broken promises." 22 November 2021. *Washington Post.* https://www.washingtonpost.com/nation/interactive/2021/klamath-river-basin-drought/

Lodge, Michael W. Remarks, UN Global Compact Action Platform for Sustainable Ocean Business, High Level meeting on Ocean. "Ocean as part of the solution – How industries can lead on delivering on the 17 SDGs and the opportunities of the Ocean in particular." 3 June 2019, Oslo, Norway. https://isa.org.jm/files/documents/En/SG-Stats/3_June_2019.pdf

Lyons, Katie and Todd Gartner. "3 Surprising Ways Water Depends on Healthy Forests." 21 March 2017. World Resources Institute. https://www.wri.org/insights/3-surprising-ways-water-depends-healthy-forests

Rannard, Georgina and Francesca Gillett. "COP26: World leaders promise to end deforestation by 2030." 2 November 2021. https://www.bbc.com/news/science-environment-59088498.

Rodrigues, Jill. "RWU Arboretum a Reality as Campus Earns Accreditation." 13 October 2015. Roger Williams University. https://www.rwu.edu/news/news-archive/rwu-arboretum-reality-campus-earns-accreditation.

State of California. "Water Rights Maps." 23 November 2021. https://waterrightsmaps.waterboardsca.gov/viewer/index.html?viewer=eWRIMS.eWRIMS_gvh#

States at Risk. "Preparedness Report Card: Rhode Island." Climate Central, 2021. https://statesatrisk.org

United Nations Climate Change Conference: UK 2021 in partnership with Italy. "The Global Forest Finance Pledge: Financing the protection, restoration, and sustainable management of forests." 2 November 2021. https://ukcop26.org/the-global-forest-finance-pledge/

United Nations Environment Programme. "From heatwaves to rising seas: How trees defend us." 11 September 2019. https://www.straitstimes.com/opinion/from-heatwaves-to-rising-seas-how-trees-defend-us

United States Forest Service. "Watershed Rights: Water rights on national forests and grasslands." 23 November 2021. https://www.fs.fed.us/naturalresources/watershed/water_rights.shtml

United States Forest Service. "Water rights curtailment in California's national forests." 23 November 2021. https://www.fs.usda.gov/internet/FSE_DOCUMENTS/stelprd3844946.pdf.

Whitehouse, Sheldon, and Jack Reed. "Federal delegation announces nearly $2 billion to bolster RI coastline: Grants for nature conservancy and CRMC will protect homes, businesses from rising seas." 14 July 2017. https://www.reed.senate.gov/news/releases/federal-delegation-announces-nearly-2-million-to-bolster-ri-coastline

Waterfront City Squares

The Erie Canal, completed in 1825, and flowing from lake to river to ocean, became the fastest, newest, and cheapest way to ship goods. Cargo from Syracuse to New York Harbor previously cost $100; with the canal, it cost $10. Ships became more popular and larger; the canal had to be widened (the same was also true later for the Panama Canal). The canal was soon bypassed in favor of other shipping methods. Today, while parts of the canal are active, supporting tourism and recreation in what could be termed an aquatic greenway, other segments are used very little. What could the Erie Canal do with its no-longer-used waterway segments?

One solution is Canalside, a town square in Buffalo, New York. The area was originally developed in 1825 as the western terminus for the Erie Canal. When trains and trucks took over much of the transport of goods, Buffalo's Erie Canal Harbor declined in use and was eventually filled in with dirt, stone, and pavement, with some of it used for parking lots. Thus was the state of the "harbor" at the turn of the millennium.

Buffalo's mayor and the New York Power Authority gave the state a 50-year license to draw energy from nearby Niagara Falls, with a financial incentive of $7 million annually so waterfront communities could change from an industrial focus with considerable polluting factors to cleaning up the waterfront by making it a star-studded gateway. The result? Erie Canal Harbor Development Corporation. Nearby, the town of Niagara Falls opened three new hotels, with the mayor stating: "Give us back access to our waterfront, and we'll rebuild our community" (McClelland, 2016). Just after 2000, Erie Canal Harbor returned—this time rebuilt as a waterfront, with cooperation from ECHDC and state authorities working together. The new waterfront drew visitors of every description: businesses like the views, and tourists like the businesses. Hotels began to open. Condos were built and sold. What about winter when cold winds blow and water freezes? The Dutch have known that answer for a long time: ice skating along waterways. The ice at Canalside typically freezes in mid-November and becomes a skateway until daffodils bloom. In the spring, summer, and fall, there is kayaking.

Canalside Buffalo, by Invest Buffalo Niagara, 2015.

Attribution: see p. 164

Real estate prices around Canalside skyrocketed. One developer proposed building 20 condos and 10 townhomes on Lakefront Boulevard, with unit sale prices averaging $650,000. The company, in this case Ciminelli Real Estate Corporation, acquired the land with exclusive rights to develop for $2.2 million. The residences were to be set back 100 feet from the water. Another bidder, McGuire Development Group and Impacto Consulting, proposed a similar combination of condos and townhomes set back just 50 feet. The Waterfront Village Association works with developers and community to determine setbacks.

The message was clear. Buffalo was back. Original investment? $35 million. Yield? $200 million. Added bonus? Jobs: more than 1,000 positions. Buffalo rebuilt and reached out in various directions. Among the results? Tesla Inc. opened a plant in the new RiverBend complex in western New York State.

Among the world's canal cities, Annecy, France, is sometimes called the Venice of the Alps and features the Thiou canal; Bruges, Belgium, is encircled by canals and was named a UNESCO World Heritage Site. Inland Waterways International (IWI) promotes "conservation, use, development, and proper management of inland waterways worldwide" (IWI, 2020). IWI is part of an initiative called Navigating a Changing Climate that includes ports and waterfront squares. With rising seas, coastal communities may expect challenges, and perhaps opportunities, that may spur innovation.

Sources:
Epstein, Jonathan. "Condo project approved at Waterfront Village." *Buffalo News*, 22 January 2015. https://ciminelli.com/news/article/current/2015/01/22/100007/condo-project-approved-at-waterfront-village/

Inland Waterways International. "Promoting inland waterways." https://inlandwaterwaysinternational.org/

McClelland, Edward. "How Buffalo got its waterfront back: River restoration is influencing the city's economy, public space, and environmental health." Next City: Inspiring Better Cities. 5 December 2016. https://nextcity.org/features/view/buffalo-waterfront-redevelopment-economy/

Navigating a Changing Climate Partnership. https://navclimate.pianc.org/

UNESCO. "Historic Centre of Brugge: World Heritage Site." 2000. https://whc.unesco.org/en/list/996/

Floodscapes

Climate science is clear: the water is coming, in volume greater or less, depending on us. Given this certainty, there are two ways to deal with that reality: barriers and entries. There is no doubt barriers are important and protective.

The Netherlands has been described as "a sinking country bordering a rising sea." But the Dutch have prevailed. In the past 2,000 years, the sea has overtaken 1.4 million acres (566,560 ha) of the Netherlands—but the Dutch have reclaimed 1.8 million acres (728,434 ha). And they have been doing so since the days of Pliny the Elder who reported in the first century that inhabitants of the country constructed dams in tidal creeks to protect their land from flooding. Behind the dams were hollowed tree trunks that served as sluices. Handiwork included ingenious valves on tree trunks fashioned so as to close at high tide. The sluice/valve principle worked so well that it is still popular today.

Barriers continue to be useful and essential. The Dutch city of Rotterdam built *Maeslantkering*, a storm barrier system. Construction started in 1991, with completion and opening on 10 May 1997. If Rotterdam is threatened by floods, a supercomputer closes the gates. It is one of the largest moving structures on Earth. To make the storm surge barrier more understandable to citizens, a Public Water Management Information Center was built in 1996 to showcase Dutch water management. There's also a webcam to observe the massive barrier.

October 2020 brought high tides and floods to Venice, Italy. Floods of a similar sort inundated the city in 2019 when the deluge was the most severe in half a century, causing more than $1 billion in damage. But in 2020, a new barrier called MOSE, formed by a system of 78 floodgates, protected the city. In normal conditions, the barriers are invisible: they rest on the bottom of the lagoon. But when a storm surge occurs, barriers inflate, float to the surface, and seal off three key lagoon inlets. Venice has waited for MOSE since the 1980s, but various factors caused delays. While the system worked well in 2020, environmentalists worry that sea-rise would have consequences, causing the floodgates to be used more than 100 days per year, sealing off the lagoon from the sea and stopping natural flows that nourish the lagoon.

"*Maeslantkering,* northern half 3," by Joop van Houdt and Rijkswaterstaat, 2010.

Attribution: see p. 164

But assuming water will get in (a probability that may increase as seas warm and rise), what about directing floods into prepared floodscapes? Letting water come in is a different approach to rising seas, one that may provide an opportunity to rebuild coastal areas with a future of benefit rather than prevention. For example, Rotterdam, once the world's largest port and a city that is 90% below sea level. In addition to the *Maeslantkering* barrier, this city found a creative solution by building the *Eendragtspolder*, where flood water is allowed to fill a waterway for aquatic sporting competitions. In August 2016, the World Rowing Championships were held there.

In the United States, a comprehensive coastal map of the so-called "Lower 48" revealed that more than 100 communities will be subject to chronic flooding by

2030. And it gets worse. By 2100, more than 600 cities and towns will likely be underwater. Four of the five boroughs in New York City will be inundated.

As warming seas increase the ferocity of hurricanes and threaten coastal areas, scholars are beginning to see changes in public opinion. According to a study conducted by the Yale Program on Climate Change Communication, "Florida has been directly hit by 117 hurricanes between 1851 and 2017, ranking first among all states for direct hits. Texas, Louisiana, North Carolina, and South Carolina have also experienced frequent direct hits. More than half of the residents of these five states believe global warming is affecting the weather, and that global warming will harm people in the United States" (Talaty, et al., 2020).

WINDOW ON THE ECONOMY

Top 9 U.S. Tidal Flooding Towns:

Miami, Florida
Florida Keys, Florida
Savannah, Georgia
Annapollis, Maryland
South Jersey Shore, New Jersey
Jamaica Bay, New York
Outer Banks, North Carolina
Charleston, South Carolina
Norfolk, Virginia

Source:

VIDEO: Verge Science. "This is what sea level rise will do to coastal cities." 23 April 2019. https://www.youtube.com/watch?v+6tesHVSZJOg.

Responses? Among recommended policies are incentives for households and businesses to flood-proof their buildings. Another approach? Rethink zoning laws in flood-prone areas where overbuilding is prevalent. Instead, build sea walls or consider natural floodscapes. Residential and business areas could move back from encroaching seas. Cities could rebuild waterfronts in a new way. Waterfront design may be one of the biggest areas of innovation and success in the future.

"It takes decades for us to get our act together and build things," warns landscape architect Kristina Hill of the University of California, Berkeley. "Future generations won't have the luxury of decades. They're going to be coping with two feet of sea level rise over 25 years potentially" (Bird, 2016). Hill recommends planning for worst consequences, because even if it doesn't happen immediately, it's going to happen eventually. Instead of trying to wall out water, Hill advises a landscaping hybrid—a mix of beaches, levies, ponds and wetlands that can absorb several feet of storm surge.

The combination of natural and built environments was once termed "cyborg" by Elizabeth Meyer of the University of Virginia when describing Frederick Law

Olmstead's design of the Back Bay Fens in Boston, Massachusetts. Olmstead restored the muddy, bug-infested Fens area, making it part of a ring of parks now known as the Emerald Necklace. San Francisco took note. Hill developed "horizontal levees" in the Bay Area, adding a levee to land that abuts an ocean, creating a wedge that breaks inundating sea-rise waves and reduces their height. Coasts in Florida, New York, and North Carolina, require preparations as well. More wetlands, more dunes and beaches might restrain high waves, and houses on pilings might survive severe flood damage.

But it's more than just houses on pilings. What about sewage systems? Roadways? Hill predicts: "If sea level rise goes to four feet [1.2 m], we will have so many infrastructure investments we have to make, sewage treatment plants, sewage pipes, which will fill with groundwater, contaminated soil that will be remobilized by rising water tables" (Hill, 2010).

Sources:

Abraham, John. "Sea level rise is accelerating; how much it costs is up to us." *Guardian*, 11 March 2016. https://www.theguardian.com/environment/climate-consensus-97-per-cent/2016/mar/11/sea-level-rise-is-accelerating-how-much-it-costs-is-up-to-us

Aridi, Rasha. "Venice's Controversial Inflatable Floodgates Save City for the Second Time: The barriers may not be permanent solutions, but they've now protected Venice from two floods this month." 19 October 2020. *Smithsonian Magazine*. https://www.smithsonianmag.com/smart-news/venices-new-floodgates-deployed-second-time-shielding-city-potentially-destructive-floods-180976087/

Bird, Winifred. "Rethinking urban landscapes to adapt to rising sea levels." https://e360.yale.edu/features/rethinking_urban_landscapes_to_adapt_to_rising_sea_levels_climate_change_new_york_city

Boettle, M., D. Dybski, J.P. Kropp. "Quantifying the effect of sea level rise and flood defence – a point process perspective on coastal flood damage." *National Hazards and Earth System Sciences: An interactive open-access journal of the European Geosciences Union*. Volume 16, issue 2. 29 February 2016. https://nhess.copernicus.org/articles/16/559/2016/

Brooke, Kathleen Lusk. "Rising Seas." May 2020. Building the World Blog. University of Massachusetts Boston. http://blogs.umb.edu/buildingtheworld/2020/05/09/water-pulitzer-prize-and-climate-change/

Hill, Kristina and Jared Green. Interview with Kristina Hill. 2010. American Society of Landscape Architects. https://www.asla.org/ContentDetail.aspx?id=28548

Kimmelman, Michael. "The Dutch have solutions to rising seas. It's an opportunity." Changing Climate, Changing Cities series. *New York Times*. 15 June 2017. https://www.nytimes.com/interactive/2017/06/15/world/europe/climate-change-rotterdam.html

Neumann, Barbara, Athanasios T. Vafeidis, Juliane Zimmerman, and Robert J. Nicholls. "Future coastal population growth and exposure to sea-level rise and coastal flooding – a global assessment." 11 March 2015. *PLOS ONE* 10(3):e0118571. https://pubmed.ncbi.nlm.nih.gov/25760037/

Radford, Tim. "Scientists set out costs of sea level rise." 15 March 2016. *Climate News Network*. https://climatenewsnetwork.net/scientists-work-out-costs-of-sea-level-rise/

Ramirez, Rachel. "Floods are getting worse, and the number of people exposed is 10 times higher than previously thought." CNN.com. 4 August 2021. https://www.cnn.com/2021/08/04/weather/global-flood-risk-climate-change/index.html

Talaty, Urvi, Peter Howe, Matto Mildenberger, Jennifer Marlon, and Anthony Leiserowitz. "Are hurricane-prone states more concerned about climate change?" 24 July 2020. Yale Program on Climate Change

Communication. https://climatecommunication.yale.edu/publications/are-hurricane-prone-states-more-concerned-about-climate-change/

Union of Concerned Scientists. "Encroaching tides: How sea level rise and tidal flooding threaten US East and Gulf Coast communities over the next 30 years." 2014. https://www.ucsusa.org/resources/encroaching-tides

Welby, Justin. "Our moral opportunity on climate change." 3 November 2017. *New York Times.* https://www.nytimes.com/2017/11/03/opinion/faith-climate-change-justin-welby.html

Renewing Aquifers and Springs

Aquifers and springs worldwide are sources of water for drinking and agricultural irrigation. Several factors threaten these resources: climate change, deforestation, land use, and population growth. In 2018, the International Centre for Integrated Mountain Development (ICIMOD) created a protocol for reviving springs in the Hindu Kush Himalayan region. The

"Panoramique mont Everest," by Fabien1309, and Lerian, 2005.
Attribution: see p. 164

Centre serves Afghanistan, Bangladesh, Bhutan, China, India, Myanmar, Nepal, and Pakistan. In partnership with the Advanced Centre for Water Resources Development and Management (ACWADAM), an aquifer-based, participatory groundwater management organization, a study led by Professor Rajendra B. and team created a manual of practices and programmatic applications to revive and preserve these springs. There are six steps: 1) mapping springs and springsheds; 2) setting up a data monitoring system; 3) understanding social and governance systems; 4) performing hydrological mapping of the recharge area; 5) establishing springshed management protocols; and 6) measuring the impact of actions and refining the approach (Shrestha, 2018. Fig. 21, p. 23).

While the Himalayan initiative works with supporting processes to recharge water resources, another approach is Aquifer Storage and Recovery (ASR). Likening the process to a savings account in a bank, water is deposited by injection into aquifers, stored, and accessed when needed. One concern is what might happen when inserted water mixes with natural water.

Another process, Managed Aquifer Recharge (MAR), is widely practiced in the United States, with projects in every region of the country. Arizona, California, Florida, Idaho, New Jersey, New Mexico, Ohio, and Oregon are among states that use recharge methods for aquifers. The oldest system dates to 1967 in New Jersey, where ASR wells still provide drinking water for the influx of summer visitors to the Jersey shore. In both ASR and MAR processes, water filtration and treatment are mandatory before water is released for public consumption.

With climate warming, land use change, and population growth, every area of the world needs to conserve water. Aquifer and spring management is one effort to provide water for an increasingly thirsty world.

Sources:
Advanced Centre for Water Resources Development and Management (ACWADAM). http://www.acwadam.org

Environmental Protection Agency (EPA). "Aquifer recharge and aquifer storage and recovery." https://www.epa.gov/uic/aquifer-recharge-and-aquifer-storage-and-recovery

International Centre for Integrated Mountain Development (ICIMOD). https://www.icimod.org/

National Groundwater Association. "Managed Aquifer Recharge." https://www.ngwa.org.

Shrestha, Rajendra B., et al. *Protocol for Reviving Springs in the Hindu Kush Himalayas: A Practitioner's Manual*. April 2018. Kathmandu: ICIMOD. ISBN: 9789291156078. https://lib.icimod.org/record/34040

Reinventing the Toilet

Sanitation is one of the greatest needs of water equality and water rights. United Nations' Sustainable Development Goal 6 urges universal access to safe water, including equitable sanitation by 2030. Meeting that target will require new infrastructure investment of $114 billion per year.

Sustainable Development Goal 6: Clean Water and Sanitation
by United Nations, 2016.

Attribution: see p. 164

An initiative of the Bill & Melinda Gates Foundation, Reinvent the Toilet Challenge, seeks to bring increased health to more than 2.5 billion people in the world who do not have proper access by encouraging new and innovative designs. Gates explained: "If we apply creative thinking to everyday challenges, such as dealing with human waste, we can fix some of the world's toughest problems" (Gates, 2012). This challenge is part of the Water, Sanitation & Hygiene section of the foundation for which the initiative reserved $370 million for sustainable sanitation.

The toilet of the future could incorporate several benefits and features:
- captures and processes human waste
- transforms human waste into useful resources such as water and energy
- does not use piped water, sewer
- does not require electricity
- an affordable price.

Once Gates announced the challenge in 2012, the race was on. The first year's winners met goals in innovative ways. One design from the California Institute of Technology was a solar-powered toilet that generates hydrogen and electricity; it won first prize of US$100,000.

"Solar septic tank toilet prototype, front view,"
by SuSanA Secretariat (Sustainable Sanitation Alliance), 2014.
Attribution: see p. 164

A toilet that produces minerals, biological chemicals, and clean water merited $60,000 for a second-place entry by Loughborough University, United Kingdom. The University of Toronto won the $40,000 third-place price with a toilet that sanitizes bodily outputs while also recovering used water resources. A fourth prize recognized the importance of user interface; the Swiss Federal Institute of Aquatic Science and Technology won that award.

Because infrastructure supporting toilets may be complex in some situations, there are innovations that promise considerable progress. For example, there are more than 4,000 toilets in India, each powered by so-called 'Tiger' worms. The worms reside in a container placed below the toilet. These toilets look like latrines but have no scent, do not require hook-up to a sewer, do not flush but compost waste, and remove 99% of pathogens leaving behind usable compost—all at a cost of $350 per unit. Wastewater returns to the ground.

The Bill & Melinda Gates Foundation, as part of the Reinventing the Toilet challenge, awarded $4.8 million to the London School of Hygiene and Tropical Medicine (LSHTM) to accelerate the technology; there was also testing supported by the U.S. Agency for International Development (USAID) for locations in India, Myanmar, and Uganda. Lixil Group, with divisions including American Standard and Grohe, signed a letter of intent to bring Tiger Toilets to market worldwide. According to Bill Gates, it's a significant market, worth $6 billion by 2030.

An expansion of the Gates idea invited engineers and designers in China to research, develop, and produce a "next generation toilet." The Chinese challenge was the first country-specific initiative, launched in Beijing with the Chinese People's Association for Friendship with Foreign Countries, China Friendship Foundation for Peace and Development, and the University of Science and Technology Beijing.

India's progress on sanitation, a goal raised by Prime Minister Narendra Modi during his first national speech, resulted in a campaign called *Swachh Bharat* (Clean India) which would install 75 million toilets. In 2017, three years into the mission, *Swachh Bharat* has reached 1,334 cities, achieving waste-to-energy production of 88.4 megawatts. To monitor progress, India commenced *Swachh Survekshan*, a survey to update progress on Clean India; in 2020, the survey covered 4,242 cities in 28 days.

WINDOW ON THE ECONOMY

Three in ten people worldwide lack access to safe water at home;
six in ten live without managed sanitation.

Sources:
http://sanitationandwaterforall.org/.

VIDEO: World Merit.org. "United Nations SDG6 Explained," 1 March 2016.
https://www.youtube.com/watch?v=hYfZw-bpfJw.

Mt. Everest is a peak so legendary that many strive to climb it; in so doing, mountaineers leave more than memories: 28,000 pounds of human waste, some deposited in open pits. Everest climber Zuraina Zaharin partnered with Imad Agi to invent a waterless sanitation station using microbes to turn human waste into fertilizer so safe it can be used in organic farming. ECOLOO, their product, has been installed in remote locations, like Everest and some island vacation retreats. Several units are now available at Petra, a UNESCO World Heritage Site. ECOLOO also is planning to make units available for disaster response.

September 2020: toilet delivery to the International Space Station represented a new era for space sanitation. Referred to by the acronym UWMS (Universal Waste Management System), the new loo is 65% smaller and 40% lighter than the ISS's current amenity.

Two sanitation fixtures will sit side-by-side in Node 3 of the station. One of the innovations in the new model: fittings that are universally suitable to both male and female use. Like the older model, UWMS has a mechanism to collect and treat urine to recycle as reclaimed water. If successful, UWMS could be used on future missions and space environments including the moon. Some engineers may see in UWMS adaptive possibilities to help solve the terrestrial need for universal sanitation.

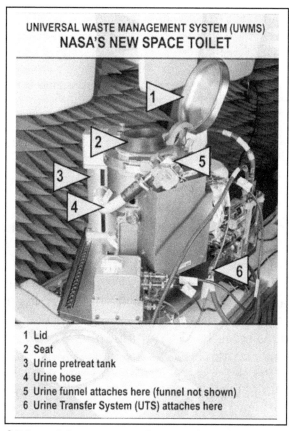

"Universal Waste Management System (UWMS): NASA's New Space Toilet,"
by NASA, 2020.

Attribution: see p. 165

Sources:
Brueck, Hilary. "A $350 toilet powered by worms may be the ingenious future of sanitation that Bill Gates has been dreaming about." *Business Insider*. 13 January 2019. https://www.businessinsider.com/ bill-gates-foundation-helps-invent-tiger-toilets-powered-by-worms-2019-1

Ecoloo Group. "Sustainable Toilet for All." https://www.ecoloogroup.com/

Gates Foundation. "Bill Gates names winners of the Reinvent the Toilet Challenge." August 2012. https://www.gatesfoundation.org/ideas/media-center/press-releases/2012/08/bill-gates-names-winners-of-the-reinvent-the-toilet-challenge

Gates Foundation. "Reinvent the Toilet Challenge: A brief history." 2021. https://www.gatesfoundation.org/our-work/programs/global-growth-and-opportunity/water-sanitation-and-hygiene/reinvent-the-toilet-challenge-and-expo

Government of India, Ministry of Housing and Urban Affairs. "Swachh Bharat." http://www.swachhbharaturban.in/sbm/home/#/SBM.

Mathewson, Samantha. "NASA's new $23 million space toilet is ready for launch." 25 September 2020. https://www.space.com/nasa-space-toilet-ready-for-launch/

Modi, Narendra. "Swachh Bharat Abhiyan." https://www.pmindia.gov.in/en/major_initiatives/swachh-bharat-abhiyan/

Rai, Arpan. "4,242 cities, 92 Ganga towns and 1.87 *crore* citizens: All you need to know about Swachh Survekshan 2020." 18 August 2020. *Hindustan Times*. https://www.hindustantimes.com/india-news/swachh-survekshan-2020-all-you-need-to-know-4-242-cities-92-ganga-towns-and-1-87-crore-citizens/story-bhOZzRPG5khHyL1VHanQ4K.html

United Nations. Department of Economic and Social Affairs (DESA). "The Sustainable Development Goals explained: Clean water and sanitation." Leanne Burney, 17 September 2015. https://www.youtube.com/watch?v=LCKsU4bPFOQ

World Health Organization (WHO). "WHO calls for increased investment to reach the goal of a toilet for all." 1 October 218. https://www.who.int/news/item/01-10-2018-who-calls-for-increased-investment-to-reach-the-goal-of-a-toilet-for-all

Water Credit

Gary White, co-founder with Matt Damon of Water.org, introduced micro-financing to bring safe drinking water and sanitation to more than seven million people in ten countries. White observed that many people living in areas with scarce water spent 20% of their income on water. Working with existing financial systems not yet offering loans for water and sanitation, Water.org and WaterCredit developed ways to include such household improvements in loans; 99% of the loans are repaid. Another fact? $1.00 put into WaterCredit yields $24.00 of impact. Microcredit is often cited as the idea of Muhammad Yunus, recipient of the 2006 Nobel Peace Prize along with Grameen Bank, and Dr. Akhtar Hameed Khan, founder of the Pakistan Academy for Rural Development (PARD).

Sources:
Salzman, James. *Drinking Water: A History*. 2012. Peter Mayer Publishers. ISBN: 9781468306750.

United Nations. "Sustainable Development Goals: 17 Goals to Transform Our World: Goal 6: Ensure access to water and sanitation for all." https://www.un.org/sustainabledevelopment/water-and-sanitation/

Water.org. "WaterCredit Toolkits for Financial Institutions." https://water.org/solutions/watercredit/lending-for-water-sanitation/watercredit-toolkits/

White, Gary. "Commencement Address, Missouri University of Science & Technology, December 13, 2013." See also, "An Interview With: Water.org's White," by Carlos David Mogollón, *WaterWorld*, 1 October 2009. https://www.waterworld.com/international/article/16217882/an-interview-with-waterorgs-gary-white

Yunus, Muhammad. "Nobel Lecture." 10 December 2006. https://www.nobelprize.org/prizes/peace/2006/yunus/lecture.

Meat-Free Mondays

Those who have plenty of water, and means enough to eat plentifully, may wonder what they can do personally to help the world retain and preserve water. Animal agriculture and the related effects on land, water, energy, and climate change were the subject of a 2017 video by Sir Paul McCartney. In 1964, John Lennon and McCartney wrote a song titled "Eight Days a Week."

"Musical Notes" from Wikimedia Commons.
Sir Paul McCartney challenges you to compose a song for Meat Free Mondays (www.meatfreemondays.com).

Attribution: see p. 165

Many years later, McCartney asked the question: "What can I as an individual do?" to save the world's water. He recommended one day a week without meat. MeatFreeMondays.com, launched by Paul, Mary, and Stella McCartney, encourages people to help slow climate change by voting with their food choices. Paul also wrote a song, "Meat Free Monday," and invited people around the world to send in songs, too.

A fashion designer, Stella McCartney is among those developing sustainable fashion with fabrics and production methods that recycle, and leather made from vegetable sources. Other fashion trends include clothing and shoes made from algae and mycelia.

Meat Free Mondays reached out to school lunch programs worldwide. Another related innovation—and an important aid to fulfilling the mission—is *The Meat Free Monday Cookbook*, which features recipes from chefs worldwide.

VOICE OF THE FUTURE
— Sir Paul McCartney

"If someone gave up meat one day a week for a year, their carbon footprint is reduced to the equivalent of not driving a car for a month."

Source:
McCartney, Paul. "Paul McCartney on Meat Free Monday." https://youtu.be/1E1NDjltMvk

VIDEO: McCartney, Paul. "Meat Free Monday Song." Listen to the song: https://www.youtube.com/watch?v=NnNFryHonQo

Sources:
Hunt, Katie. "Why the search for the perfect vegan leather starts on the forest floor." CCN Style. 29 September 2020. https://www.cnn.com/style/article/vegan-leather-alternatives-fungi-biofabric-scn/index.html

McCartney, Paul. "Meat Free Monday." LISTEN to the song: https://www.youtube.com/watch?v=NnNFryHonQo

McCartney, Paul, Mary McCartney, Stella McCartney. "Meat Free Mondays: Global Campaigns." September 2020. https://meatfreemondays.com/global/

McCartney, Stella. "Materials and Innovation." https://www.stellamccartney.com/us/en/sustainability/sustainability.html.

Ramsing, Becky. "Food Trends for 2020 Show a Sustainability Focus." 7 January 2020. Johns Hopkins Center for a Livable Future. https://clf.jhsph.edu/viewpoints/food-trends-2020-show-sustainability-focus

Fashion Forward

Fashion designers and producers are leading a revolution in the garment industry, currently responsible for 5-10% of global greenhouse gas emissions and 20% of the world's untreated wastewater—the result of dyeing fabrics. Leather jackets made from mushrooms, garments produced in safe and just factories, fibers that are sustainable, shoes that biodegrade, and plastic shopping bags transformed into fabrics, are some of the trends transforming fashion.

Ralph Lauren Corporation announced "Color on Demand" in its adoption of ECOFAST™, a sustainable textile method developed by Dow, which will be used in 80% of Ralph Lauren wear by 2025. ECOFAST™ uses 40% less water, 85% fewer chemicals, and 90% less energy. The Circular Fibres Initiative launched by the Ellen MacArthur Foundation brings together industry leaders to change the life cycle and supply chain of fashion fibers and textiles. *Circular Design for Fashion* (December, 2021) features interviews with designers and offers insights from more than 80 circular design practitioners in fashion.

"Palette de teintures végétales sur soie," by Florent Beck, 2019.
(Trans: "Palette of vegetable dyes on silk")

Attribution: see p. 165

Designer Stella McCartney placed sustainability fact sheets on seats at the Palais Garnier for her 2020 spring collection show. Will garments of the future have sustainability ratings and ingredient tags along with laundering instructions? Is there a market for a fashion line in the color of blue, with a portion of the purchase supporting water sustainability?

Sources:
Ellen MacArthur Foundation. *Circular Design for Fashion*. Ellen MacArthur Foundation Publishing. December 2021. https://circulardesignfashion.emf.org

Ellen MacArthur Foundation. "Redesigning the future of fashion." https://ellenmacarthurfoundation.org/topics/fashion/overview

McCartney, Stella. "Circular Fashion/Circular Economy." StellaMcCartney.com. https://www.stellamccartney.com/experience/en/sustainability/circularity-2/

Newbold, Alice. "Stella McCartney: Sustainability is the future of fashion, not just a trend." 30 September 2019. *Vogue*. https://www.vogue.co.uk/tags/stella-mccartney

Ralph Lauren Corporation. "Ralph Lauren revolutionizes how the fashion industry dyes cotton." 22 March 2021. https://corporate.ralphlauren.com/pr_210322_ColorOnDemand.html

Water-Food-Energy Nexus

Water, food, and energy are interrelated. For instance, in California, should one choose water to produce food, generate electricity, or provide tap water? In Lebanon and Egypt, continually encroaching drought can increase competition for water resources by both the national population and each country's requirements for industrial growth.

A project with the American University of Beirut, The American University in Cairo, American University of Sharjah (UAE), Birzeit University (Palestine), Lebanese American University, and University of California, Davis, aimed to find innovations in the water-energy-food nexus. The result was "Minimizing the Losses of Water, Energy, and Food throughout the Agriculture and Supply Chain Processes," which explored case studies in Egypt, Lebanon, Palestine, the United Arab Emirates, and the United States, particularly California. One goal: to develop strategies and possible models for regions around the world that share similar resources and conditions.

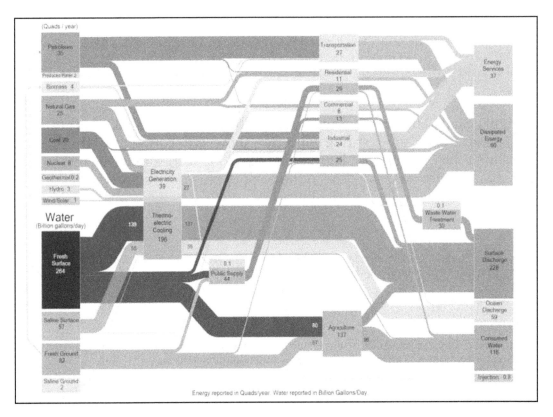

"Hybrid Sankey Diagram of 2011 U.S. Interconnected Water and Energy Flows."
by Bauer, Philbrick, and Vallario, U.S. Department of Energy, 2014.

Attribution: see p. 165

Explorations of the water-food-energy nexus also engage the next generation. *(Re)Connect the Nexus* announced a video competition open to anyone under 25. Videos from Brazil, India, Singapore, and the United Kingdom were immediately posted to the site, with viewing and voting via YouTube.

According to Upmanu Lall of the Columbia Water Center, water security has emerged as a global concern. "This creates the impetus for a broad range of innovations that should disrupt water and wastewater services. The most significant disruption I expect to see is that a much greater role will emerge for the private sector" (Lall, 2018).

The water-food-energy nexus balances three factors, increasing in demand by a rising world population. Agriculture consumes the largest portion of freshwater resources; more than 25% of global energy is used in food production and supply (United Nations, 2020). The water-food-energy nexus requires an integrated systems' approach to balance and sustain these critical resources in response to global growth.

In the next volume, we'll explore another element, energy.

Sources:

Lall, Upmanu. "Positive water sector disruptions by 2030." 2 December 2018. Columbia University, Opinion paper prepared for the Inter-American Development Bank. https://www.researchgate.net/publication/331949159_Positive_Water_Sector_Disruptions_by_2030

Spang, Edward. "New UC Davis podcast tackles food waste and loss as a way to feed the planet." 1 October 2019. https://spang.ucdavis.edu/news/new-uc-davis-podcast-tackles-food-waste-and-loss-way-feed-planet

Spang, Edward, et al., "Food-Energy-Water (FEW) Nexus: Informal Water Systems." https://spang.ucdavis.edu/food-energy-water-few-nexus

Spang Lab. https://spang.ucdavis.edu

Springmann, Marco, et al. "Options for Keeping the Food System Within Environmental Limits." *Nature*, 11 October 2018. https://doi.org/10.1038/s41586-018-0594-0

United Nations. "Water, Food, and Energy." 2020. UN Water. https://www.unwater.org/water-facts/water-food-and-energy/

WEF Nexus Working Group. "(Re)Connect the Nexus." https://www.water-energy-food.org

WEF Nexus Working Group. "Water, Energy, Food (WEF) Nexus Project." https://sjoseph.ucdavis.edu/ucdar

CASE STUDY:

COLORADO RIVER COMPACT

"Colorado River: Horseshoe Bend" by Paul Hermans, 2012.
Attribution: see p. 165

Case studies provide something we all wish we had when facing the future: hindsight. Historic cases offer in-depth exploration of a situation that can elucidate and evaluate past decisions, especially unexpected consequences. Examples with contracts or legal documents, and their subsequent revisions, may prove valuable to the development of policy for the future. Links to the laws are included in the sources for this case study of a water resource that addresses many decisions regarding the water-food-energy nexus.

COLORADO RIVER COMPACT

The Colorado River is impressive by any measure:
- more than 17 million years old.
- extends approximately 1,450 miles (2,330 kms) from northern Colorado to the Gulf of California, in Mexico.
- the river waters cover an area of 242,000 sq.mi. (632,000 sq.km.).

At such a scale, covering so much territory, and with so many parties and stakeholders involved, there was a critical need for the Colorado River Compact. It was signed in 1922, to govern the harnessing of the river for hydroelectric, agricultural, industrial, and residential needs. Seven states came together from what is known as the Upper/Lower Basins region: Arizona, California, Colorado, Nevada, New Mexico, Utah, and Wyoming. It was the first time in American history that a group of states cooperated to share water. Later, additional stakeholders asserted rights.

Water Allotment

When the Compact was signed, allotments of water to the Upper and Lower Basins were based on recorded rainfall measurements taken in the years prior to signing. Little or no consideration was given, at the time, to the possibility that rainfall patterns might change, for example, as the result of global warming. As dramatic shifts began to appear in the early 21st century, decisions were needed as to how to share water. Additional allocations were based on the river's average flow. However, tree ring studies confirmed what was suspected: the Colorado River flow is greatly reduced, and drought in the region since 2011 has only intensified the need to further evaluate how the water will be allocated.

In 2019, the Upper and Lower Basin states began to consider changes to the allotments. Originally calculated in 1922 after a series of very wet winters, the Colorado River Compact divided up the annual 15 million acre-feet allotments between the groups of states: 7.5 each. Unfortunately, two factors are stressing that allocation: the river actually yields an average of 12.5 million acre-feet; and over the past 15 years, the river has decreased by 6%. Even worse, scientists now predict that the Colorado River could shrink between 20% and 30% by 2030, and between 35% and 55% by 2100 (Finley, 2019). States might need to renegotiate Compact terms, in what some call a "grand bargain," that would assure long-term sustainability, but such a change would require an Act of Congress.

Colorado River Delta Dangers

Prior to 1922, the Colorado River ran freely from its headwaters in Colorado down to Mexico, where significant quantities of silt from the river created the vast Colorado River Delta. Spread across the northern end of Mexico's Gulf of California, the delta's tidal wetlands once covered 1.93 million acres (7,810 sq.km.) and supported a large population of plant, bird, aquatic, and terrestrial life.

Dam-building and excessive water use, exacerbated by extended drought in 2011, meant water supplies and flows from the Colorado River were heavily tapped, to the detriment of the river delta in Mexico. Environmentalists throughout southwestern United States and Mexico were concerned, and raised questions on current uses of the Colorado River. On 16 August 2021, those questions received an important answer: historic first water cuts were enacted, mandatory in 2022. The "Colorado River Drought Contingency Plan Authorization Act" brings a century-view, from 1922 to 2022, to the future of climate and water.

VOICE OF THE FUTURE
—Gabriel Eckstein

"As many as twenty aquifers straddle the Mexico/United States border, many of which serve as the primary source of fresh water for overlying populations."

—Gabriel Eckstein, Texas A&M University School of Law, and Director, International Water Law Project.

Sources:
Gabriel Eckstein. "Buried Treasure or Buried Hope? The Status of Mexico-US Transboundary Aquifers under International Law." *International Community Law Review* 13 (2011): 273-290. https://scholarship.law.tamu.edu/facscholar/129/

VIDEO: Gabriel Eckstein, "Regulating what we can't see: international law and transboundary aquifers." IAH Groundwater Congress 2019. https://vimeo.com/411756586

VIDEO: Rosario Sanchez Flores, Water Management & Hydrological Science, Texas A&M University. "Transboundary Aquifers Between US and Mexico: Where and How Do We Start?" https://vimeo.com/119554600.

Reservoirs Shrinking

Another water resource under stress is Lake Mead, the grand reservoir created by the Hoover Dam. Formed in the 1930s, the lake draws many visitors, and by 2019 tourists numbered 7.5 million; Lake Mead has more tourists per annum than Yosemite (4.5 million) or the Grand Canyon (5.9 million). Estimates indicate Lake Mead contributes $500 million each year to the local economy. Most importantly, Lake Mead provides crucially needed water to Arizona, California, and Nevada. Mexico may help. In 2012, an agreement was made whereby Mexico will store some of its water allotment in Lake Mead.

As a result of environmental changes in the Colorado River, effects on the lake are obvious and measurable. Full capacity of the lake is 1,229 feet (375 meters); by 2013, Lake Mead measured 1,122 feet (342 meters), and by 2014 just 1,081 feet (329 meters). But Lake Mead—largest water reservoir in the United States— continues to shrink. In August 2021, Lake Mead's water reservoir was at 35%; Lake Powell at 31%, and the lower Colorado River system at 40%. Rain helps; in autumn 2021, several days of precipitation added some water. But only 10% of

Lake Mead's water comes from rain: the rest is snowmelt from the Rocky Mountains.

With global climate warming, droughts are more common. The U.S. Bureau of Reclamation announced cuts in water allocations for 2022, activating provisions in the Colorado River Drought Contingency Plan Authorization Act (H.R. 2030), accompanied by a companion agreement on contingency management by the Bureau of Reclamation. Arizona, Nevada, and Mexico will suffer water allocation cuts. If Lake Mead falls below 1,045 feet (318.5 m), reductions to California's water allotment will follow. If it falls below 1,030 feet (314 m), Arizona, California, and Nevada must reconvene to decide next steps. The goal is to stop Lake Mead from getting below 1,020 feet (311 m) which is a level close to where no water may leave Lake Mead. Arizona is worried: 40% of its water comes from Lake Mead.

Water laws regarding protective measures were activated in 2021 when the lake dropped below its mandated 1,075 feet (328 m) level. Shrinking water supply has closed lakeside marinas. While some say the declining water level may be due (at least partially) to drought, others believe Lake Mead's depletion is caused by overuse. It is clear, however, the reservoir is dwindling and the region is suffering. Further consideration is needed regarding policies governing reservoirs related to dams and hydropower generation.

In 2026, the guidelines for water use in the Colorado River, last defined in 2007, will expire. Lake Mead and Lake Powell defined three drought levels: light shortage, heavy shortage, and extreme shortage, based on warnings of impacts due to climate change. In August 2021, the U.S. government declared a water shortage for Lake Mead, enforcing Tier 1 reductions for the first time.

Compact Partner: Mexico

The Colorado River Compact was signed at Bishop's Lodge, Santa Fe, New Mexico, in 1922. If one were to remove "New" from that state's name, it would highlight a crucial lesson. While countries may be defined by lines on a map, land itself determines environmental reality. Nowhere is this truer than with water resources. The Colorado River joins the Gulf of California in Mexico, a fact that was not acknowledged in 1922. Two decades later, the Compact had to be amended to recognize Mexico's rights: in 1944, a protocol provided Mexico with 1.5 million acre feet (maf) and use of the Colorado River, Tijuana River, and the Rio Grande (called the Rio Bravo in Mexico). In 2012, environmental and climate changes demanded further adjustment: an amendment known as "Minute 319" determined how Colorado River Delta flows could be shared internationally for environmental sustainability (Stanger, 2013).

Mexico recently settled some water debts with the United States, but there was conflict. In 2020, farmers occupied La Boquilla Dam in Chihuahua state to halt water diversions: Mexico's National Guard responded. During the conflict, a fatality occurred. The disputed river, Rio Conchos, is shared by U.S. and Mexico. Agreements stipulate allotment of 62% to Mexico, but recent use has been as high as 71%. Some of the terms of allocation relate to a bilateral treaty signed by the border neighbors in 1944, as an update to the Colorado River Compact (Helfgott, 2021).

In 2020, Mexico and the United States agreed upon new rules for sharing water from the Colorado River. The U.S. will send less water to Mexico during drought, but this could be balanced by allowing Mexico to store water in Lake Mead during years when rainfall is plentiful. Part of the deal includes $10 million for Mexico to repair irrigation channels damaged during a 2010 earthquake, and to restore the Colorado River Delta.

Insufficiently Recognized Partners

Water rights of indigenous Americans were poorly defined in the original Colorado River Compact of 1922—but at least they were mentioned. Herbert Hoover (for whom the dam was named) inserted the following phrase in Article VII of the Compact: "Nothing in this compact shall be construed as affecting the obligations of the United States of America to Indian Tribes" leaving the 1922 Compact implicitly clear. Hoover may have been referring to rights previously established by the United States Supreme Court in 1908 (Winters v. United States), in which the court decided that Native American tribal nations possess and retain water rights, whether they use them or not. The court further confirmed that water rights were related to where the territory was located. Such confirmation became explicit when, in 1963, apportionments for the Chemehuevi, Cocopah, Colorado River, Fort Mojave, and Quechan peoples were certified. Later, the Havasupai, Hualapai, and Navajo would also claim their rights.

The Havasupai occupy 180 miles (290 km) of frontage on the Colorado River. The Navajo have a particularly advantageous situation: their nation falls entirely within the territory covered by the Compact, and they were awarded a 5-maf share—larger than Mexico's share.

Environmental Awareness

In recent years, environmental concerns have been the focus of most amendments to the Colorado River Compact:

- 1973 Endangered Species Act contained provisions for certain fish.
- 1974 Colorado River Basin Salinity Control Act.
- 1992 Grand Canyon Protection Act, which recognized the importance of the Colorado River.

Lessons Learned

Multi-party agreements within a nation

The Colorado River Compact was the first agreement among American states regarding water sharing. The compact divided the partners into two groups: Upper Basin (Colorado, New Mexico, Utah, Wyoming) and Lower Basin (Arizona, California, Nevada). Although the 1922 original agreement determined allotments, the status was challenged and amended in 1963 by the United States Supreme Court in Arizona v. California. Balancing federal authority with relative autonomy of states and determination of rights is complex and continually evolving.

Multi-party agreements with other nations

As the U.S. discovered, other national parties were not recognized in detail in the original compact. The compact mentioned Mexico and American indigenous people, but their rights were not defined, subsequently leading to further legislation. Mexico claimed its rights in 1944; indigenous Americans did so in 1963 and after. The lesson to be learned? All stakeholders must be included, as lawsuits and adjudication can be expensive. Early determination of the full circle of stakeholders has advantages.

Realistic standards of reference

How should water allotments be determined? The Colorado River Compact used older measuring and statistical standards, such as rainfall and river flow. This resulted in overly optimistic amounts that proved to be unsustainable when environmental and climate factors affected the area.

Preservation of reservoirs

The Hoover Dam resulted in the creation of Lake Mead. How do reservoirs serve their surrounding regions? Many credit the Hoover Dam and Lake Mead as instrumental in the growth of Las Vegas. But as water levels have declined, Lake Mead law redefined drought levels, the most severe triggering restrictions to deal with low water levels. How can reservoirs be safeguarded and sustained?

Times of flood, times of drought

Both the Colorado River Compact and laws regarding Lake Mead change in times of flood and drought. When drought persists, the amount of water in both sources is severely stressed. But states in the Compact have continued to demand increasing amounts of water. How can the competing needs of urban centers and industry be balanced?

Water for sale

Most partners in the Colorado River Compact cannot resell their water rights on the open market. Such restrictions do not govern Mexico or the indigenous sovereign nations, including the Navajo, whose nation is entirely within the Compact's territory. What happens when some partners sell water rights, but not everyone can?

Environment: Emerging issue

Recent amendments to the Colorado River Compact concern water quality, especially salinity; endangered species, notably fish; and protection of national environmental wonders and treasures. What can be learned from the environmental questions and evolving responses of the Colorado River, Lake Mead, Lake Powell, and the Delta that will help protect and sustain water resources in the future?

Rights

The various agreements governing the Colorado River might suggest the consideration of rights: not water use rights allocated to parties of users, but the rights of rivers themselves.

Rights of Nature are rapidly evolving. Some environmental and legal historians date the commencement of the subject to 1972. "Should Trees Have Standing?—Toward Legal Rights of Natural Objects," an article by Christopher D. Stone, a professor at the University of Southern California, opened the issue. Stone's essay was occasioned by the Sierra Club's move to sue Walt Disney Enterprises to stop construction of a ski resort in the Sierra Nevada Mountains. When the United States Court of Appeals observed that the Sierra Club itself had not been injured by the project, and therefore could not claim rights to sue, Stone presented an argument that nature's rights should stand in court. Regarding the rights of water, Lidia Cano Pecharromán wrote in 2018 that "court rulings on the rights of rivers are the ones setting precedent."

Colombia established legal rights for the Atrato River, and the surrounding Amazon forest in an intergenerational pact. India initiated legal status consideration for the Ganges and Yamuna Rivers. In the United States, the State of Ohio voted legal rights for Lake Erie. What implications do agreements, laws, and rights have for transboundary bodies of water like the Mekong or Nile rivers? New Zealand's Whanganui River, sacred to the Māori, achieved personhood legal status in 2017.

Sources:
Dineen, Sally. "Feds Slash Colorado River Release to Historic Lows." *National Geographic*. 16 August 2013. http://news.nationalgeographic.com/news/2013/08/130816-colorado-river-drought-lake-powell-mead-water-scarcity/.

Finley, Bruce. "Colorado River Water: Grand Bargain in the face of Climate Change." 25 August 2019. *The Denver Post*. https://www.denverpost.com/2019/08/25/colorado-river-water-grand-bargain-climate-change/.

Fountain, Henry. "In a first, U.S. Declares Shortage on Colorado River, Forcing Water Cuts." 16 August 2021, New York Times. https://www.nytimes.com/2021/08/16/climate/colorado-river-water-cuts.html

Gelt, Joe. "Sharing Colorado River Water: History, Public Policy and the Colorado River Compact." Summary of a conference held at the University of Arizona upon the 75th anniversary of the Colorado River Compact. *Arroyo*, August 1997, vol. 10, no. 1. Water Resources Research Center, College of Agriculture and Life Sciences, The University of Arizona. https://wrrc.arizona.edu/publications/ %20arroyo-newsletter/sharing-colorado-river-water-history-public-policy-and-colorado-river.

Healy, Meredith N. "Fluid Standing: Incorporating the Indigenous Rights of Nature Concept into Collaborative Management of the Colorado River Ecosystem." Colorado Natural Resources, Energy, and Environmental Law Review. 2019, volume 30: 2, pp. 327-360. https://www.colorado.edu/law/sites/default/files/attached-files/healy_web_edition_pdf.pdf

Helfgott, Alexandra. "Bilateral Water Management: Water Sharing between the US and Mexico along the Border." Mexico Institute, Wilson Center. 4 January 2021. https://www.wilsoncenter.org/article/bilateral-water-management-water-sharing-between-us-and-mexico-along-border

International Boundary and Water Commission (IBWC). "Fact sheet: Minute 319 environmental flow." https://www.ibwc.gov/files/minutes/min319_fact_sheet.pdf

International Boundary and Water Commission (IBWC). "Minute 319: Colorado River Limitrophe and Delta Environmental Flows Monitoring, Final Report." November 2018. https://www.ibwc.gov/files/minute_319_monitoring_report_112818_final.pdf

Kann, Drew. With video by Bryce Urbany and graphics by Renee Rigdon. "As a megadrought persists, new projections show a key Colorado River reservoir could sink to a record low later this year." 19 April 2021. https://www.cnn.com/2021/04/19/weather/western-drought-colorado-river-cutbacks-study/index.html

Karamanos, Keith. "Lake Mead: Benefits of the Largest Reservoir in the United States." California Polytechnic State University, San Louis Obispo, June 2010.

Kuhn, Eric and John Fleck. *Science Be Dammed: How Ignoring Inconvenient Science Drained the Colorado River*. University of Arizona Press, 2019. ISBN: 9789816540051.

Maffly, Brian. "Eco-groups sue feds, allege that Glen Canyon Dam plan ignores climate change." 1 October 2019. *Salt Lake Tribune*. https://www.sltrib.com/news/environment/2019/10/01/eco-groups-sue-feds/

Metz, Sam. "US West prepares for possible 1st water shortage declaration." 17 April 2021. https://apnews.com/article/business-science-general-news-government-and-politics-environment-and-nature-09302e61c5e0ef051f50459f3dcb771f

Ramirez, Rachel, with Drew Kann. "First-ever water cuts declared for Colorado River in historic drought." 16 August 2021. CNN.com. https://www.cnn.com/2021/08/16/us/lake-mead-colorado-river-water-shortage/index.html

Stanger, William F. "The Colorado River Delta and Minute 319: A Transboundary Water Law Analysis." Masters Thesis. 2013. https://environs.law.ucdavis.edu/volumes/37/1/stanger.pdf

Stone, Christopher D. "Should Trees Have Standing?—Toward Legal Rights for Natural Objects." *Southern California Law Review*, 45 (1972): 450-501. https://iseethics.files.wordpress.com/2013/02/stone-christopher-d-should-trees-have-standing.pdf.

Selection of Colorado River laws and agreements:
1963 Arizona v. California, 373 US 546 (1963). https://supreme.justia.com/cases/federal/us/373/546/

1974 Colorado River Basin Salinity Control Act. https://www.usbr.gov/lc/region/g1000/pdfiles/crbsalct.pdf

1992 Grand Canyon Protection Act, H.R. 814- 102nd Congress (1991-1992). https://www.congress.gov/bill/102nd-congress/house-bill/814/text

An ACT relating to water; prohibiting, with certain exceptions, the use of water. From the Colorado River to irrigate nonfunctional turf on certain properties. Southern Nevada Water Authority. Assembly Bill No. 356, 22 March 2021. https://www.leg.state.nv.us/Session/81st2021/Bills/AB/AB356_R1.pdf

Bureau of Reclamation USA. Complete List of All Laws Regarding the Colorado River Compact. https://www.usbr.gov/lc/region/pao/lawofrvr.html

Colorado River Compact of 1922. https://www.usbr.gov/lc/region/pao/pdfiles/crcompct.pdf

La Paz Agreement between the United States of America and Mexico. 14 August 1983. https://www.epa.gov/sites/production/files/2015-09/documents/lapazagreement.pdf

Law of the River. https://www.usbr.gov/lc/region/g1000/lawofrvr.html

Minute 319. International Boundary and Water Commission: United States and Mexico. 12 November 2012. http://www.ibwc.gov/Files/Minutes/Minute_319.pdf

Utilization of the Waters of the Colorado and Tijuana Rivers and of the Rio Grande. Treaty between the United States of America and Mexico. 3 February 1944. https://www.usbr.gov/lc/region/pao/pdfiles/mextrety.pdf

Winters v. United States, 207 US 564 (1908). https://supreme.justia.com/cases/federal/us/207/564/

Rights
        Bolivia
Ley de Derechos de La Madre Tierra – Estado Plurinacional de Bolivia.
https://www.scribd.com/document/44900268/Ley-de-Derechos-de-la-Madre-Tierra-Estado-Plurinacional-de-Bolivia

Cano Pecharromán, Lidia. "Rights of Nature: Rivers That Can Stand in Court." *Resources*, 2018, 7, 13. doi:
10:3390/resources7010013. https://www.mdpi.com/2079-9276/7/1/13

        Colombia
"Climate Change and Future Generations Lawsuit in Colombia: Key Excerpts from the Supreme Court's
Decision." 13 April 2018. Dejusticia. https://www.dejusticia.org/en/climate-change-and-future-generations-lawsuit-in-colombia-key-excerpts-from-the-supreme-courts-decision/

        India
Daley, Jason. "India's Ganges and Yamuna Rivers Are Given the Rights of People." 23 March 2017.
Smithsonian.com. https://www.smithsonianmag.com/smart-news/ganges-and-yamuna-rivers-given-rights-people-india-180962639/

        Navajo
Calma, Justine. "The Navajo Nation Faced Water Shortages for Generations – and Then the Pandemic Hit." 6
July 2020. The Verge. https://www.theverge.com/2020/7/6/21311211/navajo-nation-covid-19-running-water-access

DigDeep. "Americans without Water." https://www.digdeep.org/

Navajo Nation Environmental Protection Agency (NNEPA). https://www.navajonationepa.org

        New Zealand
New Zealand Parliament/Pāremata Aotearoa. "Innovative Bill Protects Whanganui River with Legal
Personhood." *Te Awa Tupua* (Whanganui River Claims Settlement Bill). 28 March 2017.
https://www.parliament.nz/en/get-involved/features/innovative-bill-protects-whanganui-river-with-legal-personhood/

WINDOW ON THE ECONOMY

When will future amendments to the Colorado River Compact include
provisions for access to household running water for all in the Compact,
including many of the Navajo Nation? Estimated cost—$700 million.

Source:
Justine Calma. "The Navajo Nation faced water shortages for generations—and then the pandemic hit." 6
July 2020. The Verge. https://www.theverge.com/2020/7/6/21311211/navajo-nation-covid-19-running-water-access

VIDEOS: CBS Sunday Morning: "Americans Without Water." updated 26 July 2020.
https://www.navajowaterproject.org/cbs
or
https://youtu.be/uC8CmOOZ300

SYSTEM DYNAMICS MODEL:

WATER SYSTEMS: A MODEL OF USE

How can one experience and explore the issues involved in the world's water problems? The field of System Dynamics, founded by Professor Jay Forrester of MIT, is useful for exploring core issues that determine the success or failure of systems. System Dynamics is a methodology that uses modeling to frame, test, and understand complex problems. It is especially useful in identifying and understanding unintended consequences of actions and policies, the nonlinear behavior of complex systems with many interacting factors, and the effects of time delays.

The following figure depicts a system dynamics model of water use, developed by Professors Khalid Saeed and Paul Mathisen of Worcester Polytechnic Institute, in Massachusetts.

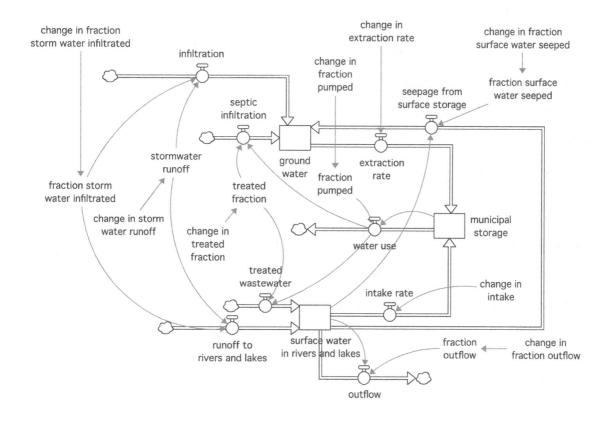

Water systems: A model of use, by Khalid Saeed.

Attribution: see p. 165

Equations for the Model

	Equation
ground water(t)	ground water(t - dt) + (septic infiltration + seepage from surface storage + infiltration - extraction rate) * dt
municipal storage(t)	municipal storage(t - dt) + (extraction rate + intake rate - water use) * dt
surface water in rivers and lakes(t)	surface water in rivers and lakes(t - dt) + (treated wastewater + runoff to rivers and lakes - intake rate - seepage from surface storage - outflow) * dt
extraction rate	100+STEP(change in extraction rate,5)
infiltration	stormwater runoff*fraction storm water infiltrated
intake rate	100+STEP(change in intake,5)
outflow	surface water in rivers and lakes*fraction outflow
runoff to rivers and lakes	stormwater runoff*(1-fraction storm water infiltrated)
seepage from surface storage	surface water in rivers and lakes*fraction surface water seeped
septic infiltration	water use*(1-treated fraction)
treated wastewater	water use*treated fraction
water use	municipal storage*fraction pumped

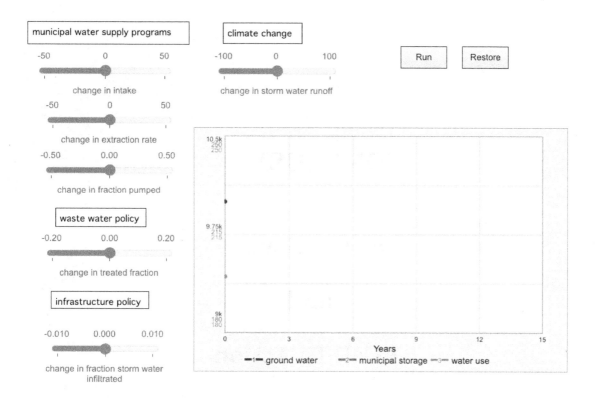

Adapted from: K. Saeed, and P. Mathisen. Watershed Simulator. Presentation at Water Symposium. Worcester, MA: Worcester Polytechnic Institute, School of Arts and Sciences. March 31, 2014.

Great respect and appreciation to Khalid Saeed and Paul Mathisen for permitting this use of their work.

CONCLUSION

Ten Challenges

and

A Call To Action

"Splash!" by José Manuel Suárez, 2008.

Attribution: see p. 165

10 Challenges

Is It Too Late?

Many great innovations were born in, and from, crisis. It is so with water. Ancient Romans didn't get serious about finding a water resource other than the Tiber—even though the river was already showing signs of pollution—until a threat of enemy poisoning. Danger warnings sent scouts to surrounding hills to identify healthy water springs. The army built aqueducts to convey water to the city.

Today, water around the world is already showing signs of crisis due to climate change, and damage approaches the catastrophic. According to economist Kenneth Boulding, there are three types of catastrophes:

- Type 1: Mishap so slight the former order is easily and quickly restored. One might imagine dropping something on the floor and picking it up.
- Type 2: Damage is so extensive that the former order cannot be restored. Imagine that object you dropped shattered.
- Type 3: Destruction so dire that there is nobody around to respond.

Climate change is a Type 2 catastrophe. Once a glacier melts, you can't refreeze it. The former order is gone, but there is still the opportunity, and the responsibility, of building back better. It will be expensive (cost figures included in this section are estimates by expert specialists, identified in sources, and may be subject to revision and update) but may also change the world for the better.

This book series presents a path to rebuilding the world. Because we are the water planet, we begin with water. What challenges should we address?

WATER: 10 Challenges

1. **Clean Drinking Water and Safe Sanitation**

2. **Contaminants—Three Factors to Watch**

3. **Infrastructure—Leaking or Lacking?**

4. **Rising Seas**

5. **Droughts and Fires**

6. **Water from Space**

7. **Renewal**

8. **Global/Regional**

9. **Respect**

10. **Rights**

Challenge 1: Clean Drinking Water and Safe Sanitation

"Drinking Water Fountain," by Darwin Bell, 2006.

Attribution: see p. 166

High on the list of the United Nations Sustainable Development Goals (SDG #6), clean water and safe sanitation will change the world, decreasing sickness and death while increasing productivity. It's urgent: every two minutes, a child dies of water-borne disease. Some families carry water for hours each day; some schools lack running water. Solve water problems and education, economy, and health will improve.

Problems: Costs—Now

For a family of six, collecting water for drinking, cooking, and basic hygiene means hauling water for an average of three hours per day. Half the world's hospital beds are occupied by patients suffering from water-related illness. Suffering and loss: these are tragic, incalculable costs.

Solutions and Benefits

Time - When everyone has access to safe, clean household-use water, time saved would amount to 200 million hours—daily. Sanjay Wijesekera, Director of the Programme Division at UNICEF headquarters, put it this way: "Just imagine: 200 million hours is 8.3 million days, or over 22,800 years. It would be as if a someone started out with an empty bucket in the Stone Age and didn't arrive home with water until 2016" (UNICEF, 2017).

Health – The benefits of universal safe, clean sanitation include reductions in medical costs to treat those who fall to water-borne disease. Plumbing, municipal water, and sewer systems will grow. But just running plumbing lines won't necessarily solve the problem. Recent findings revealed tap water in some systems contains E. coli bacteria.

Economy and Education - If the 200 million hours now spent carrying water were available for education or for remunerative work, poverty would decrease. With access to clean drinking water and sanitation, alleviated medical costs would tally over $30 billion each year.

Achieving clean water and safe sanitation will lessen disease, increase education, boost economic productivity, and generate, in combined savings and earnings from solving clean water and safe sanitation: $150 billion—per year.

Sources:
https://www.express.co.uk/news/science/1528874/climate-change-great-barrier-reef-regeneration-coral-spawning-australia-coral-bleaching?jwsource=em

Boulding, Kenneth E. Address to a joint meeting of the American Association for the Advancement of Science (AAAS) and the American Institute of Aeronautics and Astronautics (AIAA). 03 January 1980. San Francisco, CA.

Gates Foundation. "Reinvent the Toilet Challenge: A Brief History." 2020. https://www.gatesfoundation.org/our-work/programs/global-growth-and-opportunity/water-sanitation-and-hygiene/reinvent-the-toilet-challenge-and-expo

UNICEF. "Collecting water is often a colossal waste of time for women and girls." 29 August 2017. https://www.unicef.org/media/media_92690.html.

Voice of America. "The Cost of Clean Water: $150B a Year, Says World Bank." 29 August 2017. https://www.voanews.com/science-health/cost-clean-water-150b-year-says-world-bank

Water.org. "An Economic Crisis." https://water.org/our-impact/water-crisis/economic-crisis/

VOICE OF THE FUTURE
—Ingrid Waldron

"Environmental Racism can be defined as a disproportionate location or siting of polluting industries in communities of color, indigenous communities, black communities, and the working poor. And these are typically those communities that lack a base – an economic base and a political base – to fight back."

Ingrid Waldron is the author of *There's Something in the Water;* Associate Professor in the Faculty of Health at Dalhousie University; Director of the Environmental Noxiousness, Racial Inequities & Community Health Project (ENRICH Project); and Team Lead for the Health of People of African Descent Research Cluster at the Healthy Populations Institute at Dalhousie University.

Source:
Waldron, Ingrid. *There's Something in the Water: Environmental Racism in Indigenous & Black Communities.* Halifax & Winnipeg, Fernwood, 2018. ISBN: 9781773630571 (paper); Kindle: 9791773630595.

VIDEO: Waldron, Ingrid. "Environmental Justice in Mi'kmaq & African Nova Scotian Communities." TEDxMSVUWomen, 2020. https://youtu.be/itRiNmo3hq8

VIDEO: "There's Something in the Water." 2019. Documentary by Ian Daniel, Elliot Page, and Ingrid Waldron. https://www.imdb.com/title/tt10864040/releaseinfo

Challenge 2: Contaminants—Three Factors to Watch

"Plastic on corals, pockets, wakatobi, 2018" by Q. Phia, 2019.

Attribution: see p. 166

Three Factors

We've used plastic for less than a century, but it is everywhere. The Anthropocene era, whose nomenclature refers to the presence of human-made materials in Earth's layers, is in part characterized by plastic. But it's not just below ground: 80% of tap water contains micro plastic. And by 2050, there could be more plastic in the ocean than marine life.

Not only plastic, but liquid chemicals are present. Industrial dumping is a problem. Other chemicals, too: some residents of a town downriver from a major city tested positive for a range of pharmaceuticals they did not take, except by drinking their tap water. Cosmetics and household cleaners are mixing into the water, too. And it's not just plastic or pills. We are also contaminating our water in two other ways: fracking, which is about to stop, and deep sea mining, which is about to begin.

Factor #1: Plastics—Problems and Costs

Microplastics, in the form of tiny beads and fibers in cleaning products, cosmetics, and other household and industrial products including clothing, contaminate water. In 2015, eight trillion microbeads entered the aquatic supply of the United States—daily. Pharmaceuticals also enter the water supply: you may be drinking micro-doses of your neighbor's prescriptions. It's not just in drinking water: contaminants like chemicals and microplastics invade coastal, near-shore, open-ocean, and deep-sea habitats. For larger pieces of plastic trash, such as those swirling in the Great Pacific Garbage Gyre, it would take 67 ships one year to clean up just one percent of the North Pacific Ocean. Environmental damage to marine eco-systems: $13 billion per year.

Plastics: Solutions and Benefits

Removing contaminants, solid and liquid, from world water will be needed even if we stop using plastic and chemicals tomorrow. It's going to be a field of innovations. Among the first, filters that attach to washing machines to capture microfibers before they enter the water supply (Brooke, 2021).

Find ways to clear marine plastic pollution? It's worth $19 billion to 87 coastal countries (2018 figures from Viool, et al.). Removing plastic in water will improve aquaculture, fisheries, marine ecosystems, and public health. Clean water will also restore revenue in coastal real estate, marinas, ports, and waterways. Plastic production will persist, so solutions and innovations addressing water contamination will continue to be of economic importance. There will be two kinds of innovations: the first is cleanup which will be a business until we no longer use plastic; the second is revenue restoration. Here's the results of a global survey showing combined savings and earnings in removing plastic from water:

Region	Cleanup Cost ($US/mil)	Revenue Restoration ($US/mil)
Africa	25 to 69 mil	8 to 92 mil
Asia	5 to 14 bil	0.2 to 2.3 bil
Europe	73 to 309 mil	0.1 to 1 bil
Middle East	0.5 to 1 mil	2 to 29 mil
Oceania	1 to 3 mil	2 to 20 mil
North America	47 to 139 mil	44 to 465 mil
South America	196 to 401 mil	23 to 276 mil

Based on 2018 figures from Bailey, et al.; Petten, et al.; and Viool, et al. Illustration by Cherie E. Potts. Attribution: see p. 166

Sources:
Bailey, Richard, et al. "Breaking the Plastic Wave." Pew Charitable Trusts and SYSTEMIQ, 2020. https://www.pewtrusts.org/-/media/assets/2020/07/breakingtheplasticwave_report.pdf

Baldwin, Austin K., et al. "Plastic debris in 29 Great Lakes Tributaries: Relations to Watershed Attributes and Hydrology." *Environmental Science and Technology*, 2016, 50 (19): 10377-10385. DOI: 10.1021/acs.est.6b02917. https://www.researchgate.net/publication/308121939_Plastic_Debris_in_29_Great_Lakes_Tributaries_Relations_to_Watershed_Attributes_and_Hydrology

Brooke, Kathleen Lusk. "Water: Microplastic Filter Innovations." 2 August 2021. *Building the World* blog. https://blogs.umb.edu/buildingtheworld/2021/08/02/water-microplastic-filter-innovations/.

NOAA. "Garbage Patches." https://marinedebris.noaa.gov/info/patch.html

Petten, Laurens, et al., "Marine Plastic Pollution: The hefty cost of doing nothing." 2020. Deloitte. https://www2.deloitte.com/us/en/insights/topics/strategy/marine-plastic-pollution.html

Viool, Vincent, Abhishek Gupta, Laurens Petten, Jorg Schalekamp. Deloitte. "The Price Tag of Plastic Pollution. 2019, p. 10, Fig. 2: "Economic impact per geographic region." https://www2.deloitte.com/content/dam/Deloitte/my/Documents/risk/my-risk-sdg14-the-price-tag-of-plastic-pollution.pdf

Weckhuysen Research Group. "Catalytic conversion of biomass, waste, and Co2." https://bertweckhuysen.com/research/

Zhang, Fan, Manhao Zeng, Ryan D. Yappert, Jiakai Sun, Yu-Hsuan Lee, Anne M. LaPointe, Baron Peters, Mahdi M. Abu-Omar, Susannah L. Scott. "Polyethylene upcycling to long-chain alkylaromatics by tandem hydrogenolysis/aromatization." 23 October 2020. *Science*, vol. 370, no. 6515: 437-441. DOI: 10.1126/science.abc5441. https://sciencemag.org/content/370/6515/437.full

Factor #2: Hydraulic Fracturing (Fracking)

The well is an ancient symbol, sacred source of clean water. It is the center of many stories. It is the village gathering place. A source of water often determined where to locate settlements. From 2003 to 2013, of the world's 37 major aquifers, 21 declined. Drought creates stress on aquifers and wells, which are precious at any time but critical in dry times. Why, then, would we want to use the resources of underground water for anything other than drinking or irrigation?

Because water is power. Imagine a fire hose. It illustrates what happens when water, mixed with chemicals, is shot underground into shale to crack and fracture the rock, releasing natural gas and oil veined within. Shale gas and oil were always known, but only recently accessible.

"Drilling an oil well into the Bakken Fields in North Dakota," U.S. Geological Survey, 2009.
Attribution: see p. 166

Hydraulic fracturing created jobs. Between 2008 and 2012, 40,000 new jobs in North Dakota (U.S.), home of the Bakken fields. Real estate prices skyrocketed. Gas stations popped up, along with convenience stores, restaurants, and every manner of service. Energy prices fell, and cheap fuel encouraged new car buyers to go back to SUVs, eschewing gas-thrifty autos and electric vehicles because gas was relatively cheap. So there are many who favor fracking.

But there are some problems. Like the name says, hydraulic fracturing involves water for drilling wells, and tapping into aquifers. Not for the purpose of watering people, animals, or plants; not for the purpose of industry and manufacturing which also use water; but for the purpose of using water-powered hoses to crack shale and rock and pump out the liquid gold. Besides consuming limited water supplies, fracking also endangers the health of habitat and inhabitants.

Problem: *"Bubbling in the Cellar"*

That's industry lingo for methane leaks. When spent, fracked wells are sealed. Nevertheless, when leaks occur—and they do, by as much as 50%—they saturate surrounding ground with a toxic cocktail of chemicals. You don't want that leaking into your drinking water or your farming field.

Problem: Seismic Shifts

Since 2005, in the U.S., 679,000 acres of land have been damaged by fracking. That drilling, often at angles due to the process of working on shale rock, disturbs terrain with repeated seismic blows, so fracked areas are vulnerable to shifts, earthquakes, and shocks.

Problem: Lost Water Supply

Finally there's water supply itself: since 2005, just in the U.S., 239 billion gallons of water have been used for fracking. *The fracking fluid itself is 90% water.* Yes, fracking will stop eventually because it's based on a finite supply of a fossil-based fuel. But it's popular, especially in some countries that have a lot of shale to frack. In 2000, energy from fracking comprised just 2% of United States oil production; by 2016, it was 50%.

In 2011, France outlawed fracking; in 2017, Uruguay followed suit, as did the American states of Maryland, New York, and Vermont. In 2019, Oregon banned fracking, as did Washington State, the same year Brazil, Costa Rica, Mexico, and South Africa declared bans or a moratorium (Herrera, 2020).

Fracking: Solutions and Benefits

What happens to closed fracking wells? In North Dakota (U.S.), there are more than 100,000 abandoned wells. It is estimated that the U.S. had 1.5 million fracking wells in 2015. And that's just one country.

As with plastic, if we can find some positive use for fracked wells, it will be better than just sealing them, which is both an expense and a ticking time bomb. The land around closed wells suggests some rehab practices. For example, post-fracking land tends to be deforested, compacted from the weight of heavy equipment, and strewn with rocks. Before a site is sealed, frackers could dig up and loosen compacted ground, restore topsoil, and plant grasses, shrubs, and trees to rehabilitate the land. Should that be mandated in contracts?

It might be relatively easy to restore land, but what about those wells? Picture a crowded cemetery, except the monuments are underground. It is an inverse graveyard or a future yet unimagined. Like inverted tombstones filled with sand or concrete, what is the future of these dormant monuments of the Anthropocene era? Perhaps not even dormant, but slowly leaking. There will be millions of post-fracked wells worldwide. What can we do about these hidden artifacts of the fossil-fuel era?

Sources:
Herrera, Hector. "The legal status of fracking worldwide: An environmental law and human rights perspective." 6 January 2020. The Global Network for Human Rights and the Environment (GNHRE).

https://gnhre.org/human-rights/the-legal-status-of-fracking-worldwide-an-environmental-law-and-human-rights-perspective/

Nikiforuk, Andrew. "Shale gas: How often do fracked wells leak?" 10 January 2013. Resilience.org. https://www.resilience.org/stories/2013-01-10/shale-gas-how-often-do-fracked-wells-leak/

North Dakota State University. "A guide to plugging abandoned wells." July 2016. AE966. Revised by Tom Scherer. https://www.ndinvasives.org/publications/landing-pages/environment-natural-resources/guide-to-plugging-abandoned-wells-ae966

Rogers, Nala. "2019: The year fracking earthquakes turned deadly." 21 February 2020. *Inside Science.* https://www.insidescience.org/news/2019-year-fracking-earthquakes-turned-deadly

SGK Planet. "Magazine: All about fracking." https://sgkplanet.com/en/magazine-all-about-fracking/

Townsend, Dina. "The legal status of fracking worldwide: An environmental law and human rights perspective." Global Network for Human Rights and the Environment. 6 January 2020. https://gnhre.org/2020/01/06/the-legal-status-of-fracking-worldwide-an-environmental-law-and-human-rights-perspective/.

Factor #3: Deep Seabed Mining

"Seamount," NOAA, National Ocean Service, 2011.

Attribution: see p. 166

If hydraulic fracturing is coming to an end, deep seabed mining is just getting started. We are about to move from exploration of seabed mining to exploitation in this realm lower than 656 feet (200 meters), where it is cold and dark, with pressures greater than 1,000 bars (equivalent to two elephants standing on your big toe) (Heffernan 2019). Deep seas cover 65% of Earth.

An interesting legal aspect of this mining is that it is not in national waters. The deep sea is that part of the ocean that is beyond 200 nautical miles—recognized as the standard boundary of national rights. Most of the world's oceans and seas are large enough to have a shared middle. In fact, deep sea is considered the property of all the nations on Earth, not just coastal countries with beaches, ports, and shores.

The International Seabed Authority (ISA) adjudicates deep seabed mining. There's a significant treasure trove out there for those seeking cobalt and other valuable elements. We don't hear much about deep seabed mining but it's an industry now moving from exploration (finding the cobalt and other deposits) to exploitation (mining).

Problem: Underwater Gold Rush?

Cobalt, copper, manganese, platinum, zinc, and other minerals are in these deep seabeds. Some are essential to the digital age which uses rare earth elements like erbium, europium, and yttrium. It's estimated there may be 15 million tons of rare earth elements in the Clarion-Clipperton Zone of the Pacific.

Of course, as with fracking, drilling will cause damage, in this case not only to the ocean floor but to the marine habitat. It's not that easy to just say no, so how should we proceed? Contracts are approved by ISA in Kingston, Jamaica; cases and disputes are adjudicated by the Tribunal in Hamburg, Germany. What should be the role of the United Nations Convention on the Law of the Sea (UNCLOS)?

Deep Seabed Mining: Solutions and Benefits

Perhaps it is ironic that materials found in deep seabeds are those used for building renewable energy devices such as batteries, solar panels, wind turbines, and smartphones.

What guidelines should be in place as we move to the next phase of deep seabed mining? As a source of cobalt and other materials essential to aspects of manufacturing and technology, deep sea mining will become increasingly valuable. Alternatives may be discovered on asteroids, but will be even more difficult to harvest.

BMW, Google, Samsung, and Volvo are among businesses that have called for a moratorium on deep seabed mining. Such calls may not end deep seabed mining but they will strengthen the need for more research. Looking at the most valuable elements sought in deep seabed mining, and their uses in certain applications, can substitutes be found and introduced?

Sources:
Ballard, Barclay. "Deep-sea mining could provide access to a wealth of valuable minerals." 13 May 2019. *The New Economy.* https://www.theneweconomy.com/energy/deep-sea-mining-could-provide-access-to-a-weath-of-valuable-minerals

Deep Sea Conservation Coalition. "Deep-Seabed Mining: The Main Players." 2020 http://www.savethehighseas.org/deep-sea-mining/the-main-players/

Gallagher, M. B. "Understanding the Impact of Deep-Sea Mining." 5 December 2019. MIT News. With VIDEO. https://news.mit.edu/2019/understanding-impact-deep-sea-mining-1206

Heffernan, Olive. "Seabed mining is coming -bringing minerals riches and fears of epic extinctions." 24 July 2019. *Nature.* https://www.nature.com/articles/d41586-019-02242-y

International Seabed Authority. www.isa.org.jm

International Union for Conservation of Nature (IUCN). "Deep-sea mining." https://www.iucn.org/resources/issues-briefs/deep-sea-mining

MarketWatch. "2021 Deep Sea Mining Technology Market Top Vendor Performance Analysis with Impact of COVID-19, Manufacturer Strategies, Recent Developments, Growth Overview, Latest Trends, Opportunities, and Forecast to 2026." 11 June 2021. https://www.marketwatch.com/press-release/2021-deep-sea-mining-technology-market-top-vendor-performance-analysis-with-impact-of-covid-19-manufacturer-strategies-recent-developments-growth-overview-latest-trends-opportunities-and-forecast-to-2026-2021-06-11

Miller, K.A., et al., "Challenging the need for deep seabed mining from the perspective of metal demand, biodiversity, ecosystems services, and benefit sharing." 29 July 2021. *Frontiers in Marine Science.* https://doi.org/10.3389/fmars.2021.706161, and https://www.frontiersin.org/articles/10.3389/fmars.2021.706161/full

Shukman, David. "Companies back moratorium on deep sea mining." 3 April 2021. BBC. com. https://www.bbc.com/news/science-environment-56607700

United Nations. "United Nations Convention on the Law of the Sea." https://www.un.org/depts/los/convention_agreements/texts/unclos/unclos_pdf

World Wildlife Fund. "In too deep: What we know, and don't know, about deep seabed mining." 9 February 2021. https://www.worldwildlife.org/publications/in-too-deep-what-we-know-and-don-t-know-about-deep-seabed-mining

---

VOICE OF THE FUTURE
—Christiana Figueres

"This decade is a moment of choice unlike any we have ever lived. I invite each of you to ask yourself: What is the future you want, and what are you doing to make that future a reality?"

—Christiana Figueres, architect of the United Nations Framework Convention on Climate Change and the 2015 Paris Agreement, and founder of Global Optimism.

Sources:
Figueres, Christiana and Tom Rivett-Carnac. *The Future We Choose: The Stubborn Optimist's Guide to the Climate Crisis.* New York: Vintage, 2021. ISBN: 9780593080931

Global Optimism. https://globaloptimism.com

VIDEO: Figueres, Christiana. "The case for stubborn optimism on climate." October 2020. https://www.ted.com/talks/christiana_figueres_the_case_for_stubborn_optimism_on_climate?language=en
OR
"The TED Interview: Christiana Figueres on how we can solve the climate crisis." With Chris Anderson, December 2019.
https://www.ted.com/talks/the_ted_interview_christiana_figueres_on_how_we_can_solve_the_climate_crisis

Challenge 3: Infrastructure—Leaking or Lacking?

"Water on Tap (Unsplash)" by Luis Tosta, 2017.

Water infrastructure has two problems. One problem: leaking; another problem: totally lacking.

Problem 1: Leaking water infrastructure

Leaking water infrastructure is mainly due to the age of installations and pipe networks in areas that have had plumbed municipal water for more than 100 years. Underground iron pipes date back to the 1800s, in some instances, with more "recent" installations 75 to 100 years old.

In the United States, there are 1.6 million miles of water pipes (ASCE 2017). In Chicago, Illinois, the Jardine Water Purification Plant—world's largest by volume—draws water from the Great Lakes and delivers it to 390 million people. But an estimated 6 billion gallons (23 billion liters) *per day* may be lost to old leaky pipes in the network. Across the U.S., 2.1 trillion gallons (8 trillion liters) of water per year are lost to leaks, enough to put Manhattan under 300 feet (91.4 meters) of water. The American Society of Civil Engineers (ASCE) notes that the U.S. has no central water authority; rather, water is handled locally by 58,000 municipalities across the country.

In Europe, the Water Framework Directive (WFD) monitors water systems that serve 17 countries via an extensive network. Europe has 4.4 million miles (7 million km) of pipes that have been in use for more than a century. It is estimated that one-quarter of Europe's treated water leaks out of those older pipes. In the region that gave us the Roman aqueducts and the sanitation innovations of the sewers of Paris, can Europe restore its water systems and rise to today's challenges? In Africa, the Priority #2 goal of drinking water and sanitation systems (part of the African Continental Free Trade Area (AfCFTA)) will support significant advances in water infrastructure. In Asia, the Grand Canal of China led the ancient world in water engineering and is still under improvement construction today, with the current phase concluding in 2050.

Cost to rebuild or replace leaking water/sewer pipes		
United States: Source: Tabuchi 2017	1.6 mil mi (2.6 mil km)	$300 billion
Europe (Poland): Source: Ramm, 2018	47,200 mi (76,000 km)	€14 billion ($16.9 billion

"Cost to rebuild or replace leaking water/sewer pipes." Illustration by Cherie E. Potts, 2021.

Attribution: see p. 166

Problem 2: Totally lacking water infrastructure

Cities like Chicago or Paris may have leaks but at least they have water pipes. Some cities don't even have full water infrastructure. In Nigeria, fewer than one-tenth of urban residents had piped water in 2015, a decline from 29% in 1990 (Hares, 2017). Many rural locations around the world totally lack water infrastructure. In Africa, only 42% of the population has a sanitation system.

We know the cost in health and time, but funding costs are more difficult to estimate. The World Bank advises the cost may be $150 billion per year worldwide.

Solutions and Benefits

Houston, Texas (U.S.), in February 2021, suffered a winter storm that resulted in crippling and deadly electric power outages, and caused water pipes to freeze and break. Only two areas of Houston, not connected to the city's main water system, escaped disaster. The remaining population had to boil water, and some residents were asked to shut off their water connection to conserve the vital resource for hospitals and fire stations. Water treatment plants were fine because they had generators, but the water distribution system suffered significant damage.

A potential solution: self-healing pipes, inspired by human biology. When we experience a skin cut, blood comes to the surface and soon clots. It's the work of platelets. That is what inspired engineer Ian McEwan of the University of Aberdeen and founder of Brinker Technology Ltd., to develop "artificial platelets" made from elastomeric material that can be injected into pipelines. When a leak occurs, pressure change conveys platelets to the leak and they clog it. Developed for pipelines carrying fuel and tested by British Petroleum and Shell, can the concept be adapted for municipal water systems? The method is currently being studied for use in water pipes in the United Kingdom where 951 million gallons (3,600 million liters) of water leak from pipes every day, causing water companies to dig and replace pipes.

Self-healing pipes and other technologies that improve water will be needed as we rebuild aging, existing water infrastructure. In areas that now lack water distribution systems, how can new technologies lead to a healthier way to bring water to all?

Sources:
American Society of Civil Engineers. "Drinking Water: Infrastructure Report Card, 2017." https://www.infrastructurereportcard.org/cat-item/drinking_water/

Fluence. "Aging Water Infrastructure in the US." 31 May 2018. *Fluence News.* https://www.fluencecorp.com/aging-water-infrastructure-in-the-us/

Graham-Rowe, Duncan. "Self-healing pipelines." 21 December 2006. *Technology Review.* https://www.technologyreview.com/2006/12/21/130692/self-healing-pipelines/.

Hares, Sophie. "The cost of clean water: $150 billion a year, says World Bank." 28 August 2017. Reuters. https://www.reuters.com/article/us-global-water-health-idUSKCN1B812E

Molle, François. "Water pricing in Thailand: Theory and practice." Doras Center-Delta Project. Research Report #7. Kasetsart University/IRD. 2001. ISBN: 9475538981. https://citeseerx.ist.psu.edu/viewdoc/download?doi=10.1.1.578.7869&rep=rep1&type=pdf

Ramm, Klara, Chair, EurEau Committee on Economic and Legal Affairs. "Time to invest in Europe's water infrastructure." 2 May 2018. *Euractiv.* https://www.euractiv.com/section/energy-environment/opinion/time-to-invest-in-europes-water-infrastructure

Sukphisit, Suthon. "Troubled waters." 28 July 2019. *Bangkok Post.* https://www.bangkokpost.com/life/social-and-lifestyle/170327/troubled-waters

Tabuchi, Hiroko. "$300 Billion War Beneath the Street: Fighting to Replace America's Water Pipes." 10 November 2017. *New York Times.* https://www.nytimes.com/2017/11/10/climate/water-pipes-plastic-lead.html

Thomson, Amy. "NASA Just sent a New $23 Million Space Toilet to the International Space Station." 9 October 2020. Smithsonian Magazine. https://www.smithsonianmag.com/science-nature/nasa-just-sent-new-23-million-space-toilet-international-space-station-180976037/

Tiseo, Ian. "Global Water Industry – Statistics & Facts." Statista/Energy & Environment/Water & Wastewater. 29 October 2020. https://www.statista.com/topics/1575/water/

Wray, Dianna. "City of Houston has Lifted the Boil Water Notice." 17 February 2021. *Houstonia Magazine.* https://www.houstoniamag.com/news-and-city-life/2021/02/city-of-houston-has-issued-a-boil-water-notice

Challenge 4: Rising Seas

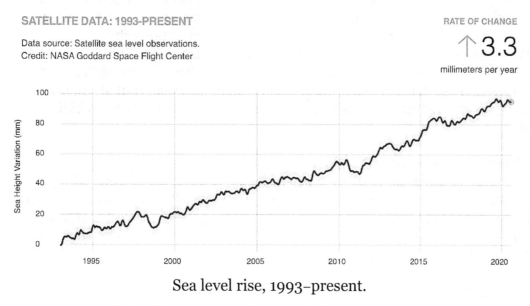

SATELLITE DATA: 1993-PRESENT

Data source: Satellite sea level observations.
Credit: NASA Goddard Space Flight Center

RATE OF CHANGE

↑ 3.3

millimeters per year

Sea level rise, 1993–present.

"Sea level rise, 1993–present" by NASA Goddard Space Flight Center.

Attribution: see p. 166

When (or if) we meet the goals of the 2015 Paris Agreement and reduce Earth's warming to an increase of no more than 1.5 C or even 2.0 C, we will still have already-melting glaciers and ice sheets raising water levels at our shores. We've seen a 6-8 inch (16-21 cm) sea level rise since 1900, with a rise of 2.4 inches (3 cm) in the last two decades.

In summary, there's going to be sea level rise. How much, we'll know as we go, but more than we might think. According to a recent Intergovernmental Panel on Climate Change (IPCC) study, we may endure sea level rise of 39 feet (11.8 meters). It's time now to prepare. Sea level rise will be traumatic if we wait until it's dangerous. But there is also the possibility of starting now to anticipate then. It's an opportunity to rethink, reimagine, rebound. Sea level rise may cause the biggest rebuilding project in history.

Cost of sea level rise for U.S. cities	
Boston, Massachusetts	$2.4 bil
Charleston, South Carolina	$2.0 bil
Houston, Texas	$30 bil
New York City	$10 bil
all U.S. cities (est.)	$400 bil

Based on Schinko, et al., 2020. Illustration by Cherie E. Potts, 2021.
Attribution: see p. 167

Problem: Real Estate

The pleasures of a waterfront condo are many; a beach house is the prized possession of few; marinas and harbor hotels and restaurants beckon with promise of refreshing pleasures: waterfront economy is powerful.

Worldwide figures are dramatic, but let's look just at the United States. A study by the Union of Concerned Scientists valued threatened American real estate property at $1.07 trillion. More than 300,000 commercial, industrial, and residential properties will be affected by sea level rise, causing $135 billion in damage.

Problem: Relocation

Climate migrants and refugees will increase. Whole islands may disappear, and residents there may rebuild or perhaps relocate. Globally, more than 630 million live on land below flood levels predicted by 2100. It is estimated that one billion people live in areas less than 33 feet (10 meters) above high tide (Kulp, 2019). Where will those people go?

Problem: Insurance

Live in a flood plain? Try affording insurance—if you can get it. Insurance companies are questioning whether to fund rebuilding in the same location with repeating storm damage or flood claims. Insurance companies may lead the way to financing rebuilding in safer locations, saving vulnerable coastal land to be restored. American Property Casualty Insurance Association stated: "We can't, as an industry, continue to just collect more and more money, and rebuild and rebuild and rebuild in the same way" (D. L. Griffin, quoted in Flavelle, 2021).

Problem: Habitat

Marine habitat will be affected. Fishing and aquaculture will be threatened. There has been reef degradation as warmer rising seas bleach coral and damage marine life. Corals reefs cover 0.2% of the seafloor, but support 25% of marine species (UN Environment Programme, 2021). The Great Barrier Reef extends 1,429 miles (2,300 kms), but over half of its living coral was lost between 1986 and 2012. The Great Barrier Reef Marine Park Authority (GBRMPA) instituted a series of "Reef Snapshot" reports on conditions during successive summer when most damage occurs. Australia allocated $2 billion for reef health improvement, after three bleaching events from 2016 to 2020. Bleaching that occurred in 2016 and 2017 was so severe that not enough adult corals remained to regenerate lost areas. Marine scientists warn that the Great Barrier Reef will continue to suffer damage from ocean acidification and warming until climate change is halted and reversed. In 2021, Great Barrier Reef's status as a World Heritage site was changed to include an "in danger" designation because of the bleaching events of 2016, 2017, and 2020. In November 2021, regenerative measures began to show some success (GBRMPA, 2021).

Some of this degradation is due to predation by the crown-of-thorns starfish (*Acanthaster planci*), but 48% is due to typhoon damage, also increased by warming waters. More than 80% of the coral reefs in the Caribbean have been damaged in the last three decades. The Caribbean Institute for Meteorology and Hydrology reported several Alert Level 1 and Level 2 situations in September 2021.

Human actions can make a difference and reefs can recover, but action is needed now (Knowlton, 2012).

Problem: Floods and Storms

While sea level rise will cause its own consequences, particularly on coasts, the effects of climate change don't stop at the shore. Bigger, warmer, increasingly turbulent seas will cause flooding, not just of coastal areas but also rivers. And then there are the typhoons and hurricanes that will grow stronger, due to warmer waters.

In 2020, the Atlantic Ocean saw 30 named hurricanes. Cyclone Amphan struck Bangladesh and India, that same year, resulting in damages of $14 billion. In 2021, a glacier burst in the Himalayas and caused sudden floods in Uttarakhand in northern India. Two hydroelectric dam projects, one of which was the Rishiganga Hydroelectric Project (RGHEP), were damaged. Some workers perished in the rushing waters. Experts question the safety of building future hydroelectric facilities on rivers such as the Ganges and its tributaries, especially as Himalayan glaciers continue to melt. The relationship of glaciers and their runoff, and hydropower, could be a concern in Asia, Europe, and North and South America. Flooding can also be the result of storms. Here's a partial tally of storms in the United States that each cost more than $1 billion:

2020 U.S. Storms	Est. Costs
Hurricane Laura	$19 billion
Hurricane Sally	$7.5 billion
Hurricane Zeta	$3.5 billion
Hurricane Delta	$2.9 billion
2021 U.S. Storms	
Hurricane Ida	$20 billion
Hurricane Nicholas	$950 million
Hurricane Grace	$330 million
Hurricane Elsa	$290 million

Sources:
Center for Disaster Philanthropy. "2021 Atlantic Hurricane Season." 5 October 2021. https://disasterphilanthropy.org/disaster/2021-atlantic-hurricane-season/

National Centers for Environmental Information. National Oceanic and Atmospheric Administration (NOAA). "Billion-Dollar Weather and Climate Overview." 2020. https://www.ncdc.noaa.gov/billions/

Illustration by Cherie E. Potts, 2021.
Attribution: see p. 167

Problem: What to do With Flood Water

We already know we should not rebuild in flood plains. We already know we must build storm surge protection. We already know we can anticipate damage until we rebuild differently. Meanwhile, will an idea of Jessica Jones (CEO of Pivot to Growth) to form an advertising and public service media "Hurricane Network," help business and residential response to be more timely and effective? How can the insurance industry advise on wise rebuilding? Or consider the proposal by François Lempérière and Luc Deroo: avoid flooding in Paris by pumping from strategic canals into reservoirs.

Storms and floods produce unplanned water. Unplanned, but not unexpected. We can find ways to collect, filter, channel, and store inundations, and develop methods to bring water to places in drought.

Solutions and Benefits

Coastal solutions will begin as local, expand to national, and ultimately must be regional. Boston's Center for Coastal Environmental Sensing Networks (CESN) might lead the way. On a regional level, will Canada, Mexico, and the United States—from (rising) Atlantic to (rising) Pacific—develop an educational and service exchange network, a new CCC perhaps called Climate Conservation Corps? The goal could be two-fold: respond to disaster and rebuild coasts for the future.

Coastal innovations might originate from three approaches:

- **Land-based**: Rebuild raised roads; upgrade storm sewer and runoff systems; review locations of airports and other facilities near coasts; ports and related industrial activities may demand redesign.
- **Land/Water interface**: Sea walls, stilt-assisted buildings, elevated sidewalks and beachwalks may be required.
- **Water-based**: Barriers, floodgates, and new kinds of canals with reservoirs are among future engineering possibilities.

According to a recent study comparing hundreds of restoration projects, the cost to restore marine ecosystems was median $80,000/ha and average $1,600,00/ha. Coral reefs have a 64% success restoration rate; seagrass was lower at 38% (Bayraktarov, et al., 2015).

Sea Walls

Taking the U.S. as an example, if seawalls were built to protect coastal cities with more than 25,000 people, the additional economic activity would be worth some $42 billion. If seawall building is expanded to smaller towns, the figure jumps to more than $400 billion. Would costs of a Boston Harbor barrier outweigh the benefits? Will findings from the Sustainable Solutions Lab and the Stone Living Lab, both at University of Massachusetts Boston, develop nature-based solutions to prevent flooding, improve ecosystems, and enhance urban coastal life?

Breakwaters

Breakwaters are "sea-backed" in the sense that they have water on both sides. A smaller structure than a sea wall, a breakwater can be as simple as a pile of stones that dissipates energy from waves. Other structures include caissons and wave attenuators. Another option is revetment, a land-backed structure.

Canals

Sea level rise will impact existing canals, and there are many worldwide. According to David Edwards-May, author of *Inland Waterways of France* (2010), there are more than 80 French rivers and canals, in eight waterway regions: Northern France, North-Eastern France, Seine, Central France, Western France, South-Eastern France, South-Western France, and Southern France. Will the proposal by Lempérière and Deroo, to siphon and store excess water, offer a solution?

Ports

After sea walls and breakwaters are built, and canals are rebuilt, what about the city, especially if it is also a port? How will Miami, Florida, rebuild its waterfront? Perhaps like the harbor at Alexandria, Egypt, with a new vision inspired by the ancient city? Coastal regions at a sea level of less than 32 feet (10 meters) produce $1 trillion of global wealth. For example, after Superstorm Sandy, New York City engaged Bjarke Ingels Group (BIG) and others to redesign "The Big U," the low-lying area from West 57th Street to The Battery and up to East 42nd Street. It's home to 220,000 people and generates $500 billion in business activity. The design award: $335 million (BIG, 2017).

What's the total economic activity that will happen due to sea level rise? In the United States, maybe $400 billion: globally, $14 trillion—annually.

Sources:
Bayraktarov, Elisa, et al. Data from "The cost and feasibility of marine coastal restoration." https://esajournals.onlinelibrary.wiley.com/doi/full/10.1890/15-1077. For data, see Dryad: http://dx.doi.org/10.5061/dryad.rc0jn

Bjarke Ingels Group (BIG). "The Big U." 2017. https://big.dk/#projects

Breuck, Hilary. "The heart of Paris is underwater." 29 January 2018. *Business Insider.* https://www.businessinsider.com/see-paris-underwater-as-the-seine-floods-the-streets-hundred-year-flood-2018-1

Brooke, Kathleen Lusk. "Year 2020: Climate Conservation Corps." Building the World Blog, University of Massachusetts Boston. https://blogs.umb.edu/buildingtheworld/year-2020-climate-conservation-corps-ccc/

Caribbean Regional Climate Centre, and Caribbean Institute for Meteorology and Hydrology (CIMH). *Caribbean Coral Reef Watch*, vol. VI, no. VI (October 2021). https://rcc.cimh.edu.bb/caribbean-coral-reef-watch-vol-vi-issue-vi-october-2021/

Center for Coastal Environmental Sensing Networks (CESN). University of Massachusetts Boston. Online archive of scholarly articles and theses: https://scholarworks.umb.edu/do/search/?q=Center%20for%20coastal%20environmental%20sensing%20networks&start=0&context=1332317%facet=#query-results

Chen, Robert F. "CP24G – Transdisciplinary Research and Education in Coastal Systems Posters," and "Social-Ocean Science Interactions and SDGs." 18 February 2020. Ocean Sciences Meeting, San Diego, CA, USA. https://agu.confex.com/agu/osm20/meetingapp.cgi/Session/85229

Church, J. A., et al. *Climate change 2013: The Physical Science Basis. Contribution of Working Group to the Fifth Assessment Report of the Intergovernmental Panel on Climate Change.* UK: Cambridge University Press, 2013.

Dal Cin, Francesca, Fransje Hooimeijer, and Maria Matos Silva. "Planning the urban waterfront transformation, from infrastructures to public space design in a sea-level rise scenario: The European Union prize for contemporary architecture case." 18 January 2021. *Water* 13(2): 218. https://doi.org/10.3390/w13020218

Duvat, Virginie K. E., et al. "Risks to future atoll habitability from climate-driven environmental changes." 23 December 2020. WIREs Climate Change. Wiley. DOI: 10.1002/wcc.700. https://onlinelibrary.wiley.com/doi/epdf/10.1002/wcc.700.

Edwards-May, David. "French Waterways." https://www.french-waterways.com/waterways/canals-rivers-france/

European Environment Agency. "Global and European sea level rise." 11 December 2020. https://www.eea.europa.eu/data-and-maps/indicators/sea-level-rise-7/assessment/

Flavelle, Christopher. "Climate change could cut world economy by \$23 trillion in 2040, insurance giant warns." 23 April 2021. *New York Times.* For the insurance study, see: Swiss Re. "The economics of climate change." 22 April 2021. https://www.swissre.com/institute/research/topics-and-risk-dialogues/climate-and-natural-catastrophe-risk/expertise-publication-economics-of-climate-change.html

Flavelle, Christopher, quoting Donald L. Griffin, American Property Casualty Insurance Association. In: "US disaster costs doubled in 2020, reflecting costs of climate change." 7 January 2021. *New York Times.* https://www.nytimes.com/2021/01/07/climate/2020-disaster-costs.html

Great Barrier Reef Marine Park Authority (GBRMPA). "Reef Snapshot: Summer 2020-2021." https://www.gbrmpa.gov/au/the-reef-/reef-health/reef-snapshot

Jones, Jessica. "Hurricane Network." Pivot to Growth. www.pivottogrowth.com.

Kirezci, Ebru, et al., "Projections of global-scale extreme sea levels and resulting episodic coastal flooding over the 21st Century." *Sci Rep* 10, 11629 (2020). https://doi.org/10.1038/s41598-020-67736-6

Kirshen, Paul, et al., "Integrated assessment of storm surge barrier systems under present and future climates and comparison to alternatives: a case study of Boston, USA." 13 July 2020. *Climatic Change* (2020) 162:445-464. https://doi.org/10.1007/s10584-020-02781-8

Knowlton, Nancy of Smithsonian Museum of Natural History talks with Gwen Ifill. "Storms, Starfish Wiped out Half of the Great Barrier Reef Coral." PBS NewsHour. 2 October 2012. VIDEO: https://www.youtube.com/watch?v=M7b6gRUi820

Kulp, Scott A. and Benjamin H. Strauss. "Author Correction: New elevation data triple estimates of global vulnerability to sea-level rise and coastal flooding." December 2019. https://www.nature.com/articles/s41467-019-13552-0

Kulp, Scott. A. and Benjamin H. Strauss. "New elevation data triple estimates of global vulnerability to sea-level rise and coastal flooding." *Nat. Commun* 10, 4844 (Oct. 2019). https://doi.org/10.1038/s41467-019-12808-z

Lempérière, François and Luc Deroo. "Peut-on éviter les inondations à Paris?" 25 January 2018. Comité français des barrages et reservoirs (CFBK).

Litwin, Evan. "The climate diaspora: Indo-Pacific emigration from small island developing states." 1 May 2011. Thesis. McCormack Graduate School of Policy and Global Studies. University of Massachusetts Boston.

Mashal, Mujib, and Hari Kumar. "Glacier bursts in India, leaving more than 100 missing in floods." 7 February 2021. *New York Times*. https://www.nytimes.com/2021/02/07/world/asia/india-glacier-flood-uttarakhand.html

Morrison, Jim. "Who will pay for the huge costs of holding back rising seas?" Yale Environment 360. 5 August 2019. https://e360.yale.edu/features/who-will-pay-for-the-huge-costs-of-holding-back-rising-seas

Normile, Dennis. "'Australia's inaction on climate puts Great Barrier Reef in danger, UNESCO report says.'" 22 June 2021. *Science*. https://www.science.org/content/article/australias-inaction-climate-puts-great-barrier-reef-danger-unesco-report-says

Penn, Allison Rebecca. "What Climate Change means for Coastal Real Estate Values and Property Investors." 27 June 2019. All Property Management. https://www.allpropertymanagement.com/blog/ post/what-climate-change-means-for-coastal-real-estate-values/

"Rising sea levels could cost the world $14 trillion a year by 2100." *Science Daily,* 3 July 2018. https://www.sciencedaily.com/releases/2018/07/180703190745.htm.

Schinko, Thomas, et al. "Economy-wide effects of coastal flooding due to sea level rise." 2020 Environ. Res. Commun. 2.015002. https://iopscience.iop.org/article/10.1088/2515-7620/ab6368/

Sever, Megan. "Economic costs of rising seas will be steeper than we thought, unless we prepare. A study estimates 4 percent in annual global GDP losses by 2100 unless coast regions prepare." https://www.sciencenews.org/article/climate-economic-costs-rising-seas-will-be-steeper-than-thought

Shaw, Jonathan. "Controlling the global thermostat." *Harvard Magazine*, November-December 2020, pp. 42-47, 82-83. https://www.harvardmagazine.com/2020/11/features-controlling-global-thermostat

Stone Living Lab. https://www.stonelivinglab.org

Sustainable Solutions Lab. "Feasibility of harbor-wide barrier systems: preliminary analysis of Boston Harbor." Principal Investigator: Paul Kirshen. May 2018. University of Massachusetts Boston. https://www.umb.edu/editor_uploads/images/centers_institutes/sustainable_solutions_lab/umb_rpt_Bos Harbor_5.18_15-optimized.pdf

UN Environment Programme (UNEP). "Status of Coral Reefs of the World 2020." https://www.unep.org/resources/status-coral-reefs-world-2020

Wuebbles, D. J., et al., editors. National Climate Assessment (NCA4). "Climate Science Special Report: Fourth National Climate Assessment (NCA4), Volume I." US Global Change Research Program. https://science2017.globalchange.gov/

Challenge 5: Droughts and Fires

"Trees torching at the High Park Wildfire," U.S. Department of Agriculture, 2012.

Attribution: see p. 167

It seems ironic that rising seas will lead to droughts and fires. Warmer temperatures mean not only melting glaciers, rising seas, and flooding; a hotter Earth will parch land and starve trees and plants. Globally, our average surface temperature has risen steadily since 1900.

Problem: Droughts

Droughts can come in cycles, lasting years or decades, but they may also be more frequent and more intense. In the United States, California, Oregon, Texas, and Washington all experienced severe drought in 2021. In Australia, driest continent on Earth, an intense drought in 2019 left 10 cities and towns nearing zero water supply. Droughts choke agriculture, diminish drinking water supply, cripple industry, and ultimately set up conditions for fire.

Problem: Fires

In 2020, drought-induced fires in Australia burned an area bigger than the state of Florida (U.S.). Western U.S. fires destroyed 10.3 million acres (4.2 million hectares) that same year.

Solutions and Benefits

Canals. China built the Grand Canal in part as an internal waterway (we'll talk about that in the Transport volume), but also as a way to bring water from south to north. It's the oldest continuous construction project in the world, and continues to be improved. As China pursues its Belt and Road Initiative, will ways to channel water to needed areas be similarly inspired?

Reservoirs. How can we learn from the Colorado River Compact? Will reservoirs continue to be a strategic asset, and how will they be monitored and replenished?

Ever-normal water supply. It's as old as the Biblical story of Joseph and the ever-normal granary, an idea revisited by Henry A. Wallace, U.S. Secretary of Agriculture from 1933 to 1940. The concept of an ever-normal water supply was suggested by Frank P. Davidson referencing discoveries such as a vast lake under the Sahara Desert, perhaps termed Lake Hope, with water systems powered by solar energy abundant in the desert area.

Tubes of the future. In addition to hidden lakes to be explored, we might find a way to use excess water from inundations (rising seas, storms, and floods) to supplement drought-parched water reservoirs such as shrinking Lake Mead or Lake Chad. Additionally, could pipelines now carrying fossil fuels be rebuilt (rights of way are already in place) to convey water? A tube is uniquely suited to be fitted with a series of successive filters: by the time water reaches the end of the tube, it would be clean, safe, and saved.

Sources:

Carlowicz, Michael. "Drought threatens millions in South Africa." 1 December 2019. https://earthobservatory.nasa.gov/images/146015/drought-threatens-millions-in-southern-africa

Davidson, Frank P., Kathleen Lusk Brooke, with design and illustrations by Cherie E. Potts. *Building the Future.* "Lake Hope." pp. 14-20. Boston, 8 August 2012. LOC Reg. No. TXU001842617

Ghosh, Pallab. "Climate change boosted Australia bushfire risk by at least 30%." 4 March 2020. BBC.com. https://www.bbc.com/news/science-environment-51742646

Lindqvist, A.N., R. Fornell, T. Prade, L. Tufvesson, S. Khalil, and B. Kopainsky. "Human-water dynamics and their role for seasonal water scarcity: A case study." *Water Resources Management* 35 (2021): 3043–3061. https://doi.org/10.1007/s11269-021-02819-1

Wait, Andrew, and Kieron Meagher. "Climate change means Australia may have to abandon much of its farming." 6 September 2021. Phys.org. https://phys.org/news/2021-09-climate-australia-abandon-farming.html

Challenge 6: Water from Space

"The Solar System and Beyond is Awash in Water," by NASA, 2015.

The moon rocks were wet. When NASA's Apollo astronauts brought back some lunar samples, the wrapping was moist. Why? Decades later, it was confirmed: there is water on the moon—also detected on Mars and on asteroids. All this is very good news; we need water if we are to live in space. And if we wish to travel in space, farther afield than rocket fuel carried from Earth can presently take us, we could use hydrogen found in water for power.

There appears to be water throughout the universe. If we could get there, a black hole 12 billion light years from Earth may have a water-vapor cloud large enough to supply every person on earth with needed water—some 20,000 times over (Fishman, 2011). In the future, those who find ways to filter and treat water found in space, to make it usable for human consumption, to nurture plants, and to provide energy, will reap great benefits.

We have always dreamed about space, and imagined ourselves there as we looked upward at the stars. But now that humans are there, the most immediate benefit may come from looking down. From space, we can now monitor Earth and spot trending climate changes before it is too late.

Problem: Rising Seas

Sea level rise will not be felt equally on Earth. Regions will notice vast differences, and must respond differently, too. For example, according to 23 years of satellite data from NASA and partners, overall sea level rise is still less than an inch (2.5 cm), but on the east coast of the United States, sea rise is developing two or three times faster, while the Yellow River Delta in China has suffered an increase of more than 9 inches (25 cm) per year (Rasmussen & Buis, 2015). It's predicted that Boston, Massachusetts, and certain other Atlantic coastal locations, might experience sea rise of 15 inches (38 cm) or more. According to the National Oceanography Centre in Liverpool, England: "In some places, it may very well be that regional processes will be the most important signal" (Rasmussen & Buis, 2015).

Solutions and Benefits

We have eyes in the skies. Earth observation satellites already monitor sea level rise, and by 2030 the Copernicus/Jason/Sentinel series will give us a decade of data. A team in the Himalayas made use of Google Earth to observe the status of watersheds and develop renewal programs to bring essential water to a landlocked mountainous area.

As we address rising seas, Earth observation satellite data will suggest ways not only to monitor potential inundations, but may point to areas that should have the highest priority for rebuilding.

In addition, there are other important benefits regarding space as a location where water may be found. Water discovered on Earth's moon or Mars or asteroids, would be crucial for human habitation, potential agriculture, and also for energy.

Sources:
Brooke, Kathleen Lusk. "SPACE: Here's looking at you, Earth." 10 August 2020. Building the World Blog. University of Massachusetts Boston. https://blogs.umb.edu/buildingtheworld/2020/08/10/space-heres-looking-at-you-earth/

Fishman, Charles. "Scientists discover the oldest, largest body of water in existence—in space." 29 July 2011. *Fast Company.* https://www.fastcompany.com/1769468/scientists-discover-oldest-largest-body-water-existence-space

Rasmussen, Carol and Alan Buis. "The fingerprints of sea level rise." 26 August 2015. Jet Propulsion Laboratory (JPL). https://www.jpl.nasa.gov/news/the-fingerprints-of-sea-level-rise

Challenge 7: Renewal

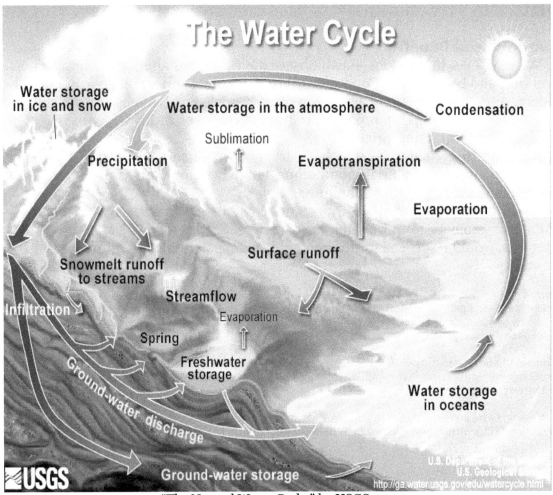

"The Natural Water Cycle," by USGS, 2005.

Attribution: see p. 167

One of the ways to renew water is filtration. Wole Soboyejo and team combined nanotechnology and traditional ceramics to renew the usability of water previously thought non-potable. Another example of renewal is Askwar Hilonga's invention using sand and nano filters to remove bacteria and pesticides from water; the achievement received the Africa Prize for Engineering Innovation. Rajendra Shrestha and a Himalayan team use traditional and new innovative methods to conserve mountain springs, allowing them to renew and revive water sources. Finally, there is vast potential in desalination: our world has relatively little fresh water compared to the huge quantity of sea water. In the future, we may be able to transform sea water in ways not yet fully utilized. All these methods will help a thirsty world to renew available water.

Problem: Wasted water

We now waste water at an alarming rate. Aging infrastructure results in leaks in pipes. Every time it rains and we do not capture and store what one innovator calls the "river from the sky," we waste water. There is potential to recover water from fog, which is now wasted. Our lack of innovation in water storage is, in effect, wasting water.

Solutions and Benefits

Reuse. The first way to renew water is reuse. Systems that utilize filters, whether on Earth such as those by Soboyejo and Hilonga mentioned above, or on the International Space Station, can bring water back for a second and third act. Other ways to reuse water triage the resource for uses requiring more, or less, purity: drinking the clearest portion but conserving other forms like water from household washing (sometimes called gray water) to hydrate gardens.

Retention can renew water. Certain plants develop root systems that hold water from the sky with two results: reduction of soil degradation, and renewal of groundwater. An example: the Great Green Wall, a 4,971 mile (8,000 km) stretch of green across the African continent.

Desalination. Water from the oceans gives Earth its characteristic blue color. It is certain that advances in desalination will change the future. In 2004, Israel derived all its potable water from rain or aquifers; in 2010, 20% came from the sea; by 2019, up to 80% flows from desalination plants (Weiss, 2019). Israel Desalination Enterprises (IDE) Technologies spent $500 million on Sorek, a reverse osmosis facility that produces 165,636 cubic gallons (627 cubic meters) of water daily at a cost of about $0.58 per person. IDE won the Sorek B BOT Tender for the next phase from 2020 to 2045 (IDE Technologies, 2020).

A promising innovation, developed at the Korea Institute of Civil Engineering and Building Technology (KICT), features a membrane composed of nanofibers using co-axial electrospinning. The membrane showed a capability to filter 99% of salt from seawater (Woo, et al., 2021).

Innovations that show us how to renew water may ultimately be the most important discoveries for the future of the water planet. While desalination is proving to be highly important, and surely will be among future solutions for water availability, the process is not without some negative consequences. Once salt has been removed from water, it is often returned to the ocean. This eventually makes the ocean saltier. There is the possibility of chemical pollution from the desalination process. There is also a concern about the energy consumption needed to run desalination plants.

Renewal. Water renewal marked achievements of ancient engineers. Thera (now Santorini) in Greece was an early instance of climate migrants: drought-plagued citizens left their homeland to found Cyrene: a new city located in an area with abundant water and perhaps a special plant. Rome built aqueducts to allow urban expansion beyond limits of the Tiber river.

The water cycle is one of renewal. Water is in constant recirculation. Because Earth is the water planet, all the systems of land and sea are driven by feedback processes of renewal. But to address the renewal of water, we will need to think beyond the national, because water is trans-boundary by nature. Many rivers run through more than one country and therefore require regional policy. Oceans, our largest bodies of water, are always multi-boundary. And our planet itself is mainly water. By observing Earth from space, we now have the opportunity—and obligation—to learn how to sustain and renew water. As we recognize the global/regional nature of world water, two challenges must be met: respect and rights.

Sources:

Annan, Ebenezer, et al. "Clay mixtures and the mechanical properties of microporous and nanoporous ceramic water filters." *Journal of Materials in Civil Engineering* 28 (10), May 2016. https://www.researchgate.net/publication/302918873_Clay_ Mixtures_and_the_Mechanical_ Properties_of_Microporous_and_Nanoporous_Ceramic_Water_Filters

Chang, Kenneth. "Under icy surface of a Saturn moon lies a sea of water, scientists say." 3 April 2014. *New York Times.* https://www.nytimes.com/2014/04/04/science/space/a-moon-of-saturn-has-a-sea-scientists-say.html

Davidson, Frank P. and Kathleen Lusk Brooke. "Founding of Cyrene," pages 11-21; "Aqueducts of Rome," pages 21-35. In *Building the World: An Encyclopedia of the Great Engineering Projects in History*. Volume One. Greenwood Press, ABC-CLIO, Bloomsbury, 2006. ISBN: 0313333734.

IDE Technologies. https://www.IDE-tech.com/en/

Jacobsen, Rowan. "Israel proves the desalination era is here." 29 July 2016. *Scientific American.* https://www.scientificamerican.com/article/israel-proves-the-desalination-era-is-here/.

Massachusetts Institute of Technology (MIT). "Rainwater harvesting." WATER FOR ALL. Mission 2017: Global Water Security. http://12.000.scripts.mit.edu/mission2017/

Shrestha, Rajendra, Jayesh Desai, Aditi Mukherji, Madhav Dhakal. "Protocol for reviving springs in the Hindu Kush Himalayas: A Practitioner's Manual." September 2018. *International Centre for Integrated Mountain Development (ICIMOD)*. ISBN: 9789291156078. https://lib.icimod.org/record/34040

Talbot, David. "Megascale desalination: The world's largest and cheapest reverse-osmosis desalination plant is up and running in Israel." *Technology Review.* https://www.technologyreview.com/technology/megascale-desalination/

United Nations. Convention to Combat Desertification. "The Great Green Wall Initiative." 2020. https://www.unccd.int/actions/great-green-wall-initiative

Weiss, Mark. "How Israel used desalination to address its water shortage." 18 July 2019. *Irish Times.* https://www.irishtimes.com/news/ireland/irish-news/how-israel-used-desalination-to-address-its-water-shortage-1.3959532

Woo, Yun Chul, et al. "Co-axially electrospun superhydrophobic nanofiber membranes with 3D-hierarchically structured surface for desalination by long-term membrane distillation." *Journal of Membrane Science*, vol. 623 (2021). https://doi.org/10.1016/j.memsci.2020.119028. https://www.sciencedirect.com/science/article/pii/S0376738820316008

Challenge 8: Global/Regional

"Earth from Space," by NASA, 2000.

Attribution: see p. 167

Global Vision

Look at Earth from space. The first thing you'll notice is blue; the Earth is 70% water. The next thing you'll observe is land: 30%. What you won't see are lines of division or names of countries. Earth is not a map. Whatever political entities result in lines on maps, our planet remains composed of land surrounded by water: oceans and seas. Water is also within land: aquifers, lakes, rivers. Water is an essential element of the global commons.

How did we get to this point? The years 1952, 1962, 1972, 1982, and 1992 marked milestones on humanity's road to a global vision, as developed and refined by the United Nations. What is it about the second year of a decade? Here is a summary:

1952: The United Nations formed resolutions 523 (VI) on 12 January and 626 (VII) on 21 December concerning rights over natural resources.

1962: Building upon resolutions a decade earlier, the United Nations General Assembly Resolution 1803 (XVII) established rights of "Permanent Sovereignty Over Natural Resources."

1972: The United Nations Conference on the Human Environment, held in Stockholm, Sweden, introduced a new vision linking natural resources to the global commons.

1982: The United Nations General Assembly's 37th session convened in New York to bring forth the "World Charter for Nature."

1992: Brazil hosted the United Nations Conference on Environment and Development, producing an extensive agenda for global action on environmental and developmental issues to shape the 21st century. The resultant Rio Declaration, agreed by 172 governments, introduced 27 principles that now guide nations and states to "act in a spirit of global partnership to conserve, protect, and restore the integrity of Earth's ecosystem" (UNCED, 1992).

Regional Missions

As a dominant component—70%—of the global commons, water will be affected by climate change, but differing topographies will experience varying effects. Some areas may be plagued by drought and vulnerable to fires; others may suffer inundations. As noted, rising seas are one of the effects of climate change that will move beyond national borders, so response might need to be on a macro scale: regional missions, reflecting global goals. *Our Common Future* by the World Commission on Environment and Development (WCED), also known as the Brundtland Report in recognition of WCED's Chair and three-term Prime Minister of Norway, Gro Harlem Brundtland, recognized: "An accelerating interdependence among nations. Ecology and economy are becoming ever more interwoven—locally, regionally, nationally, and globally—into a seamless net of causes and effects" (WCED, 1987). As *Our Common Future* and the Rio Declaration decreed, nations and states, and perhaps contiguous groups such as regions, must enact and sustain the global vision. Winston E. Langley likened the global/regional relationship to an umbrella: each panel protects its own section, but all sections depend upon, and find strength in, the overarching whole.

Global/Regional Relations

The Rio Declaration, and preceding resolutions, might be said to be milestones of rights for natural resources and the role of human civilization in those rights. In 1952, we started with nations' rights to their own natural resources. By 1992, we established nations' responsibilities to treat all natural resources as part of a connected, and shared, ecosystem. With climate change, there may be further evolution and testing of those rights and responsibilities. Nature's rights, as we will see in Challenge #10, are part of that evolution.

Regional Agreements and Treaties

While some may find fault with regional trade agreements, existing cooperative frameworks could play a role in climate response. Such agreements affect how a region will respond. As a start for regional water use and renewal policies, trade agreements might be a framework. For example:

African Continental Free Trade Area
https://www.worldbank.org/en/topic/trade/publication/the-african-continental-free-trade-area

European Union
https://ec.europa.eu/trade/policy/countries-and-regions/negotiations-and- agreements/)

North America
https://ustr.gov/trade-agreements/free-trade-agreements/united-states-mexico-canada-agreement/agreement-between

Post-Brexit EU/UK
https://ec.europa.eu/commission/presscorner/ detail/en/ip_20_2531

RCEP
https://www.trade.gov.tw/Files/PageFile/697972/RCEP10709.pdf

Solutions and Benefits

While climate change is global, the effects will be regional and therefore responses should be determined by regions. It is not enough to address rising seas at a national level; coasts extend beyond lines on a map that denote countries. We might consider a new phrase: *climate diplomacy*. Regions may need to analyze, design, and recommend a coordinated and cooperative response to climate change. For example, what are the management and governance processes necessary for a region to address rising seas?

Should there be regional education programs and perhaps a service-based response corps? Proposals have included deploying military coast guard or disaster response units that may train together on a regional basis. Included in this training would be a common frame of reference and a use-based working vocabulary shared by respondents who have received educational introductions to the languages of the region.

After World War II, the need to rebuild nations and economies gave rise to the International Monetary Fund and World Bank. Since then, International Development Financial Institutions (DFI) and Multilateral Development Banks (MDB) have funded infrastructure improvements like water systems or road networks. Among such development banks are African Development Bank (AFDB), Asian Development Bank (ADB), European Bank for Reconstruction and Development (EBRD), European Investment Bank (EIB), Inter-American Development Bank (IDB), International Finance Corporation (IFC), and the Islamic Development Bank (ISDB).

Could regional development banks work with educational institutions and service corps to sponsor an **Idea Bank** where innovations solving problems in water or energy could be collected and accessed? Emulating social media models like Facebook and Twitter, an Idea Bank could become an interactive depository resource for the future.

Sources:

Brundtland, Gro Harlem. "Conversations with History: Interview with Gro Harlem Brundtland." With Harry Kreisler. 29 April 2014. Institute of International Studies, University of California, Berkeley. University of California Television (UCTV). https://youtu.be/pHBW_Ng62QI
See also: https://theelders.org/profile/gro-harlem-brundtland

Cash, David W., and Susanne C. Moser. "Linking global and local scales: designing dynamic assessment and management processes." 14 April 2000. *Global Environmental Change* 10 (2000), 109-120. https://doi.org/10.1016/S0959-3780(00)00017-0

Chen, R. F. "Energy and natural resources." In: *Teaching Energy Across the Sciences: K-12.* Jeffrey Nordine, ed. National Science Teachers Association (NSTA) Press, 2015 . ISBN 9781941316016.

Eckstein, Gabriel. "International law and transboundary aquifers." In: *Routledge Handbook of Water Law and Policy.* Alistair Rieu-Clarke, Andrew Allan, Sarah Hendry, eds. Pp. 217-233. New York: Routledge, 2017. ISBN: 9781138121201.

Hardin, Garrett. "The tragedy of the commons." *Science*, vol. 162, no. 3859 (13 December 1968): 1243-1248. https://www.science.org/doi/abs/10.1126/science.162.3859.1243

Langley, Winston E., ed. "General Assembly Resolution 1803 (XVII) of 14 December 1962, Permanent Sovereignty Over Natural Resources." Pp. 343–345. In: *Human Rights: Sixty Major Global Instruments.* Jefferson, NC and London: McFarland, 1992. ISBN: 0899506690.

Litwin, George H., John J. Bray, and Kathleen Lusk Brooke. *Mobilizing the Organization: Bringing Strategy to Life.* London: Prentice Hall/Pearson, 1996. ISBN: 0131488910.

MacNeill, Jim. "Brundtland Revisited." 4 February 2021. Open Canada. https://opencanada.org/brundtland-revisited/

OECD. "Development finance institutions and private sector development." https://www.oecd.org/development/development-finance-institutions-private-sector-development.htm.

Ostrom, Elinor. *Governing the Commons: The Evolution of Institutions for Collective Action.* New York: Cambridge University Press, 1990. ISBN: 9780521405997

United Nations. Conference on Environment and Development (UNCED). "Rio Declaration," 3-14 June 1992, Rio de Janeiro, Brazil. https://www.un.org/en/events/pastevents/UNCED_1992.shtml

United Nations. "Declaration of the United Nations Conference on the Human Environment." Stockholm, Sweden, 5-16 June 1972. https://www.ipcc.ch/apps/njlite/srex/njlite_ download.php?id=6471

United Nations. "General Assembly Resolution 1803 (XVII) Permanent Sovereignty Over Natural Resources." 1962. United Nations Audiovisual Library of International Law. https://legal.un.org/avl/pdf/ha/ga_1803/ga_1803_ph_e.pdf

United Nations. "Right to exploit freely natural wealth and resources." 21 December 1952. A/RES/626(VII), https://digitallibrary.un.org/record/211441

United Nations. "World Charter for Nature." 1982. https://digitallibrary.un.org/record/39295?ln=en

World Commission on Environment and Development (WCED). *Our Common Future, From One Earth to One World: An Overview.* Oxford: Oxford University Press, 1987. ISBN: 019282080X. Available online: https://digitallibrary.un.org/record/129811

VOICE OF THE FUTURE
—Gro Harlem Brundtland

"Either we will change our ways and build an entirely new kind of global society, or they will be changed for us."

—Gro Harlem Brundtland, three-term Prime Minister of Norway, Director-General of the World Health Organization, Deputy Chair of The Elders, UN Special Envoy on Climate Change, Chair of the World Commission on Environment and Development (WCED), often referred to as the Brundtland Commission, which published *Our Common Future*.

VIDEO: "Conversations With History: Interview with Gro Harlem Brundtland." Institute of International Studies, University of California, Berkeley. 2014. https://conversations.berkeley.edu/index.php/brundtland_2014.

Challenge 9: Respect

"O Praise Him" by JFXie, 2012.

Engineering, science, and technology are the means to solve water problems, and this book has a central focus on problems as seen through action and solution. This is the visible hand. But what of the heart?

Water is reverenced in many cultures' spiritual rituals. For example, the practice of *Wudu* in Islam, *Mikveh* (sometimes spelled *Mikvah*) in Judaism, the water of baptism in Christianity, immersion in the Ganga (Ganges) River in Hindu sacred practice, and water offerings at Buddhist shrines.

Water is also part of important ceremonies around the world. In Thailand, water pouring over the hands of a wedded couple marks the moment of marriage; *Songkran*, the New Year, is celebrated by *Song Nam Phra*, a water ceremony. African traditions honor water as a source of life, a means of purification, and a locus of regeneration. Every culture honors water.

The arts reach a part of our perception that deepens appreciation and understanding. President Joseph R. Biden invited National Youth Poet Laureate Amanda Gorman to deliver her poem titled "The Hill We Climb" at the presidential inauguration on 20 January 2021. When the Whanganui River rights were recognized at the New Zealand Parliament on 20 March 2017, the moment was marked by the singing of a traditional song sacred to the Māori.

Filmmaker James Cameron, first person to make a solo descent to the bottom of the ocean's deepest floor in the Mariana Trench, and contributor to advanced underwater filming technologies with a digital 3D Fusion camera system, raised awareness of oceans. When filming *Titanic*, a movie about a ship that struck an iceberg, Cameron made several dives to the bottom of the Atlantic Ocean to film vessel wreckage. Later, Cameron explored the Mariana Trench, after which he presented a film titled *Deepsea Challenge 3D* to bring awareness about the deepest areas of the oceans. He then launched a series on ocean exploration in several key areas of the world.

Raising Awareness

Days of the week intersect the quotidian with the sacred. While year, month, and day are given to us by nature, people developed the week. Many traditions have dedicated specific days to natural elements. Ancient China named the first day of the week for fire; the next day for water. Wednesday is the day of water in Japan. As we commit to global and local water goals, should we add a focus on water to a day of the week? For example, schools might present a brief lesson on water, once a week, in the classroom.

Color is another way to raise awareness. Most people associate water with blue. Designers might develop accessories, apparel, and environments to raise awareness of water, perhaps adding a contribution to water sustainability upon purchase. An example of the power of color linked to a cause is the pink ribbon supporting breast cancer research. Estée Lauder Company is credited with the idea of the pink ribbon campaign: Evelyn Lauder and Alexandra Penney, editor-in-chief of *Self Magazine*, began the campaign in 1992, financing production of pink ribbons distributed to cosmetic counters in department stores. When customers sought advice about personal care, they were given a ribbon to remind them to schedule a breast exam. Lauder also started the Breast Cancer Research Foundation. The campaign proved powerful. Campbell Soup placed pink labels on two soups and doubled sales (Houtz 2006).

WINDOW ON THE ECONOMY
The Money of Color

Business generated by the licensing portion of Pantone Color outpaces that from graphic standards, in Japan. London-based nail polish company, Butter London, reported a 34% increase in web sales, and an increased conversion rate of 37% , on the day their color announcement matched Color of the Year.

Sources:
Budds, Diana. "How Pantone Became the Definitive Language of Color." 18 September 2015. *Fast Company*. https://www.fastcompany.com/3050240/how-pantone-became-the-definitive-language-of-color

Sandler, Emma. "Butter London Sees Brand Awareness Opportunity with Pantone Color of the Year." 6 December 2018. https://www.glossy.co/platform-effect/butter-london-sees-brand-awareness-opportunity-with-pantone-color-of-the-year/

VIDEO: "Pantone Color of the Year 2021." https://www.youtube.com/watch?v=pu9zLAKpntM.

How to link color to cause? An expert advises: "Examine the *Zeitgeist*. What's going on in the world around us? What is it people are aspiring to, that they're hoping for, and how does color best serve that? We look at fashion because fashion is always a forerunner. We look at the world of entertainment. We also look at the world of art," stated Leatrice (Lee) Eiseman, Executive Director of the Pantone Color Institute, originator of Pantone Color of the Year, in a 2021 interview (Karlinsky, 2021).

Respect and reverence for Earth's water should be like Janus—looking back and forward. Great water traditions should be honored. Composer Philip Glass, whose work *Itaipú* honors the hydroelectric technology of the "Singing Stone" of the Paraná River shared by Brazil and Paraguay, may be an inspiration in a future direction.

Organizations like Only One and SeaLegacy channel the power of photography, video, digital, and social technologies, to help build healthy oceans through visual storytelling, expeditions, and solutions. We should encourage and sponsor the creation of new art, dance, music, poetry, and ritual to honor developments in water sustainability as we build a better future.

Sources:
Cameron, James. "Aliens of the Deep." 2005. With NASA, an exploration of the Mid-Ocean Ridge, a submerged chain of mountains in the Atlantic and Pacific Oceans. https://movies.disney.com/aliens-of-the-deep

Cameron, James. BBC Studies, and National Geographic. "OceanXplorers." Featuring waters around the Arctic, Azores, Dominican Republic, and West Indies. Filming begun in 2021 for six-part series. https://nationalgeographicpartners.com/2021/02/oceanxplorers-ocean-exploration-series/

Cameron, James, and National Geographic. "Deepsea Challenge 3D." 2014. Film about an expedition that discovered 68 new species. www.deepseachallenge.com. VIDEO: https://youtu.be/ZZD_nbS1_ll

Glass, Philip. *Itaipú*. Guaraní text of libretto translated by Daniela Thomas. © 1988. Dunvagen Music Publishers. Sony Cat. #: 46352. ASIN: B00000277F.

Glass, Philip. "Itaipú: Singing Stone." https://www.wisemusicclassical.com/work/6072/Itaipu-Philip-Glass/

Houtz, Jolayne. "Buying pink: How much of your purchase goes to breast-cancer research?" 10 October 2006. *Seattle Times*. https://www.seattletimes.com/life/lifestyle/buying-pink-how-much-of-your-purchase-goes-to-breast-cancer-research/

Karlinsky, Malia. "Pantone's Color of the Year expert lives on Bainbridge Island." *Seattle Refined*. 11 January 2021. http://seattlerefined.com/lifestyle/pantone-colors-of-the-year-2021

Only One. https://only.one

SeaLegacy. https://www.sealegacy.org/our-work

Shearer, Arial. "Meet the Seattle-area woman behind Pantone's 2020 Color of the Year." December 2019, *Seattle Magazine*. https://www.seattlemag.com/life-style/meet-seattle-area-woman-behind-pantones-2020-color-year

Zerubavel, Eviatar. *The Seven Day Circle: The History and Meaning of the Week*. New York: Free Press, 1985. Chicago: University of Chicago Press, reprinted 1989. ISBN: 0226981657.

Challenge 10: Rights

"Whanganui River between Pipiriki and Jerusalem" by Prankster, 2012.
Attribution: see p. 167

Civilization can be seen as the history of increasing recognition of rights. While human rights have been an evolving area of inclusion and justice, the evolution of rights is not restricted to humans. Recognition of water's nature and spirit dates back to ancient times when water deities inhabited springs and oceans had gods. Grecian springs were believed to be homes of water naiads and nymphs who died if the spring dried up. Every culture on Earth has myths about water, many of them about water spirits.

Examples of Personhood Rights
- Legal rights of nature have a history that some date to a 1972 seminal article by Christopher D. Stone, "Should trees have standing?" written about the rights of trees threatened by development activities in California (U.S.).
- "World Charter for Nature," 1982. What many believe to be the first code of conduct for global habitat and natural resources, outlined in five principles.
- Rights of nature are moving beyond natural resources to all forms of life, including the animal kingdom.
- Rivers have seen rights established into law. Whanganui River personhood rights became law on 20 March 2017. The New Zealand water resource is sacred to the Māori, and essential to the land where the river serves many purposes. In *Te Awa Tupua* (Whanganui River Claims Settlement) Act 2017, *Te Awa Tupua* "means the legal person created by section 14."

- After the Whanganui River was recognized as a legal person, two rivers of India—Ganges and Yamuna, site of the Taj Mahal—received proposals for similar legal standing, although these rights were challenged.
- Toledo, Ohio (U.S.) sought special rights to its harbor on Lake Erie: *"Lake Erie, and the Lake Erie watershed, possess the right to exist, flourish, and naturally evolve. The Lake Erie Ecosystem shall include all natural water features, communities of organisms, soil as well as terrestrial and aquatic subsystems that are part of Lake Erie and its watershed."* (Lake Erie Bill of Rights (LEBOR), Section 1. Statements of Law—A Community Bill of Rights, 4 December 2018 Ordinance 497-18).

Use Rights

- While personhood rights were not established by the Colorado River Compact, use of water was. The Colorado River is essential to the Lower and Upper Basins of the U.S., the nation of Mexico, as well as the sovereign lands of the Native American peoples. As drought increases in areas of the Colorado River, will rights of the river emerge in future legislation? What will happen if rights of the Colorado River are recognized? If so, all of the laws and agreements concerning use rights may need review.
- Will there also be discussion of the Nile, and rights of the river essential to all nations through which it flows?
- Will agreements concerning the Paraná River shared by Brazil and Paraguay, the Guaraní and other peoples, be considered when developing future aspects of Itaipú, the hydroelectric facility? (We will discuss hydroelectricity in the volume on Energy.)
- Following the precedent of Lake Erie, will nations forming a circle around Lake Chad decide on principles that govern water so essential to regional livelihood?
- Transboundary aquifers will be another area needing determination. Mexico and the United States share many waters beneath their connected lands. Can the work of Gabriel Eckstein elucidate the future of this vital common resource?
- When water is discovered on celestial bodies and used for energy, habitation, transport—who will own the rights?

Renewal Rights

- Another milestone for the rights of nature is the constitution of Ecuador, revised and updated in 2008. Title Two, Chapter Seven "Rights of Nature," Articles 71–74 establish the right of nature to exist; the right to maintain and regenerate its life cycles, structures, functions, and evolutionary processes; and the right to be restored.
- Rights of Nature may include the right to regenerate through essential cycles. In addition to Ecuador's constitution, there have been developing laws and policies regarding renewal of rivers. The Rio Atrato of Colombia,

and the Ganges and Yamuna of India have seen new policies for regeneration and renewal. In Canada, the Innu Council of Ekuanitshit and the Minganie Regional County Municipality granted recognition of rights by tandem resolutions for the Mutehekau Shipu/Magpie River in 2021 (Challe, 2021). Notable also is the "Te Awa Tupua Act" of the Whanganui River of New Zealand and the Māori.

- There are new legal developments concerning renewal rights of the Colorado River, specifically for times of drought and water scarcity.

VOICE OF THE FUTURE
— **Whanganui River**

VIDEO: Listen to *Te Awa Tupua* : https://www.youtube.com/watch?v=BX0IFd-4Kp0.

Sources:

Challe, Tiffany. "The Rights of Nature – Can an Ecosystem Bear Legal Rights?" 22 April 2021. Sabin Center for Climate Change Law, Columbia Climate School, Columbia University, New York, USA. https://news.climate.columbia.edu/2021/04/22/rights-of-nature-lawsuits/

Davidson, Frank P. and Kathleen Lusk Brooke. *Building the World: An Encyclopedia of Great Engineering Projects in History.* Volumes 1 and 2. Contains texts of original laws including Roman Aqueducts, Grand Canal of China, New River of England, Colorado River Compact, and others. Westport: Greenwood Press/ABC-CLIO, 2006. ISBN-10 : 9780313333545.

Eckstein, Yoram, and Gabriel E. Eckstein. "Transboundary aquifers: Conceptual models for development of international law." National Groundwater Association. *Groundwater*, vol. 43, no. 5 (2005): 679-690. https://ngwa.onlinelibrary.wiley.com/doi/abs/10.1111/j.1745-6584.2005.00098.x .

Hutchinson, Carrie. "An underwater museum is opening inside the world's most famous reef." 29 April 2020. CNBC.com, includes video. https://www.cnbc.com/2020/04/29/museum-of-underwater-art-to-open-inside-australia-great-barrier-reef.html

Lepore, Jill. "The elephant who could be a person." 16 November 2021. *The Atlantic.* https://www.theatlantic.com/ideas/archive/2021/11/happy-elephant-bronx-zoo-nhrp-lawsuit/620672/?utm_campaign=mb&utm_medium=newsletter&utm_source=morning_brew

Stone, Christopher D. "Should trees have standing—Toward legal rights for natural objects." *Southern California Law Review* 45 (1972): 450-501. https://iseethics.files.wordpress.com/2013/02/stone-christopher-d-should-trees-have-standing.pdf

Laws and Links
Bolivia. "La Ley de Derechos de Madre Tierra." Ley 071. 21 December 2010. Text in Spanish. http://extwprlegs1.fao.org/docs/pdf/bol144985.pdf .

Bolivia. "Revised Framework of Ley de Derechos de Madre Tierra – La Ley Marco de la Madre Tierra y Desarrollo Integral para Vivir Bien." Ley 300. 15 October 2012.

Conseil Des Innu De Ekuanitshit. "919-082/919-01-18" 18 January 2021. http://files.harmonywithnatureun.org/upload1072.pdf

Ecuador. "Constitución Política de la República del Ecuador." Asamblea Constituyente. Text in Spanish. https://pdba.georgetown.edu/Parties/Ecuador/Leyes/constitucion.pdf

Ecuador. "Constitution of the Republic of Ecuador, 20 October 2008. English language translation: https://pdba.georgetown.edu/Constitutions/Ecuador/english08.html .

India and Bangladesh. "Treaty between the Government of the Republic of India and the Government of the People's Republic of Bangladesh on sharing of the Ganga/Ganges waters at Farakka." 12 December 1996. https://iea.uoregon.edu/treaty-text/1040

"Lake Erie Bill of Rights." Jason A. Hill, CCM, CCE, Court Administrator, Sixth District Court of Appeals. LEBOR. https://farmoffice.osu.edu/blog-tags/lake-erie-bill-rights.

Municipalité Régionale de Comté de Minganie. "Résolution 025-21: Reconnaissance de la personnalité juridique et des droits de la rivière Magpie – Mutehekau Shipu." 16 February 2021. http://files.harmonywithnatureun.org/uploads/upload1069.pdf

New Zealand Parliament. "Te Awa Tupua (Whanganui River Claims Settlement) Act, 2017. 20 March. Reprint 7 August 2020. https://www.legislation.govt.nz/act/public/2017/0007/latest/whole.html

United Nations. Convention on the Law of the Non-navigational Uses of International Watercourses, 1997. Entered into force in 2014. https://legal.un.org/ilc/texts/instruments/english/ conventions/8_3_1997.pdf

United Nations. World Charter for Nature, 1982. See: UN Document A/37/L.4, and ADD.1. https://digitallibrary.un.org/record/39295?LN=EN .

United States Congress. Colorado River Compact. Signed At Santa Fe, New Mexico, November 24, 1922. https://www.usbr.gov/lc/region/g1000/pdfiles/crcompct.pdf

Yurok Tribe. "Yurok Tribe, et al., Plaintiffs, v. U.S. Bureau of Reclamation. et al., Defendants." United States District Court Northern District of California, 29 May 2020. Case No. 19-cv-04405-WHO (N.C. Cal. May.29, 2020) Court of Appeals. https://casetext.com/case/yurok-tribe-v-us-bureau-of-reclamation-3

A CALL TO ACTION

If you would like to share your ideas,

learn more about the how you might become the next Voice of the Future,

or perhaps win the Success Award,

please visit:

renewingtheworld.com

Please scan this QR code to visit the website.

Declaiming Waters none may dread

by Emily Dickinson

Declaiming Waters none may dread—
But Waters that are still
Are so for that most fatal cause
In Nature — they are full—

Source:
Dickinson, Emily. *The Poems of Emily Dickinson.* Edited by R. W. Franklin, 1998. Poem no. 1638, p. 597.
Cambridge, MA: Harvard University Press. ISBN: 9780674676220.

Thanks to the Emily Dickinson Museum, Amherst, Massachusetts (U.S.), and Harvard University Press for permission to include this poem.

Database of Laws About Water
(Acts, Compacts, Contracts, Conventions, Laws, Regulations, and Treaties)

Introduction: Three Stages of Water Laws
Laws concerning water have evolved in response to the times. Therefore, representative legal and regulatory instruments are listed by date, with links to texts. Following the timeline, it might seem that water laws and treaties show three stages:

Stage One: —> ongoing
1908—: Rights to use a natural resource such as water.

Stage Two: —> ongoing
1972—: Rights of natural resources themselves for protection and sustainability.

Stage Three: —> ongoing
2007—: The above two continue, but there now appear laws concerning rights of access to natural resources such as water in conditions of change or crisis.

Stage One: Rights to use water
1908
Winters v. United States, 207 US 564 (1908).
https://supreme.justia.com/cases/federal/us/207/564/

1922
Colorado River Compact of 1922.
https://www.usbr.gov/lc/region/pao/pdfiles/crcompct.pdf

1922-1974 inclusive
Law of the River. Compacts, contracts, guidelines, laws ranging from 1922 to 1974, collectively known as the "Law of the River." United States Bureau of Reclamation.
https://www.usbr.gov/lc/region/g1000/lawofrvr.html

1944
Utilization of the Waters of the Colorado River and Tijuana Rivers and of the Rio Grande Treaty between the United States of America and Mexico. 3 February 1944.
https://www.usbr.gov/lc/region/pao/pdfiles/mextrety.pdf

1952
Right to Exploit Freely Natural Wealth and Resources.
United Nations. 523 (VI) and A/RES/626 (VII).
https://digitallibrary.un.org/record/211441

1962
Permanent Sovereignty over Natural Resources.
United Nations, General Assembly Resolution 1803 (XVII).
https://legal.un.org/avl/pdf/ha/ga_1803_ph_e.pdf

1963
Arizona v. California, 373 US 546 (1963).
https://supreme.justia.com/cases/federal/us/373/546/

Stage Two: Rights of water itself, for protection and sustainability

1972
Declaration of the United Nations Conference on the Human Environment.
https://www.ipcc.ch/apps/njlite/srex/njlite_download.php?id=6471

1973
Endangered Species Act of 1973.
https://www.fws.gov/endangered/laws-policies/esa.html

1974
Colorado River Basin Salinity Control Act.
Public Law 93-320, June 24, 1974. An Act to authorize the construction, operation, and maintenance of certain works in the Colorado River Basin to control the salinity of water delivered to users in the United States and Mexico.
https://www.usbr.gov/lc/region/g1000/pdfiles/crbsalct.pdf

1982
United Nations "World Charter for Nature."
https://digitallibrary.un.org/record/39295?ln=en

United Nations Convention on the Law of the Sea.
https://www.un.org/Depts/los/convention_agreements/texts/unclos/unclos_e.pdf

1983
La Paz Agreement between the United States of American and Mexico. 14 August 1983.
https://www.epa.gov/sites/production/files/2015-09/documents/lapazagreement.pdf

1992
Grand Canyon Protection Act, H.R. 814 -102nd Congress (1991-1992).
https://www.congress.gov/bill/102nd-congress/house-bill/814/text

United Nations "Rio Declaration."
https://www.un.org/en/events/pastevents/UNCED_1992.shtml

1997
Convention on the Law of the Non-navigational Uses of International Watercourses." United Nations General Assembly, 1997, entered into force in 2014.
https://legal.un.org/ilc/texts/instruments/english/conventions/8_3_1997.pdf

1998
European Union Council Directive 98/83/ED of 3 November 1998 on the quality of water intended for human consumption.
https://eur-lex.europa.eu/legal-content/EN/TXT/?uri=celex%3A31998L0083

2000
EU Water Framework Directive.
Directive 20000/60/EC of the European Parliament and of the Council establishing a framework for the Community action in the field of water policy, or, for short, the EU Water Framework Directive (WFD).
https://ec.europa.eu/environment/water/water-framework/index_en.html

Stage Three: Rights of access to water in times of change or crisis

2007
Colorado River Interim Guidelines for Lower Basin Shortages and the Coordinated
Operations for Lake Powell and Lake Mead.
https://www.usbr.gov/lc/region/programs/strategies/RecordofDecision.pdf

2008
Constitución Política de la República del Ecuador.
https://pdba.georgetown.edu/Parties/Ecuador/Leyes/constitucion.pdf

2010
Ley de Derechos de La Madre Tierra.
Estado Plurinacional de Bolivia.
https://www.scribd.com/document/44900268/Ley-de-Derechos-de-la-Madre-Tierra-
Estado-Plurinacional-de-Bolivia

2011
Loi No. 2011-835 du 13 juillet 2011 visant à interdire l'exploration et l'exploitation des mines
d'hydrocarbures liquides ou gazeux par fracturation hydraulique de à abroger les permis
exclusifs de recherches comportant des projets ayant recours à cette technique.
République Française Légifrance.
https://www.legifrance.gouv.fr/loda/id/JORFTEXT000024361355/

2012
Minute 319. International Boundary and Water Commission: United States and Mexico. 12
November 2012.
http://www.ibwc.gov/Files/Minutes/Minute_319.pdf

No. 152. An Act relating to hydraulic fracturing of wells for natural gas and oil production. (H.
464) General Assembly of the State of Vermont, 2012.
http://www.leg.state.vt.us/docs/2012/Acts/ACT152.pdf

Rule § 3.29 Hydraulic Fracturing Chemical Disclosure Requirements.
Texas Administration Code. Title 16: Economic Regulation. Part 1: Railroad Commission of
Texas. Chapter 3: Oil and Gas Division. Rule § 3.29 Hydraulic Fracturing Chemical Disclosure
Requirements. January 2012.
https://texreg.sos.state.tx.us/public/readtac$ext.TacPage?sl=R&app=9&p_dir=&p_rloc=&p
_tloc=&p_ploc=&pg=1&p_tac=&ti=16&pt=1&ch=3&rl=29

South Georgia and South Sandwich Islands Marine Protected Area.
Marine Protected Areas Order 2012. S.R. & O. No: 1 of 2012, February 2012.
https://www.gov.gs/docsarchive/Legislation/SGSSI%20Marine%20Protected%20Areas%20
Order%202012.pdf

2015
Microbead-Free Waters Act of 2015. U.S.
An Act to amend the Federal Food, Drug, and Cosmetic Act to prohibit the manufacture and
introduction or delivery for introduction into interstate commerce of rinse-off cosmetics
containing intentionally-added plastic microbeads. H.R. 1321, 2015.
https://www.govinfo.gov/content/pkg/BILLS-114hr1321enr/pdf/BILLS-114hr1321enr.pdf

Microbead-Free Waters Act. New York, U.S.
An Act to amend the environmental conservation law, in relation to prohibiting the distribution and sale of personal cosmetic products containing microbeads.
State of New York, Senate Bill S3932, February 2015.
https://legislation.nysenate.gov/pdf/bills/2015/S3932

Microbead Elimination and Monitoring Act of 2015. Canada.
Bill 75/*Projet de loi 75*. An Act with respect to microbeads/*Loi concernant les microbilles.*
2015. https://www.ola.org/en/legislative-business/bills/parliament-41/session-1/bill-75

2016
Sentencia T-622/16.
Principio de precaucion ambiental y su aplicacion para proteger el derecho a la salud de las personas – Caso de comunidades étnicas que habitan la Cuenca del río Atrato y manifiestan afectaciones a la salud como consecuencia de la actividad mineras ilegales. Republic of Colombia Constitutional Court (Sixth District) 2016. Judge Jorge Ivan Palacio. Case T-622 of 2066. Proceeding T-5.016.242, regarding the Atrato River.
https://www.corteconstitucional.gov.co/relatoria/2016/t-622-16.htm

2017
Salim v. State of Uttarakhand. Writ Petition (PIL) No. 126 of 2014, decision 20 March 2017. Reserved judgment in the High Court of Uttarakhand at Nainital.
https://www.elaw.org/salim-v-state-uttarakhand-writ-petition-pil-no126-2014-december-5-2016-and-march-20-2017. See also: http://www.ielrc.org/content/e1704.pdf

Ley No. 19.585. Prohibese del uso del procedimiento de fractura hidráulica para la exploitación de hidrocaburos no convencionalis.
Normative y Avisos Legales del Uruguay, IMPO, Centro de Información Oficial.
https://www.impo.com.uy/bases/leyes/19585-2017

Ley No. 10477 – Prohibición de la prospección, exploración y exploitación de hidrocarbures líquidoes y gaseos. Poder Legislativo Provincial 2017. La legislature de la provincial de Entre Ríos, Argentina.
https://argentinambiental.com/legislacion/entre-rios/ley-10477-prohibicion-la-prospeccion-exploracion-explotacion-hidrocarburos-liquidos-gaseosos/

Title: Environment – Hydraulic Fracturing – Moratorium and Referenda.
Maryland General Assembly 2017.
https://mgaleg.maryland.gov/mgawebsite/legislation/details/sb0862?ys=2017rs

Te Awa Tupua (Whanganui River Claims Settlement Bill). 20 March 2017.
https://www.legislation.govt.nz/act/public/2017/0007/latest/whole.html

2019
An Act to amend the environmental conservation law, in relation to prohibiting horizontal drilling and high-volume fracturing, December 2019.
Title 29: Horizontal drilling and high-volume hydraulic fracturing. Section 23-2019: Prohibition on horizontal drilling and high-volume hydraulic fracturing.
New York State.
https://legislation.nysenate.gov/pdf/bills/2019/S6906

Colorado River Drought Contingency Plan Authorization Act. H. R. 2030, Public Law 116-14.
https://www.congress.gov/bill/116th-congress/house-bill/2030/text? overview=closed

2020
Review of the Colorado River Interim Guidelines for Lower Basin Shortages and Coordinated
Operations for Lake Powell and Lake Mead: Upper and Lower Colorado Basin Regions. U.S.
Department of the Interior. December 2020.
https://www.usbr.gov/ColoradoRiverBasin/documents/7.D.Review_FinalReport_12-18-
2020.pdf

Lake Erie Bill of Rights.
Drewes Farm Partnership and State of Ohio v. City of Toledo.
Case No. 3:19 CV 434. 02/27/20. Page ID# 822.
https://www.utoledo.edu/law/academics/ligl/pdf/2019/Lake-Erie-Bill-of-Rights-GLWC-
2019.pdf

2021
An Act relating to water; prohibiting, with certain exceptions, the use of water
from the Colorado River to irrigate nonfunctional turf on certain properties.
(Note: this is the first permanent U.S. law of its kind. Previously, there have been injunctions
or temporary restrictions. This is permanent: residents have until 1 January 2027 to get
ready.)
Southern Nevada Water Authority. Assembly Bill No. 356, 22 March 2021.
https://www.leg.state.nv.us/Session/81st2021/Bills/AB/AB356_R1.pdf

The life of the law has not been logic;
it has been experience.

—Oliver Wendell Holmes, Jr.

Index of Organizations

Index of Topics

Index of People
(**Bold** indicates *Voice of the Future* box featuring an interview or presentation)

*Never doubt that a small group of committed citizens can change
the world; indeed, it is the only thing that ever has.*

— Margaret Mead

Index of *Windows on the Economy*, featuring video links

Index of Images, with Attributions
(Charts, Graphics, Illustrations, Images, Models, Photos)

Cover — Created for the author by Ben Paul and Holly Sullo (https://holly-sullo.squarespace.com), Harvard Bookstore, with thanks. The cover features the photo, "The Blue Marble." For attribution, see below for p. iv entry.

p. iv — "The Blue Marble."
Attribution: National Aeronautics and Space Administration (NASA), 7 December 1972. Photo ID: AS17-148-22727. Taken by either Harrison Schmitt or Ron Evans, from a distance of about 18,000 miles (29,000 kms). This photo is located at https://commons.wikimedia.org/wiki/File:The_Earth_seen_from_Apollo_17_(Rescan).jpg. This image is in the U.S. public domain because it was solely created by NASA. It is included here with thanks to the crew of *Apollo 17* and NASA.

p. 4 — "Splash!" by José Manuel Suárez, 2008.
Attribution: Posted to Flickr by jmsuarez at https://www.flickr.com/photos/47918845@N00/2631718740.
Image link: https://commons.wikimedia.org/wiki/File:Water_drop_001.jpg
Reviewed 22 August 2008 by FlickreviewR; confirmed to be licensed under the terms of cc-by-2.0:Creative Commons Attribution 2.0 Generic license CC BY 2.0. The Flickr user has since stopped distributing the file under this license. As Creative Commons licenses cannot be revoked in this manner, the file is still free to use under the terms of the license specified. No changes were made to this photo; it was not remixed or transformed. This photo was a finalist in Picture of the Year 2012. It is with appreciation that it is included here, with thanks to José Manuel Suárez.

p. 4 — "Electricity (sanded and polished) by Andrew Fysh, 2013.
Attribution: This photo may be found at https://www.flickr.com/photos/andrewfysh/8745938723/. Photo taken on 24 February 2013 at the Powerhouse Museum, Sydney, Australia, and is part of the Powerhouse Museum Group on Flickr. Licensed under Creative Commons CC BY 2.0. It is included here with thanks to the Powerhouse Museum, and to photographer Andrew Fysh.

p. 5 — "Skyscrapers with Lit Windows at Night" by Vita Vilcina
Attribution: vita@vivivi.co.uk. Photo taken 20 October 2012. Located at https://www.flickr.com/photos/image-catalog/21488737010. Copyright to Vita Vilcina with source of Unsplash, is licensed under CC0 1.0 Universal (CC0 1.0) with Public Domain Dedication. It is included here with thanks to Vita Vilcina.

p. 5 — "Heatpipe tunnel Copenhagen 2009.jpg" by Bill Ebbesen, 2009.
Attribution: Image link: https://en.wikipedia.org/wiki/User:Atomicbre.
Photo taken 25 November 2008, the tunnel between the National Hospital (Rigshospitalet) in Copenhagen and the Amager Powerplant (Amagerværket) in Amager. Tunnel exemplifies the relationship between water, energy, cities, and transport: "The tunnel transfers heated water and steam for the city" (Ebbesen, 2008). Found at: https://commons.wikimedia.org/wiki/File:Heatpipe_tunnel_copenhagen_2009.jpg Licensed under the Creative Commons Attribution 3.0 Unported license. This photo is included here with thanks to Bill Ebbesen.

p. 6 — "Solar System Montage – High Resolutions 2001 Version," Jet Propulsion Laboratory, 2001.
Attribution: NASA/JPL. This image may be found at https://www.jpl.nasa.gov/images/solar-system-montage-high-resolution-2001-version. This montage includes Mercury (taken from *Mariner 10*), Venus (by *Magellan*), Earth and Moon (by *Galileo*), Mars (by *Mars Global Surveyor*), Jupiter (by *Cassini*), and Saturn, Uranus, and Neptune (by *Voyager*). Note: Pluto is not shown – no spacecraft has yet visited there. Two other versions of the montage, with data from earlier missions, may be found at https://photojournal.jpl.nasa.gov/catalog/PIA01341 and https://photojournal.jpl.nasa.gov/catalogue/PIA00545. For more information on the planets, visit: http://solarsystem.nasa.gov/planets/index.cfm This image of "Solar System Montage" is included here with thanks to NASA and Jet Propulsion Laboratory, California Institute of Technology.

p. 13 — "Splash!" by José Manuel Suárez, 2008.
Attribution: see earlier entry on p. 159 of this list.

p. 15 — "Aerial view of the Innoko River in summer," by Keller Jo, U.S. Fish and Wildlife Service, 2013.
Attribution: Image link: https://commons.wikimedia.org/wiki/File:Aerial_view_of_the_Innoko_river_in_summer.jpg
Creative Commons CC0 License. This image is the work of a U.S. Fish and Wildlife Service employee, taken or made as part of that person's official duties. As a work of the U.S. federal government, this image is in the public domain. This image is included with thanks to Keller Jo and the U.S. Fish and Wildlife Service.

p. 16 — "Niagara Falls, from the American Side" by Frederic Edwin Church, 1867.
Attribution: This image is located at: https://en.wikipedia.org/wiki/Niagara_Falls,_from_the_American_Side#/media/File:Frederic_Edwin_Church_-_Niagara_Falls,_from_the_American_Side_-_Google_Art_Project.jpg, and is from the Scottish National Gallery. Photographer for this inclusion is the Google Cultural Institute at qQE5jAFm16XHjQ, with link at https://artsandculture.google.com/asset/qQE5jAFm16XHjQ and was selected as picture of the day on English Wikipedia for 9 November 2016. This image is a faithful photographic reproduction of a two-dimensional work of art that is in the public domain because it is more than 100 years old. This image is included here with thanks to Frederic Edwin Church, the Scottish National Gallery, and the Google Cultural Institute.

p. 19 — "A Water Carrier," photo illustration from *Madeira, Old and New* by William Henry Koebel, 1909. Attribution: Image link:
https://commons.wikimedia.org/wiki/File:A_Water_Carrier,_MON_1909.jpg
Authorship of each illustration is not specified in this book, so there is no specific credit except to the book. The image is ascertained to be in the public domain because of the book's publication date of 1909. This image is included here with appreciation to Wikimedia, Creative Commons, and William Henry Koebel.

p. 21 — "Sustainable Development Goals" by United Nations 2019.
Attribution: Image link:
https://commons.wikimedia.org/wiki/File:Sustainable_Development_Goals.svg
This document, published by the United Nations without a copyright notice was left in the public domain in order to disseminate "as widely as possible the ideas." It is among the categories outlined in Administrative Instruction ST/AI/189/Add.9/Rev.2. This graphic was not remixed or transformed. It is included here, with appreciation to the United Nations.

p. 22 — "Ten indicators of global warming." NOAA. 2010.
Attribution: Image link: https://commons.wikimedia.org/wiki/
File:Diagram_showing_ten_indicators_of_global_warming.png
This diagram, by the U.S. National Oceanic and Atmospheric Administration (NOAA), National Climatic Data Center, is from its 2010 report "State of the Climate in 2009." This image is in the public domain because it contains materials that originally came from NOAA, taken or made as part of official duties. It is included here with thanks to NOAA.

p. 25 — "Operation IceBridge View of Larsen C," by NASA Goddard Space Flight Center, 2017.
Attribution: Image link: https://commons.wikimedia.org/wiki/
File:Operation_IceBridge_View_of_Larsen_C_ (26376302328).jpg. NASA Goddard Space Flight Center, 31 October 2017. Author NASA ICE. NASA's Operation IceBridge flies over Antarctica to measure changes in land and sea ice. Original image uploaded from https://flickr.com/photos/24662369@N0y/26376301518 and is available at http://www.nasa.gov/mision_pages/icebridge/index.html. Image license Creative Commons CC-BY-2.0. This image is included with thanks to NASA, Goddard Space Flight Center.

p. 27 — "Mobile phone evolution," by Anders
(https://commons.wikimedia.org/wiki/User:Anders).
Attribution: Image link: https://commons.wikimedia.org/wiki/File:Cell_phone_icon.svg and also http//:www.norman.cx/photos/showphotonew.asp_Q_path_E_20060108%20PAD%2C%20AND Y/IMG_6075.JPG. This work is in the public domain, released by Anders, and is included with thanks to its creator, Anders.

p. 28 — "Hydraulic Fracturing-Related Activities," by U.S. EPA, 2012.
Attribution: "Hydraulic Fracturing-Related Activities" by U.S. Environmental Protection Agency (EPA), Office of Research and Development, Washington, D.C., USA, 2012.
Image link: https://commons.wikimedia.org/wiki/File:Hydraulic_Fracturing-Related_Activities.jpg and the link to the study is: http://www2.epa.gov/hfstudy/hydraulic-fracturing-water-cycle
This image is in the public domain and is included here with thanks to the EPA.

p. 29 — "Oil production from hydraulically fractured wells in the U.S. (2000-2015)."
Attribution: Image link: https://commons.wikimedia.org/wiki/
File:Oil_production_from_hydraulically_fractured_wells_in_the_United_States_(2000-2015)_(25690743312).png. This work is in the public domain and is included because it is a work prepared by an officer or employee of the U.S. Government as part of that person's official duties under the terms of *Title 17, Chapter 1, Section 105 of the US Code*.

p. 33 —"Lake Mead," photograph by Michael Rosen, USGS, 2016.
Attribution: Image link: https://www.usgs.gov/media/images/lake-mead-1
Description: "At the edges of Lake Mead, the nation's largest reservoir, a 'bathtub ring' of mineral deposits approximately 100 ft. high shows the drop in water level after years of drought along the Colorado River."
This photo is in the public domain, and is included here with thanks to Michael Rosen and USGS.

p. 35 — "Lake Chad Map," by United Nations, 2006.
Attribution: Image link: https://commons.wikimedia.org/wiki/File:Lakechad_map.png
Image is adapted from https://www.un.org/Depts/Cartographic/map/profile/niger.pdf.
This image is a map derived from a United Nations map, and considered to be in the public domain. UN requests that user delete the UN name, logo, and reference number upon any modification of the map. License Creative Commons CC0. This image is included with thanks to the United Nations.

p. 38 — "Oceanic Gyres," by U.S. National Oceanic and Atmospheric Administration (NOAA), 2008.
Attribution: Image link: https://commons.wikimedia.org/wiki/File:Oceanic_gyres.png, and also at https://oceanservice.noaa.gov/education/for-students.html This image is in the public domain and is included here with thanks to NOAA.

p. 40 — "Plastic microbead," by Andrew Watts, 2016.
Attribution: "Plastic microbead" by Andrew Watts Face to Face with Plastic, University of Exeter, UK https://www.flickr.com/people/26126239@N02 Note: "This is an image of a plastic microbead from a facewash, taken via scanning electron microscopy" from https://commons.wikimedia.org/wiki/ File:Plastic_microbead_Andrew_Watts_research.jpg and is also located at https://flickr.com/photos/261262239@N02/27177934554. License: Creative Commons Attribution 2.0 Generic. This image is included with thanks to Andrew Watts and the University of Exeter, UK.

p. 42 — "Medicine Drugs." Clip art by ernes, 2009.
Attribution: Image link: https://en.wikipedia.org/wiki/File:Medicine_Drugs.svg
This work is in the public domain CC1.0 Universal Public Domain Dedication and is included with appreciation to ernes and Open Clip Art Library.

p. 44 — "Bear Seamount guyot," U.S. National Oceanic and Atmospheric Administration (NOAA), 2007.
Attribution: Image link:
https://upload.wikimedia.org/wikipedia/commons/a/a4/Bear_Seamount_guyot.jpg. This image is a 3-D depiction of Bear Seamount, with Physalia Seamount in the background. Because it contains materials that came from the U.S. NOAA, this image is in the public domain. It is included here with thanks to NOAA.

p. 45 — "Location of the Clarion-Clipperton Zone," by Coastal Marine Hazards and Resources Program, U.S. Geological Survey, 2018.
Attribution: Image link: http://www.usgs.gov/images/locations-clarion-clipperton-zone and also at https://commons.wikimedia.org/wiki/File:Location_of_the_Clarion_Clipperton_Zone.png shows the Mariana Arc, Lau Basin, Cook Islands, and Clarion-Clipperton Zone (CCZ). Because it is a work prepared by the United States Government, it is in the public domain. This image is included with thanks to the Coastal Marine Hazards and Resources Program, United States Geological Survey.

p. 47 — "Fresh fruits and vegetables," by Peggy Greb, 2013. U.S. Department of Agriculture.
Attribution: Image link:
https://commons.wikimedia.org/wiki/File:Fresh_cut_fruits_and_vegetables.jpg
This work is in public domain, and is included here with thanks to the U.S. Department of Agriculture and photographer Peggy Greb.

p. 49 — "Water on Tap (Unsplash)" by Luis Tosta, 2017. https://unsplash.com/@luis_tosta
Attribution: Image link:
https://commons.wikimedia.org/wiki/File:Water_on_tap_(Unsplash).jpg and also in archive at: https://unsplash.com/photos/SVeCm5KF_ho. This photo, dated 24 May 2017, was published prior to 5 June 2017 under the Creative Commons CC0 1.0 Universal Public Domain Dedication. The person who associated a work with this deed has dedicated the work to the public domain. This photo has not been remixed or transformed. It is included here, with appreciation and thanks to Luis Tosta.

p. 54 — "Reed Bed" by Pixella, 2016.
Attribution: Image link: https://flickr.com/photos/137643065@N06/24218834162 and also https://commons.wikimedia.org/wiki/File:Reed_bed_2.jpg. This photo is in the public domain, CC0 1.0 Universal Public Domain Dedication and is included here with thanks to Pixella and FlickreviewR.

p. 55 — "Rainwater collector" by Jonathan Wilkins 2009.
Attribution: "Rainwater collector" by Johnathan Wilkins
https://www.geograph.org.uk/profile/7090
Image link: https://commons.wikimedia.org/wiki/File:Rainwater_collector_-_geograph.org.uk_-_1470877.jpg and also https://www.geograph.org.uk/photo/1470877. License: Creative Commons Attribution-ShareAlike 2.0, CC-BY-SA-2.0. This image is included with thanks to Jonathan Wilkins and the Geograph project
https://commons.wikimedia.org/wiki/Commons:Geograph_Britain_and_Ireland.

p. 56 — Rainwater harvesting system" by Genetics4good and Fred the Oyster, 2010.
Attribution: Image Link: https://commons.wikimedia.org/wiki/User:Genetics4good and modified derivative work by Fred the Oyster https://commons.wikimedia.org/wiki/User:Fred_the_Oyster. This is a hand-drawn picture of a rainwater harvesting system in which potable water production (through filtering) is embedded. It is based on a drawing from the book "Duurzaam en Gezond Bouwen en Wonen" by Hugo Vanderstadt (Wikimedia 2021). This image has been digitally vectorized and is located at
https://commons.wikimedia.org/wiki/File:Rainwater_harvesting_sysem.svg and the original is
https://commons.wikimedia.org/wiki/File_Rainwater_harvesting_system.JPG
The copyright holder of this work, KVDP/Genetics4good, released this work into the public domain with the Creative Commons CC0 License. It is included here with thanks to Fred the Oyster and Genetics4good.

p. 58 — "Former Ryōgoku Kokugikan Sumo Hall Interior c1910" by unknown photographer.
Image link: https://commons.wikimedia.org/wiki/File:Former-Ryogoku-Kokugikan-Sumo-Hall-Interior-c1910.png and also https://www.mai-b.co.jp/guide/2014/09/post-484.html. This is a faithful reproduction of a two-dimensional work of art that is more than 100 years old, and therefore is in the public domain. It is under the terms of Creative Commons CC0 License. It is included here with thanks to Ryōgoku Kokugikan Sumo Wrestling Arena.

p. 61 — "Water detected at high latitudes on the moon," by NASA.
Attribution: NASA's Moon Mineralogy Mapper, an instrument on the Indian Space Research Organization's Chandrayaan-1 mission. Moon Mineralogy Mapper (M3) is an imaging spectrometer developed by Jet Propulsion Laboratory (JPL) and Carle Pieters of Brown University. Chandrayyan-1 was a mission launched in 2008 by the Indian Space Research Organization (ISRO), Department of Space, Government of India, https://www.isro.gov.in/Spacecraft/chandrayaan-1. The image "Water Detected at High Latitudes on the Moon" is located at https://commons.wikimedia.org/wiki/
File:Water_Detected_at_High_Latitudes_on_the_Moon.jpg and at https://www.nasa.gov/multimedia/imagegallery/image_feature_1478.html with image credit ISRO/NASA/JPL-Caltech/Brown Univ./USGS.
    "This image is a three-color composite of reflected near-infrared radiation from the sun, and illustrated the extent to which different materials are mapped across the side of the moon that faces Earth. Small amounts of water were detected on the surface of the moon at various locations. This image illustrates their distribution at high latitudes toward the poles. Blue shows the signature of water." ISRO/NASA/JPL-Caltech/Brown Univ./USGS, 2017.
    This image is in the public domain because it was created by NASA, and was selected as Image of the Day on 25 September 2009. It is included here with thanks to ISRO, NASA, JPL, USGS, Caltech, and Brown University.

p. 63 — "View of the Zarchin Desalination Plant on the Red Sea in Eilat" by Moshe Pridan, 1964.
Attribution: Image link:
https://commons.wikimedia.org/wiki/File:Water_desalination_plant_in_Eilat.jpg
This photo, from the Israel National Photo Collection, is in the public domain. It is included here with thanks to Moshe Pridan and the Israel National Photo Collection.

p. 65 — "Pōhutukawa tree, taken at Cornwallis Beach, West Auckland" by Ed323.
Attribution: Link to photograph: https//en.wikipedia.org/wiki/User:Ed323
Link to image: https://en.wikipedia.org/wiki/Metrosideros_excelsa
This image was dedicated to the public domain by the photographer and is included here with thanks to Ed323.

p. 68 — "Canalside 2015," by Invest Buffalo Niagara.
Attribution: Image link: https://commons.wikimedia.org/wiki/File:Canalside_2015.jpg and also https://www.flickr.com/photos/149734909@N04/36443454975/in/album-72157684060082204/
This image is in the public domain, available under Creative Commons CC0 1.0 Universal Public Domain Declaration and is included here with thanks to Invest Buffalo Niagara.

p. 70 — "*Maeslantkering*, northern half 3" by Joop van Houdt, 2010.
Attribution: Image link:
https://commons.wikimedia.org/wiki/File:Maeslantkering_northern_half_3.jpg and also at https://beeldbank.rws.nl. and also at https://beeldbank.rws.nl/MediaObject/Details/387608 This image shows the northern half of the Maeslantkering storm surge barrier. The authors, Joop van Houdt, and Rijkswaterstaat have placed this image in the public domain, but the intellectual ownership of the image material lies with the Rijkswaterstaat, Data-ICT-Dienst, Beeldarchief Rijkswaterstaat. This image is under the Creative Commons CC0 License. It is included here with thanks to Joop van Houdt, and the Rijkswaterstaat.

p. 73 — "Panoramique mont Everest" by Fabien 1309
Attribution: Fabien https://commons.wikimedia.org/wiki/User:Fabien1309) and Lerian (https://fr.wikipedia.org/wiki/Utilisateur.Lerian), 2005.
Image link: https://commons.wikimedia.org/wiki/File:Panoramique_mont_Everest.jpg
This image is in the public domain and included here with thanks to Fabien1309 and Lerian.

p. 74 — "Sustainable Development Goal (SDG) 6: Clean Water and Sanitation" by United Nations, 2016.
Image link: https://commons.wikimedia.org/wiki/File:Sustainable_Development_Goal_6.png
This image is the public domain and is included here with thanks to the United Nations.

p. 75 – "Solar septic tank toilet prototype, front view (13359494235).jpg" by SuSanA Secretariat of Sustainable Sanitation Alliance https://www.susana.or/en/ 2014.
Image link: https://www.flickr.com/photos/gtzecosan/13359494235/ and also at https://commons.wikimedia.org/wiki/File:Solar_septic_tank_toilet_prototype,_front_view_(13359494235).jpg This image shows the Exhibit of the Asian Institute of Technology (AIT) (https://www.ait.ac.th) at Reinvent the Toilet Fair in Delhi, India, 21-22 March 2014. The Sustainable Sanitation Alliance is a network of individuals and organizations that want to contribute to the UN Sustainable Development Goals, in particular SDG6. The organization began in 2007 and offers a library, project database, and discussion forum. The secretariat is currently located in Eschborn, Germany. The Asian Institute of Technology (AIT) is an international university with special programs in engineering, environment, advanced technologies, sustainable development, management and planning. This image is licensed under the Creative Commons Attribution 2.0 Generic license. It is included here with thanks to AIT and the Sustainable Sanitation Alliance.

p. 77 — "Universal Waste Management System (UWMS): NASA's New Space Toilet" by NASA 2020."
Attribution: Image link: https://www.nasa.gov/feature/boldly-go-nasa-s-new-space-toilet-offers-more-comfort-improved-efficiency-for-deep-space . The UWMS, installed on the International Space Station (ISS), offers an improved design that can be integrated into different spacecraft and support systems. UWMS is adaptable to longer missions as those on the ISS, but can be adapted to shorter missions like Artemis II for a 10-day mission. According to astronaut Jessica Meir, "We recycle about 90% of all water-based liquids on the space station, including urine and sweat. What we try to do aboard the space station is mimic elements of Earth's natural water cycle to reclaim water from the air" (NASA, 2020). This image from the U.S. National Aeronautics and Space Administration (NASA) is in the public domain. It is included here with thanks to NASA editor Darcy Elburn, astronaut Jessica Meir, the International Space Station, and NASA.

p. 79 — "Musical Notes" from Wikimedia Commons. "Musical Notes" is the refined work of many contributors and artists who are linked here with the image history:
https://commons.wikimedia.org/wiki/File:Musical_notes.svg
This image is in the public domain and is included here with thanks to Wikimedia and to the artists who contributed to its creation.

p. 81. — "Palette de teintures végétales sur soie" by Florent Beck, 2019. (Tr: Palette of vegetable dyes on silk.)
Attribution: Author link: https://commons.wikimedia.org/wiki/User:FlorentBeck
Image link: https://commons.wikimedia.org/wiki/
File:20190629_palette_de_teinture_végétales_sur_soie.jpg
This image was placed in the public domain by the author/photographer: it is made available under the Creative Commons CC0 1.0 Universal Public Domain Dedication and is included here with thanks to Florent Beck.

p. 82 — "Hybrid Sankey Diagram of 2011 U.S. Interconnected Water and Energy Flows," from "The Water-Energy Nexus: Challenges and Opportunities," by D. Bauer, M. Philbrick, and B. Vallario, U.S. Department of Energy, 2014.
Attribution: Image link:
https://commons.wikimedia.org/wiki/File:Green_equilateral_triangle_point_up.svg
This image is the public domain and is included here with thanks to Bauer, Philbrick, and Vallario, and the U.S. Department of Energy.

p. 84 — "Colorado River: Horseshoe Bend," by Paul Hermans, 2012.
Attribution: https://commons.wikimedia.org/wiki/File:Horseshoe_Bend_TC_27-09-2012_15-34-14.jpg
by Paul Hermans (https://commons.wikimedia.org/wiki/User:Paul_Hermans). Licensed under GNU Free Documentation License (GNU FDL) published by the Free Software Foundation. No Front-Cover Texts, and no Back-Cover Texts. This file is licensed under the Creative Commons Attribution-Share Alike 3.0 Unported, 2.5 Generic, 2.0 Generic, and 1.0 Generic. This photo was not remixed or transformed. It is with appreciation that it is included here, with thanks to Paul Hermans.

p. 93 — "Water Systems: A Model of Use," by Khalid Saeed.
Attribution: Khalid Saeed and Paul Mathisen, Worcester Polytechnic Institute.
http://www.wpi.edu. It is with appreciation that it is included here, with thanks to Khalid Saeed and Paul Mathisen.

p. 97 — "Splash!" by José Manuel Suárez, 2008.
Attribution: see earlier entry on p. 159 of this list.

p. 99 — "Drinking Water Fountain," by Darwin Bell, 2006.
Attribution: "Drinking Water Fountain" by Darwin Bell:
https://www.flickr.com/photos/darwinbell/286131360/
and https://commons.wikimedia.org/wiki/File:Drinking_fountain.jpg
Licensed under Creative Commons Attribution 2.0 Generic license, CC BY 2.0. This photo was not remixed or transformed. It is with appreciation that it is included here, with thanks to Darwin Bell.

p. 101 — "Plastic on corals, pockets, wakatobi, 2018" by Q. Phia, 2018.
Attribution: "Plastic on corals, pockets, wakatobi, 2018" by Q. Phia
(https://www.flickr.com/people/60477809@N03).
The photo is from Wikimedia Commons (44900243615):
https://commons.wikimedia.org/wiki/File:Plastic_on_corals,_pockets,_wakatobi,_2018_(49900243615).jpg. This file is licensed under Creative Commons Attribution 2.0 Generic license. This photo was not remixed or transformed. It is with appreciation that it is included here, with thanks to Q. Phia.

p. 102 — "Region, Cleanup Cost, Revenue Restoration."
Attribution: Chart by Cherie E. Potts, WordWorks. Composed in 2021 from data based on sources in the text.

p. 103 — "Drilling an oil well into the Bakken Fields in North Dakota" by U.S. Geological Survey, 2009.
Attribution: "Drilling an oil well into the Bakken Formation in North Dakota, by United States Geological Survey, 2009. Image location: https://www.usgs.gov/media/images/drilling-oil-well-bakken-formation-north-dakota. This image is in the public domain. This photo was not remixed or transformed. It is with appreciation that it is included here, thanks to the United States Geological Survey.

p. 105 — "Seamount" by NOAA, National Ocean Service, 2011.
Attribution: "Seamount: a map of a seamount in the Arctic Ocean created by NOAA's Office of Coast Survey by gathering data with a multibeam echo sounder." 19 January 2011. This image is licensed under Attribution 2.0 Generic (CC BY 2.0). This image may be found at: https://www.flickr.com/photos/usoceangov/5369581627. This image has not been remixed or transformed. It is with appreciation that it is included here, thanks to NOAA, National Ocean Service.

p. 108 — "Water on Tap (Unsplash)" by Luis Tosta, 2017. https://unsplash.com/@luis_tosta
See earlier entry on p. 162 of this list.

p. 198 — "Cost to rebuild or replace leaking water/sewer pipes," by Cherie E. Potts, 2021.
Attribution: Graphic created by Cherie E. Potts, WordWorks. Data from sources discussed in the text, including Klara Ramm, EurEau Committee on Economic and Legal Affairs. "Time to invest in Europe's water infrastructure," 2 May 2018. Euractiv. https://www.euractiv.com/section/energy-environment/opinion/time-to-invest-in-europes-water-infrastructure

p. 111 — "Sea level rise, 1993–present" by NASA Goddard Space Flight Center.
Attribution: "Sea level rise, 1993–present" is a chart located at https://climate.nasa.gov/vital-signs/sea-level/. The data source: Satellite sea level observations. Credit: NASA's Goddard Space Flight Center. If you wish to see latest available data, you may create an Earthdata account: register here: https://urs.earthdata.nasa.gov/home. This chart of sea level rise, 1993 to present has not been changed, remixed, or transformed. It is in the public domain through nasa.gov. It is with appreciation that it is included here, with thanks to NASA.

p. 111 — "Cost of sea level rise for U.S. cities" by Cherie E. Potts, 2021.
Attribution: table created by Cherie E. Potts, WordWorks, to illustrate sea level rise costs. Based on data sources in the text including "Economy-wide effects of coastal flooding due to sea level rise" by Thomas Schinko and others: https://www.sciencenews.org/article/climate-economic-costs-rising-seas-will-be-steeper-than-thought. This graphic is included here, with thanks to Cherie Potts and to Thomas Schinko and team.

p. 113 — U.S. Storms, and Estimated Costs, by Cherie E. Potts, 2021.
Attribution: table created by Cherie E. Potts, WordWorks. Illustrates costs of recent U.S. storms. Based on data from the National Centers for Environmental Information, and National Oceanic and Atmospheric Administration (NOAA). Available at https://www.ncdc.noaa.gov/billions/. This graphic is included here, with thanks to Cherie E. Potts, and to NOAA.

p. 118 — "Trees torching at the High Park Wildfire," by U.S. Department of Agriculture, 2012.
Attribution: Image at https://commons.wikimedia.org/wiki/File:Trees_torching_-_High_Park_Wildfire.jpg. Image originally posted to Flickr, uploaded to Wikimedia Commons on 28 June 2012. Flickr source: https://www.flickr.com/phots/usdagov/7408428590
Image is licensed under Creative Commons Attribution 2.0 Generic license. No changes were made. This photo is included here, with thanks to the U.S. Department of Agriculture.

p. 120 — "The Solar System and Beyond is Awash in Water" by NASA, 2015.
Attribution: Image link:
https://www.nasa.gov/sites/default/files/thumbnails/image/watereventfeature20150407_main.jpg . This image is from http://www.nasa.gov and is in the public domain. This image is included here, with thanks to NASA.

p. 122 — "The Natural Water Cycle" by John Evans and Howard Perlman, U.S. Geological Survey, 2019.
Attribution: https://www.usgs.gov/media/images/natural-water-cycle-0. Image credit: Howard Perlman, USGS, Public Domain. Source: The USGS Water Science School – The Water Cycle: https://www.usgs.gov/special-topic/water-science-school/science/water-cycle This image is included here, with thanks to John Evans, Howard Perlman, and the USGS.

p. 125 — "Earth from Space" by NASA, 2000.
Attribution: created by Reto Stöckli, Nazmi El Saleous, and Marit Jentoft-Nilsen, NASA GSFC.
Image link: https://earthobservatory.nasa.gov/images/885/earth-from-space
"This image is a combination of data from two satellites: The Moderate Resolution Imaging Spectroradiometer (MODIS) aboard NASA's Terra satellite collected the land surface data over 16 days, while NOAA's Geostationary Operational Environmental Satellite (GOES) produced a snapshot of Earth's clouds." Source: NASA GSFC. This image is included here with thanks to the creators, and to NASA GSFC.

p. 130 — "O Praise Him" by JFXie, 2012.
Attribution: Image created by JFXie, https://www.flickr.com/people/50249715@N06. This image was originally posted to Flickr, uploaded to Wikimedia Commons on 13 May 2014 confirmed to be licensed under Creative Commons Attribution 2.0 Generic, CC BY 2.0. The image may be found at https://commons.wikimedia.org/wiki/File:O_Praise_Him.jpg and https://www.flickr.com/photos/jfxie/7321064334. This image is included here with thanks to JFXie.

p. 133 — "Whanganui River between Pipiriki and Jerusalem," by Prankster, 2012.
Image link: https://commons.wikimedia.org/wiki/File:Whanganui-River-01.jpg
Attribution: The photographer made this image available under the Creative Commons CC0. 1.0 Universal Public Domain Dedication, waiving all their rights to the work worldwide under copyright law. It is included here with thanks to Prankster for this dedication.

p. 172 — "Splash!" by José Manuel Suárez.
See earlier entry on p. 159 of this list.

p. 173 — "Electricity (sanded and polished) by Andrew Fysh, 2013.
See earlier entry on p. 159of this list.

p. 174 — "Skyscrapers with Lit Windows at Night" by Vita Vilcina, 2012.
See earlier entry on p. 159 of this list.

p. 175 — "Heatpipe Tunnel Copenhagen 2009.jpg" by Bill Ebbesen, 2009.
See earlier entry on p. 159 of this list.

p. 176 — "Solar System Montage—High Resolutions 2001 Version," Jet Propulsion Laboratory, 2001.
See earlier entry on p. 160 of this list.

Acknowledgements

This work could never have been written without the guidance and review of George H. Litwin, co-author of *Mobilizing the Organization*; nor without the inspiration and legacy of Frank P. Davidson, co-author of *Building the World*, to whom this work is dedicated.

David H. Marks refined and guided the material on water. Lucien Deschamps and Jean Louis Bobin shaped the scope of the energy section and contributed perspectives toward a carbon-free energy system. Khalid Saeed suggested the application of system dynamics to the issues explored, and designed and contributed the water model, as well as updated terms for the urban dynamics model. John Sterman and Climate Interactive developed the energy model. Roberta L. Spencer offered guidance regarding the urban dynamics model of Jay W. Forrester. Steve Hargreaves strengthened the section on cities. In the space section, Dimitri N. Mavris and team offered the model; Matthew C. Weinzierl and Angela Acocella contributed the case. Alexandra Macmillan and James Woodcock designed the transport model. William Keene and the Atlanta Symphony Orchestra offered the libretto of *Itaipú* in the energy section. Winston E. Langley deepened and strengthened the conclusion.

Great appreciation to Harvard University, Massachusetts Institute of Technology, and the University of Massachusetts Boston for formative guidance.

Marilynn Burmeister, Richard Hantula, Lilian Kemp, Andrew C. Lemer, Rachael Rusting, Hervey (Todd) A. Ward III, and Shira P. White generously read versions of the book and significantly refined the framework. Kevin J. Downing, Michael Fisher, Brian Halley, James Levine, and George P. Richardson offered direction.

Many thanks to the Copernicus Society, Fulbright Association, Radcliffe Institute, System Dynamics Society, Whiting Foundation, and Woodrow Wilson Foundation. Greatest appreciation to the Signet Society where this book began, and to Hancock Shaker Village Museum's Writer-in-Residence program, where it found completion.

Cherie E. Potts, president of WordWorks and editor of *Building the World* and of this sequel, deserves special appreciation for excellent preparation of documents, copy editing, supporting research, and for artful design and execution of the manuscript. Howard Zaharoff provided legal advice and guidance. Yujin Asai, founder of Dotmeta, merits recognition for website development of *Building the World* and this sequel. To the Joseph P. Healey Library of the University of Massachusetts Boston, continuing appreciation for creation and development of the *Building the World Blog*. Holly Sullo and Ben Paul contributed graphic design and publication guidance.

Kind encouragement of family, friends, and colleagues contributed greatly to this exploration; many helpful ideas were suggested, discussed, and refined in conversation. Thank you.

During the development of this book, I engaged in dialogue with, and received suggestions from, several groups surveyed: Baltimore, Maryland, airport bookstore patrons; Cambridge, Massachusetts, Harvard Coop bookstore patrons; Cambridge, Massachusetts, Signet Society; Chicago, Illinois, airport bookstore patrons; Paris, France,

Fulbright Water Act and United Nations Conference of the Parties 21; Syracuse, New York, World Canals Conference; Washington, DC, Fulbright Association.

While it is with great gratitude that I acknowledge those who contributed expert guidance, it is with greater humility that I also express advance apologies for errors, mistakes, failures, omissions, and other faults that are surely my own. Exploring problems and potential solutions of some world conditions poses challenges to ensure that facts are certain and current, even as the future is rapidly changing. It is hoped that corrections, errata, and improvements may be received and included in future editions, including online updates.

Books in the Series:

Water, Energy, Cities, Transport, Space

For further information, please visit:

renewingtheworld.com

WATER

"Splash!" by José Manuel Suárez, 2008.

Attribution: see p. 168

Problems — Water is the number one at-risk element in the world's changing climate. More than 30% of the world needs safe drinking water. It is not only people who demand water; agricultural products require water, some more than others. Industry drains aquifers, so does hydraulic fracturing. Oceans will soon contain more plastic than marine life. Droughts and floods are increasing in frequency and severity. Some of the world's earliest settlements were developed from ports, and now sea rise threatens many of those cities. A key element of space exploration is the quest for water, needed both for habitation and as a source for power.

Solutions — There are promising solutions that will create opportunities and jobs. Bringing safe water and sanitation to everyone will not only save lives and reduce healthcare costs, but also liberate those who must carry water, freeing up valuable time for education and employment while adding billions to the world economy. Adjusting agriculture away from environmentally detrimental products has created a new industry of plant-based foods, bringing $13.7 billion from revenue and taxes into the American economy in 2018, along with $3.6 billion from new jobs. Even if the climate goals of the 2015 Paris Agreement are met, some amount of sea rise will continue, demanding a new era of urban design. Rising sea levels may cost $14 trillion per year by 2100. Finding water in space will enable further exploration, using hydrogen as rocket fuel.

Benefits —
- 80% of tap water contains plastic; filters will become important.
- Rebuilding coastal areas will change architecture, banking, and insurance in ways not yet imagined, worth $14 trillion annually.
- Water prices in California increased by 14% in 2009: saving water will add value to productivity, affecting cities, agriculture, industry.
- Every new job in the water and sanitation industry creates three additional jobs in the U.S. economy.

ENERGY

"Electricity (sanded and polished) by Andrew Fysh, 2013.

Attribution: see p. 168

Problems — Using fossil fuels for energy is driving climate change. More than 2.5 billion people use wood to cook and heat indoors, causing 1.2 million deaths due to smoke inhalation. Coal mining results in 24.8 per 100,000 fatal occupational injuries compared to 4.3 in private industry. Mining and fracking continue to damage the earth, endanger water supply, and delay needed energy change. Old nuclear technologies need redesign. Hydroelectricity may look very different in fifty years. Forms of renewable energy will transform every aspect of life.

Solutions —Additional investment and more jobs are generated as an outcome of energy solutions. The market growth for solar energy is expected to produce an additional $140 billion in revenue by 2023. New technologies for renewables, through wind and wave power, made history when Portugal surpassed 107 hours of electricity generated only by renewable energy. The global energy storage market predicted growth of annual installation size of 6 GW in 2017 to 40 GW by 2022. European Union decisions to achieve carbon neutrality by 2050 open opportunities for new forms of nuclear, including fusion and traveling wave. The floors we walk on may light the rooms around us, based on innovations developed by a 27-year old student who demonstrated Pavegen technology at the 2012 London Olympics. Energy may be the *unum necessarium* of this century.

Benefits —
- Electric car sales grew 32% from 2012 to 2016; greater growth is expected by 2030.
- Energy solutions may prevent 90,000 asthma attacks, and 300,000 missed work days; total savings: $15 billion.
- New kinds of refrigerators and air conditioners, both expected to double by 2030, could improve energy consumption and reduce emissions by 60%.
- Building advanced, cleaner nuclear reactors will create 3,500 jobs per plant, generating $40 million in employment income each year.
- Savings in the U.S. economy by slowing climate change: $201 billion.
- Jobs in energy efficiency field: 3 million; 11 million globally.

CITIES

"Skyscrapers with Lit Windows at Night" by Vita Vilcina.

Problems — Cities magnify climate change. Supplying clean water challenges cities from Flint to Jakarta. Energy to support megacities strains power grids and causes power disruptions. Traffic snarls cities as transport options try to meet the needs of urban life. Air pollution in some cities is so constant that children in Beijing painted the sky grey when drawing a picture of their homes. Rising seas menace coastal cities from Guangzhou, China, a port city of 15 million, to Mumbai with 18 million. Some cities are built on tectonic fault lines. Kathmandu, Nepal could lose 69,000 people in a 6.0 earthquake; Istanbul worries that tall buildings might become unintended weapons of mass destruction in a major temblor. As the world population grows, land use will drive the future.

Solutions — Cities can enact solutions more easily. Michael Bloomberg, three-time mayor of New York City, and co-founder of C40, stated that mayors can and will lead change. Cities can outlaw plastic bags, build bike lanes, and provide new forms of education and job synergies. Urban planners will open a new era of architecture in climate change, bringing jobs and improvements as cities respond to rising seas. Most cities have existing water, energy, and transit systems, some in need of repair and many in need of an upgrade to address climate change. While it is difficult to lay new work upon existing infrastructure, one critical factor is already there: obtaining right of way.

Benefits —
- Solving urban trash problems will save land and health; Hong Kong accumulates solid waste equal to the height of the Empire State Building every 27 days. Global waste may increase by 70% by 2050; it is a field ready for innovation.
- Developing apps to deal with uneaten and wasted restaurant food could serve one million people who currently rely on food pantries.
- Every $1 billion invested in city public transport creates 50,000 jobs.
- Cities are often the destination of migrants: 272 million migrated in 2019.
- One-third of Americans live in just 20 cities; those same cities are home to 65% of the country's immigrants. Programs combining education and training could transform cities in one generation.

TRANSPORT

"Heatpipe tunnel, Copenhagen 2009.jpg" by Bill Ebbesen.

Attribution: see p. 168

Problems —The great success of wheels and wings also brought problems that affect every aspect of transport. Ninety percent of everything we touch comes to us via some form of transport. Americans spend 8 billion hours annually waiting in traffic. In 2010, the world reached a milestone of one billion vehicles on the road, but the number will double in the next two decades. Traffic fatalities are disproportionately higher in low-income countries. Automated vehicles may reduce accidents but they also shift jobs, impacting millions of workers in the United States. Shipping and air transport go beyond national guidelines, making industries responsible for energy policy. Aging infrastructure, from roads and bridges to ports for sea and air, will require rebuilding.

Solutions — The vehicle market offers some solutions, with the number of electric cars rapidly increasing, spurred on by some major auto manufacturers committing to all-electric vehicles by 2035. Autonomous vehicles are already used for delivery and in beta testing for all manner of transport. Roads will change to respond to electric and autonomous vehicles. Train travel, once the means of uniting continents, will expand through advancements in magnetic levitation and tunnel building. Canals, an ancient form of transport, are perhaps a solution to climate-caused inundations in port cities. The world's first solar flight around the globe without taking on additional fuel achieved the 26,744 mile (40,000 km) milestone.

Benefits —
- Autonomous transport is more accurate and could help prevent the 1.3 million deaths each year now due to car accidents.
- Solar and electric aircraft will change regional transport: a 62-mile (100 km) stretch of e-Genius test-flight cost just $3.00 to power the electric plane.
- Hyperloop systems may connect San Francisco to Los Angeles in 35 minutes.
- Electric bikes, using paths in elevated tubes, could change traffic in cities and reduce air pollution; millions of e-bikes now traverse urban lanes.
- Battery storage markets could attract investor capital of $620 billion by 2040.
- Rebuilding transport infrastructure will redefine the world.

SPACE

"Solar System Montage – High Resolutions 2001 Version," Jet Propulsion Laboratory, 2001.
Attribution: see p. 168

Problems — Space problems are just starting. It has been over half a century since humans landed on the moon, leaving behind objects—a small problem compared to the considerable amount of space debris in orbit. There are now so many satellites that astronomers soon may not be able to study the sky, and traffic control of satellites will be an issue. Peace agreements among nations need support: space, because it is truly shared, may be our last chance for peace.

Solutions — Everything we have learned on Earth we will need in space. Water, for example. Celestial bodies can contain substantial quantities of frozen water. Space explorers need water to support themselves and plants they may grow aloft. Water can be split into oxygen and hydrogen: the first to provide breathable air, the second as a source of fuel. Space holds vast economic promise. Goldman Sachs estimates the value of just one asteroid (there are millions) at $50 billion. NASA pegs asteroid mining at $700 quintillion—enough, theoretically, to give each person on Earth $100 billion. Space is important for climate change. It is only from space that we can see the Earth as a whole. Through weather satellites, we can pinpoint places with high methane emissions, observe melting ice, monitor pollution. Many consider space an exit strategy. But peace and cooperation may be the true benefit. The International Space Station has welcomed people from 17 countries, tested experiments submitted by 2 million teachers and 43 million students—each one proof that space belongs to all of Earth's citizens equally.

Benefits —
- Cleaning up space debris could be worth $15 million per object.
- Innovations from space: solar panels (increased market by 40% worldwide); implantable heart monitors ($83.7 billion market); water purification systems (saving or improving 159 million lives); cordless tools ($32 billion market).
- Eye in the Sky: from space we can finally see Earth as a whole system. ESA's *Sentinel* satellite series and NASA's Landsat measure atmospheric levels critical to climate change. We can spot problems and test solutions.

References

OVERVIEW

American Road & Transportation Builders Association (ARTBA). "Bridge Report," 2019. And https://artbabridgereport.org/reports/2020%20ARTBA%20Bridge%20Report.pdf

American Society of Civil Engineers. "Infrastructure Report Card." https://infrastructurereportcard.org

Biden, Joseph R. "Fact Sheet: The American Jobs Plan," 31 March 2021. The White House. https://www.whitehouse.gov/briefing-room/statements-releases/2021/03/31/fact-sheet-the-american-jobs-plan/

Building the World: A Finding Aid for the Research Collection. University of Massachusetts Boston Healey Library, February 2013. https://cpb-us-w2.wpmucdn.com/blogs.umb.edu/dist/5/707/files/2012/07/Finding-Aid-2jaiazs.pdf.

Carrington, Damian. "Plastic Fibres Found in Tap Water Around the World, study reveals." 5 September 2017. *The Guardian*. https://www.theguardian.com/environment/2017/sep/06/plastic-fibres-found-tap-water-around-world-study-reveals .

Chandler, Alfred D., Jr. *The Visible Hand*. Cambridge: Harvard University Press, 1977. ISBN: 9780674940529.

Davidson, Frank P. *Macro: A Clear Vision of How Science and Technology Will Shape Our Future*. New York: William Morrow, 1983. ISBN: 0-688-02182-4.

Davidson, Frank P. and Kathleen Lusk Brooke. *Building the World: An Encyclopedia of the Great Engineering Projects in History*. Greenwood/ABC-CLIO, 2006. ISBN: 0313333548.

DeCamp, L. Sprague. *The Ancient Engineers*. London: Ballantine Books, Random House, 1960. ISBN: 0-345-32029-8.

Gates, Bill. Quoted in: Bennet, James. " 'We Need an Energy Miracle' – Bill Gates has committed his fortune to moving the world beyond fossil fuels and mitigating climate change." November 2015. *The Atlantic*. https://www.theatlantic.com/magazine/archive/2015/11/we-need-an-energy-miracle/407881/

Hall D. O., and Patricia A. Moss. "Biomass for energy in developing countries," *GeoJournal*, vol. 7, no. 1 (January 1983): 5-14. Available from: https://link.springer.com/article/10.1007/BF00191854#page-1.

Hawken, Paul. *Blessed Unrest: How the Largest Social Movement in History Is Restoring Grace, Justice, and Beauty to the World*. Penguin Books, 2008. ISBN-13: 978-0143113652.

Hawken, Paul, ed. *Drawdown: The Most Comprehensive Plan Ever Proposed to Reverse Global Warming*. Penguin Book, 2017. ISBN-10: 9780143130444.

Hawken, Paul, and Bill Maher. Video. "Paul Hawken: Project Drawdown/Real Time with Bill Maher (HBO)" 30 September 2017. https://www.youtube.com/watch?v=k1wXHx2DsSU

Hotz, Robert Lee. "There's a Speeding Mass of Space Junk Orbiting Earth, Smashing into Things." 12 September 2017. *Wall Street Journal*. https://www.wsj.com/articles/we-need-satellitesa-speeding-mass-of-space-junk-puts-them-at-risk-1505226427.

International Energy Agency. "World Energy Outlook." Energy Database. https://www.iea.org/reports/world-energy-outlook-2020 .

Ivanova, Maria. *The Untold Story of the World's Leading Environmental Institution: UNEP at Fifty*. Cambridge: MIT Press, 2021. ISBN: 9780262542104.

Kimmelman, Michael. "Jakarta is Sinking So Fast, It Could End Up Underwater." 21 December 2017. *New York Times*. https://www.nytimes.com/interactive/2017/12/21/world/asia/jakarta-sinking-climate.html.

Langley, Winston E. "Declaration on the Right of Peoples to Peace," p. 93. In: *Encyclopedia of Human Rights Issues Since 1945*. Westport, CT: Greenwood Press, 1999. ISBN: 0313301638.

Litwin, George, John J. Bray, Kathleen Lusk Brooke. *Mobilizing the Organization: Bringing Strategy to Life*. London: Prentice Hall, 1996. ISBN: 0131488910

Lo, Andrea. "Why is Sydney being split into three cities?" 12 April 2018. *CNN*. https://www.cnn.com/2018/04/12/asia/sydney-three-cities/index.html .

Lobe, Jim. "Haiti: Recovery Bill Estimated at 11.5 Billion Dollars." Institute for Policy Studies. https://ips-dc.org/haiti_recovery_bill_estimated_at_115_billion_dollars/.

Luhby, Tami. "The Cost to Fix America's Crumbling Infrastructure? Nearly $2.6 Trillion, Engineers Say." 30 March 2021. CNN. https://www.cnn.com/2021/03/30/politics/infrastructure-us-investment-cost-engineers/index.html .

Meador, C. Lawrence, and Arthur C. Parthé, Jr. "Managing Macro-Development Policy, Planning and Control System Implications," 78-108. In: *How Big and Still Beautiful? Macro-Engineering Revisited.* Edited by Frank P. Davidson, C. Lawrence Meador, and Robert Salkeld. American Association for the Advancement of Science. Boulder, CO: Westview Press, 1980. ISBN: 0-89158-792-6.

MIT *Technology Review.* The Water issue, January 2022. https://www.technologyreview.com/magazines/the-water-issue/

NASA. "Space Debris and Human Spacecraft." https://orbitaldebris.jsc.nasa.gov/faq/.

Public Broadcasting Service. "Channel Tunnel (Chunnel): Wonders of the World Databank." Building Big Series. https://www.pbs.org/wgbh/buildingbig/wonder/structure/channel.html .

Revkin, Andrew C. "Disaster Awaits Cities in Earthquake Zones." *New York Times,* 24 February 2010.

Ritchie, Hannah and Max Roser. "Access to Energy." 2019. *OurWorldInData.org.* https://ourworldindata.org/energy-access.

Stine, Jeffrey K. *Mixing the Waters: Environment, Politics, and the Building of the Tennessee-Tombigbee Waterway.* Akron, OH: University of Akron Press, 1993. ISBN 0-9622628-5-4 (hrd) and ISBN 0-9622628-6-2 (pbk).

Thornton, Alex. "10 cities are predicted to gain megacity status by 2030." 06 February 2019. World Economic Forum. https://www.weforum.org/agenda/2019/02/10-cities-are-predicted-to-gain-megacity-status-by-2030/.

Timmons, David, Jonathan M. Harris, and Brian Roach. "The Economics of Renewable Energy." Global Development and Environment Institute, Tufts University, Medford, Massachusetts, U.S. 2014. https://sites.tufts.edu/gdae/

Toynbee, Arnold, ed. *Cities of Destiny.* London: Thames & Hudson, 1967. Library of Congress Catalog Card Number: 67-21688-65125.

Tyree, Chris and Dan Morrison. "Invisibles: The plastic inside us." *Orb Media,* 2017. https://www.organicconsumers.org/news/invisibles-plastic-inside-us.

United Nations. "68% of the world population projected to live in urban areas by 2050, says UN" 16 May 2018. *Department of Economic and Social Affairs, United Nations.* https://www.un.org/development/desa/en/news/population/2018-revision-of-world-urbanization-prospects.html.

United Nations. Department of Economics and Social Affairs. "World Urbanization Prospects." 2014. ISBN: 9789211515176.

Water.org website. https://water.org/our-impact/water-crisis/

Wilson, Edward O. *Sociobiology.* Cambridge, MA: Belknap Press, 1980. ISBN: 0-674-81623-4.

World Bank. "Fossil Fuel Energy Consumption." http://data.worldbank.org/indicator/EG.USE.COMM.FO.ZS .

World Health Organization (WHO). "2.1 billion people lack safe drinking water at home, more than twice as many lack safe sanitation." 12 July 2017. https://www.who.int/news/item/12-07-2017-2-1-billion-people-lack-safe-drinking-water-at-home-more-than-twice-as-many-lack-safe-sanitation

Younger, Paul L. *All that Matters: Water.* London: Hodder & Stoughton, 2012. ISBN: 9781444155812.

WHY WATER IS IMPORTANT

Damon, Matt. "Every 90 seconds," *National Geographic.* YouTube. 25 July 2017. https://www.youtube.com/watch?v=fn016bAJ4Z4/

Dizikes, Peter. "Q&A: Matt Damon on making a difference in the world." *MIT News,* 3 June 2016. http://news.mit.edu/2016/qa-matt-damon-making-difference-world-0603.

Environmental Protection Agency. "All the Water in the World." 2015. https://www.epa.gov/sites/production/files/2015-08/documents/mgwc-ww-intro.pdf/

Reed, Christopher. "How the Steel Industry Uses Billions of Gallons of Pennsylvania Water." 30 September 2016. Fresh Air/ WESA fm. https://www.wesa.fm/economy-business/2016-09-30/how-the-steel-industry-uses-billions-of-gallons-of-pennsylvania-water

Ritchie, Hannah and Max Roser. "Water use and stress: Share of freshwater withdrawals used in agriculture." July 2018. *Our World in Data.* https://ourworldindata.org/water-use-stress

Scutti, Susan, "Study: Public water supply is unsafe for millions of Americans." *CNN.* Available from: http://www.cnn.com/2016/08/09/health/contaminated-water/index.html.

Spang, Edward, William Moomaw, Kelly Gallagher, Paul Kirshen, David H. Marks. "The water consumption of energy production: An international comparison." 2014. Environmental Research Letters. 9. 105002. 10.1088/1748-9326/9/10/105002. https://www.researchgate.net/publication/266620784_The_water_consumption_of_energy_production_An_international_comparison

UNICEF and World Health Organization. "Progress on sanitation and drinking water: 2015 update and MDG assessment." ISBN: 9789241509145; https://apps.who.int/iris/handle/10665/177752

Water.org. "Effects of the Water Crisis on Health. 2020. https://water.org/our-impact/water-crisis/health-crisis/

WHO/UNICEF Joint Monitoring Program for Water Supply, Sanitation and Hygiene. "1 in 3 people globally do not have access to safe drinking water: New report on inequities in access to water, sanitation, and hygiene also reveals more than half of the world does not have access to safe sanitation services." 19 June 2019. *World Health Organization.* https://www.who.int/news/item/18-06-2019-1-in-3-people-globally-do-not-have-access-to-safe-drinking-water-unicef-who.

PROBLEMS

Lack of Water for Drinking

"2030 – SDG 6 – Clean Water and Sanitation." TEDxKish. https://www.youtube.com/watch?v=U5TxygvcmU8

Davis, Mark. "KC nonprofit taps into an innovative idea to solve global water crisis." 19 May 2017, *The Kansas City Star.* http://www.kansascity.com/living/spirit/article151406692.html.

Deere, Carmen D. and Magdalena Leon, "Gender, land and water: From reform to counter-reform in Latin America." *Agriculture and Human Values*, vol. 15, No. 4 (1998), pp. 375-386.

"India Water Crisis: 21 cities to exhaust groundwater supply." Video. 27 June 2018. Turkish Public Broadcasting Service. https://www.youtube.com/watch?v=G3Vzm5MOc90.

Shibesh Chandra Regmi and Ben Fawcett, "Integrating gender needs into drinking water projects in Nepal," *Gender and Development*, vol. 7, No. 3 (1999), pp.62-72.

Thompson, John. *Drawers of Water: 30 Years Of Change in Domestic Water Use and Environmental Health in East Africa—A Summary Report.* London: International Institute for Environment and Development, 2001. http://www.earthprint.com; http://www.drawersofwater.org

UNICEF. "Collecting water is often a colossal waste of time for women and girls." 29 August 2017. https://www.unicef.org/media/media_92690.html.

Water.org. "An Economic Crisis." https://water.org/our-impact/water-crisis/economic-crisis/

The Water Project. "Statistics of the Water Crisis." 31 August 2016. https://thewaterproject/water-scarcity/water_stats.

World Health Organization. "Drinking-water." July 2017. http://www.who.int/mediacentre/ factsheets/fs391/en/.

Water and Climate Change

Adusumilli, Susheel et al., "Interannual variations in meltwater input to the Southern Ocean from Antarctic ice shelves." 10 August 2020. *Nature Geoscience* 13, 616-620 (2020). https://www.nature.com/articles/s41561-020-0616-z?proof=t%3B

Amos, Jonathan, "Climate change: Satellites record history of Antarctic melting." 10 August 2020. *BBC.com.* https://www.bbc.com/news/science-environment-53725288 .

Davies, Bethan. "East Antarctic Ice Sheet." 22 June 2020. Antarctic Glaciers.org. http://www.antarcticglaciers.org/antarctica-2/east-antarctic-ice-sheet/

Deltares. Institute for Applied Research in the Field of Water and Subsurface: Flood Risk, Adoptive Delta Planning, Infrastructure, Water and Subsurface Resources, Environmental. https://www.deltares.nl/en/topdossiers/clean-water-is-vital/

Food and Agriculture Organization, United Nations. "Pacific leaders alarmed over climate change's negative impact of food systems and food security: call to action at COP23." http://www.fao.org/family-farming/detail/en/c/1068343/

Givetash, Linda. "Early-Warning Tools Aim to Prevent 'Water Wars', Curb Droughts." 25 December 2018. NBC News/World. https://www.nbcnews.com/news/world/early-warning-tools-aim-prevent-water-wars-curb-droughts-n917001

Hartley, Charlotte. "Antarctic ice sheet collapse could add 3 meters to sea-level rise." 23 July 2020. *Science.* https://www.sciencemag.org/news/2020/07/antarctic-ice-sheet-collapse-could-add-3-metres-to-sea-level-rise

IHE Delft. "Water, Peace, and Security Partnership. "Identifying and Addressing Developing Water-Related Security Risks, Linking Short-Term Water Shortage to Social, Political, Economic, and Hydrological Factors." https://www.un-ihe.org/water-peace-and-security-partnership

Jacobsen, Rowan. "Israel Proves the Desalination Era is Here: One of the Driest Countries on Earth Now Makes More Fresh Water Than it Needs." *Scientific American,* 9 July 2016. https://www.scientificamerican.com/article/israel-proves-the-desalination-era-is-here/

Kounang, Nadia. "El Paso to Drink Treated Sewage Water Due to Climate Change Drought." CNN, 5 December 2018. https://www.cnn.com/2018/11/30/health/water-climate-change-el-paso/index.html

UN Water website. "Water and Climate Change." https://www.unwater.org/water-facts/climate-change/

UNESCO. "World Water Day 2014: Water and Energy." http://www.unesco.org/new/en/natural-sciences/environment/water/wwap/wwdr/2014-water-and-energy/

Icebergs and Endangered Islands
Amos, Jonathan. "A68 iceberg on collision path with South Georgia." 4 November 2020. BBC.com.

Amos, Jonathan. "A68: Iceberg that became a social media star melts away." 18 April 2021. BBC.com.

European Space Agency (ESA). "South Georgia Island." 21 December 2018. https://www.esa.int/ESA_Multimedia/Images/2018/12/South_Georgia_Island

Government of South Georgia and the South Sandwich Islands. "South Georgia and the South Sandwich Islands: Marine Protected Area Management Plan." 31 August 2013. https://www.gov.gs/docsarchive/Environment/Marine%20%Protected%Area/MPA%20Management%20Plan%20v2.0.pdf.

Imster, Eleanor. "Is this the end of the A-68A iceberg?" 10 February 2021. *EarthSky.* https://earthsky.org/earth/end-of-the-a68a-iceberg-feb2021 .

Readfearn, Graham. "Giant Antarctic iceberg on collision course with British territory of South Georgia: Fears the 150km long A-68A iceberg, which broke away from Larsen C ice shelf in 2017, could disrupt wildlife and shipping routes." 4 November 2020. *Guardian.* https://www.theguardian.com/environment/2020/nov/04/giant-antarctic-iceberg-on-collision-course-with-british-territory-of-south-georgia

Schwarz, Jill and M.P. Schodlok. "Impact of drifting icebergs on surface phytoplankton biomass in the Southern Ocean color remote sensing and *in situ* iceberg tracking." October 2009. *Deep Sea Research* Part 1, Oceanographic Research Papers 56 (10): 1727-1741. doi: 10.1016/j.dsr.2009.05.003.

More People Have Cellphones Than Toilets
Silver, Laura. "Smartphone ownership is growing rapidly around the world, but not always equally." 5 Feb. 2019. Pew Research Center. https://www.pewresearch.org/global/2019/02/05/smartphone-ownership-is-growing-rapidly-around-the-world-but-not-always-equally/.

Telegraph. "India has more mobile phones than toilets: UN report." 15 April 2010. https://www.telegraph.co.uk/news/worldnews/asia/india/7593567/India-has-more-mobile-phones-than-toilets-UN-report.html

United Nations (UN). World Toilet Day. https://www.un.org/en/observances/toilet-day.

Wang, Yue. "More People Have Cell Phones Than Toilets, U.N. Study Shows: Out of the world's estimated 7 billion people, 6 billion have access to mobile phones, but only 4.5 billion have access to working toilets," 25 March 2013. *Time Magazine.* https://newsfeed.time.com/2013/03/25/more-people-have-cell-phones-than-toilets-u-n-study-shows/

Wells and Aquifers: Fracking the Future
Elgin, Ben, Benjamin Hass, Phil Kuntz. "Fracking secrets by thousands keep US clueless on wells." 1 December 2012, Bloomberg.net. https://www.bloomberg.com/news/articles/2012-11-30/frack-secrets-by-thousands-keep-u-s-clueless-on-wells.

Environment America Research & Policy Center, 14 April 2016. "Fracking by the Numbers." https://environmentamerica.org/reports/ame/fracking-numbers-0

FracFocus. https://fracfocus.org.

Herrara, Hector. "The legal status of fracking worldwide: An environmental law and human rights perspective." January 20219. https://www.researchgate.net/publication/341625371. The_legal_status_of_fracking_worldwide_An_environmental_law_and_human_rights_perspective

Howarth, Robert W., Anthony Ingraffea, Terry Engelder. "Should fracking stop? Yes, it's too high risk." 15 September 2011. *Nature,* 477, 271-275. https://www.nature.com/articles/477271a.

Levi, Michael. *The Power Surge.* Oxford: Oxford University Press, 2013. ISBN: 9780199986163.

Nacamulli, Mia. Video. "How does fracking work?" 13 July 2017. https://ed.ted.com/lessons/how-does-fracking-work-mia-nacamulli

Ridlington, Elizabeth, Norman, Kim, Frontier Group, and Richardson, Rachel. Environment America Research & Policy Center. "Fracking by the Numbers," Table ES-1.

Townsend, Dina. "The legal status of fracking worldwide: An environmental law and human rights perspective." Global Network for Human Rights and the Environment. 6 January 2020. https://gnhre.org/2020/01/06/the-legal-status-of-fracking-worldwide-an-environmental-law-and-human-rights-perspective/.

Vuleta, Branka. "25+ astonishing fracking statistics everyone should know (2021 update)." 29 January 2021. Seed Scientific. https://seedscientific.com/fracking-statistics.

Shrinking Lakes
Allison, Edward H, et al. "Vulnerability of national economies to the impacts of climate change on fisheries." *Fish and Fisheries,* 2009. https://www.researchgate.net/profile/Declan_Conway/ publication/25725762_Vulnerability_of_National_Economies_to_Potential_Impacts_of_ Climate_Change-on_Fisheries/links/0deec52b07/.

Brean, Henry. "Follow a gallon of water from Lake Mead to a Las Vegas tap." 15 April 2017, *Las Vegas Review-Journal.* https://www.reviewjournal.com/local/local-las-vegas/follow-a-gallon-of-water-from-lake-mead-to-a-las-vegas-tap/.

Brean, Henry. "War of words flares in Arizona over Lake Mead water.' 3 May 2017. *Las Vegas Review-Journal.* https://www.reviewjournal.com/local/local-nevada/war-of-words-flares-in-arizona-over-lake-mead-water/

Brown, R. Lester, and Earth Policy Institute. "Emerging Water Shortages: Lakes Disappearing," *Plan B 3.0: Mobilizing to Save Civilization.* New York: W.W. Norton & Company, 2008. Pages. 75-78. ISBN: 9780393065893.

European Space Agency. Video. "Earth from Space: Lake Chad," 22 March 2019. https://www.youtube.com/watch?v=AnQ1gRvToVA

Pope, Cody T. "Vanishing Lake Chad – A Water Crisis in Central Africa." Circle of Blue. https://www.circleofblue.org/2008/world/vanishing-lake-chad-a-water-crisis-in-central-africa/

Purvis, Katherine and Catalin Trif. "The lakes of the world are disappearing – in pictures. Climate change and human activity are threatening the existence of some of the world's largest lakes." *Guardian,* 9 December 2016. https://www.theguardian.com/global-development-professionals-network/gallery/2016/dec/09/the-lakes-of-the-world-are-disappearing-in-pictures/.

Sow, Mariama. "Figure of the week: The shrinking Lake Chad" 9 February 2017. https://www.brookings.edu/blog/africa-in-focus/2017/02/09/figure-of-the-week-the-shrinking-lake-chad/ .

Oceans of Plastic and Garbage Gyres
Cirino, Erica. "Charles Moore is now a two-time Garbage Patch discoverer." 20 July 2017, *National Geographic.* https://www.safinacenter.org/blog/charles-moore-is-now-a-two-time-garbage-patch-discoverer-and-i-can-tell-you-what-a-garbage-patch-looks-like.

Marine Debris Program, Office of Response and Restoration, NOAA. "TRASH TALK: What is the Great Pacific Garbage Patch?" 29 September 2020. https://marinedebris.noaa.gov/videos/trash-talk-what-great-pacific-garbage-patch-0

McKie, Robin. "Eco-Warrior sets sail to save oceans from 'plastic death'." 11 April 2009. *Guardian.* https://www.theguardian.com/environment/2009/apr/12/david-de-rothschild-plastiki-pacific.

NOAA. "What is the Great Pacific Garbage Patch?" https://marinedebris.noaa.gov/videos/trash-talk-what-great-pacific-garbage-patch-0

((The) Ocean Cleanup. "System 001/B – The Mission Plan." 27 June 2019. https://theoceancleanup.com/updates/system-001-b-the-mission-plan/

Williams, David. "Plan to clean up the Great Pacific Garbage Patch gets underway." CNN, 10 Sep 2018, https://www.cnn.com/2018/09/10/health/ocean-cleanup-test-trnd/index.html.

Microbeads
Baldwin, Austin K., et al. "Plastic debris in 29 Great Lakes Tributaries: Relations to Watershed Attributes and Hydrology." *Environmental Science and Technology*, 2016, 50 (19), pp. 10377-10385. DOI: 10.1021/acs.est.6b02917. http://pubs.acs.org/doi/abs/10.1021/acs.est.6b02917.

"Beat the Microbead: Scientific evidence about microplastic ingredients." www.beatthemicrobead.org/science.

Bressy, Adèle, Catherine Carré, José-Frédéric Deroubaix, Bernard de Gouvello, Mathilde Soyer, et al. "Domestic micropollutants, a diffuse industrial pollution -Part 2: Source reduction by changing personal consumption practices." 16th international conference on Chemistry and the Environment (ICCE 2017). June 2017, Oslo, Norway. https://hal.archives-ouvertes.fr/hal-01699801 .

Carré, Catherine. Fulbright Water Act, 2015. University of Paris.

Eriksen, Marcus, et al. "Microplastic pollution in the surface waters of the Laurentian Great Lakes." *Marine Pollution Bulletin*, 77, Issues 1-2, 15 December 2013, pp. 177-182. http://www.sciencedirect.com/science/article/pii/S0025326X13006097.

Gall, S. C. and R.C. Thompson. "The Impact of Debris on Marine Life." *Marine Pollution Bulletin* 92, 170-179. http://dx.doi.org/10.1016/j.marpolbul.2014.12.041.

Matsangou, Elizabeth. "Counting the cost of plastic pollution." World Finance.com . 2 July 2018. https://www.worldfinance.com/markets/counting-the-cost-of-plastic-pollution.

Microbead-Free Waters Act of 2015, see https://www.congress.gov/bill/114th-congress/house-bill/1321.

Plastic Soup Foundation. https://www.plasticsoupfoundation.org/en/

Rochman, Chelsea M., Eunha Hoh, Tomofumi Kurobe. See J. Teh. "Ingested plastic transfers hazardous chemicals to fish and induces hepatic stress." *Nature,* Scientific Reports 3, Article number 3263. http://www.nature.com/articles/srep03263.

University of Bath, "Biodegradable alternative to replace microplastics in cosmetics and toiletries." 12 August 2019. https://www.youtube.com/watch?v=iaUf2gzV7Wc

University of Plymouth. Video. "Plastic microbeads," 30 September 2016. https://www.youtube.com/watch?v=AOWrHQ8IWX4

Medicines and Pharmaceuticals in the Water
Bexfield, L. M, P. L. Toccalino, K. Belitz, W. T. Foreman, E. T. Furlong. "Hormones and Pharmaceuticals in Groundwater Used as a Source of Drinking Water Across the United States." *Environ Sci Technol.* 2019 Mar 19;53(6):2950-2960. https://pubs.acs.org/doi/10.1021/acs.est.8b05592

Borener, Leigh Krietsch. "The Complicated Question of Drugs in the Water." *NovaNext/PBS.* 14 May 2017. http://www.pbs.org/wgbh/nova/next/body/pharmaceuticals-in-the-water/.

Scheer, Roddy, and Doug Moss. EarthTalk™. "External Medicine: Discarded drugs may contaminate 40 million Americans' drinking water." *Scientific American*. https://www.scientificamerican.com/article/pharmaceuticals-in-the-water/

World Health Organization. "Pharmaceuticals in drinking-water." 2012. https://apps.who.int/iris/handle/10665/44630

Oceanic Buried Treasure
Bochove, Danielle. "Rare metal used in electric cars causes cobalt rush." *Bloomberg*. 1 November 2017. *The Toronto Star*. https://www.thestar.com/news/canada/2017/11/01/rare-metal-used-in-electric-cars-causes-a-cobalt-rush-in-cobalt-ont.html

Cobalt Institute. "Cobalt Around the World." https://www.cobaltinstitute.org/about-cobalt/cobalt-around-the-world/

Garside, M. "Cobalt's average spot price in the US 2008-2019," 18 February 2020. *Statista*. https://www.statista.com/statistics/339743/average-spot-price-of-cobalt-in-the-us/

International Seabed Authority. "ISA Strategic Directions: 2019-2023." 26 July 2018. https://www.isa.org.jm/index.php/strategic-plan.

International Seabed Authority (ISA). "Process for taking decisions during the 26th session of the Assembly." 26 October 2020. https://www.isa.org.jm/node/19747.

International Seabed Authority. "Deep Sea Mineral Resources: Cobalt-Rich Ferromanganese." https://www.isa.org.jm/deep-sea-mineral-resources-cobalt-rich-ferromanganese.

International Tribunal for the Law of the Sea. https://www.itlos.org.

Langley, Winston E. "Lecture and discussion: International Seabed Authority," 18 October 2019, University of Massachusetts Boston.

MIT Mechanical Engineering. "Visualizing Deep-sea Mining." 10 December 2019. https://www.youtube.com/watch?v=Lwq1j3nOODA

World Ocean Review. "Metal-rich crusts," Marine Resources – Opportunities and Risks, 2014. https://www.worldoceanreview.com/en/wor-3/mineral-resources/cobalt-crusts/.

Almonds and Animals: The Food of the Future
Associated Press. "California is now the world's fifth-largest economy, surpassing the United Kingdom." 4 May 2018. *Los Angeles Times*. https://www.latimes.com/business/la-fi-california-economy-gdp-20180504-story.html

Bailey, Rob, Antony Froggatt, Laura Wellesley. "Livestock–Climate Change's Forgotten Sector: Global Public Opinion on Meat and Dairy Consumption." 3 December 2014. *Chatham House: The Royal Institute of International Affairs*. https://www.chathamhouse.org/2014/12/livestock-climate-changes-forgotten-sector-global-public-opinion-meat-and-dairy-consumption.

"Best States for Business 2019: California." *Forbes*, 2019. https://www.forbes.com/places/ca/#5c37eeb93fef/

Curnow, Mandy. "Carbon farming: reducing methane emissions from cattle using feed additives." 21 November 2019. Department of Primary Industries and Regional Development, Government of Western Australia. https://www.agric.wa.gov.au/climate-change/carbon-farming-reducing-methane-emissions-cattle-using-feed-additives.

Datta, A. Shrestha, R.P., Ullah, H., He, L., Niino, Y. 2020 "Study report on Wetland Agriculture and Water Management in the Mekong Region." Bangkok: FAO and Asian Institute of Technology (AIT). ISBN: 9789251330951. https://doi.org/10.4060/cb0378en.

Poisoned Water and Aging Infrastructure
Building the World blog. "Skin-Flint." http://blogs.umb.edu/buildingtheworld/2016/01/23/skin-flint

Carvalho, Laurence, et al. "Protecting and restoring Europe's waters: An analysis of the future development needs of the Water Framework Directive." *Science of the Total Environment,* vol. 658, 29 March 2019, 1228-1238. https://www.sciencedirect.com/science/article/pii/S004896971835126X

CBS Interactive Inc. "Ohio town may be the next Flint with its water crisis." 25 January 2016. https://www.cbsnews.com/news/sebring-ohio-next-flint-water-crisis-lead-copper/

Columbia Water Center. "Building America's Water Initiative," 15 April 2016. https://www.youtube.com/watch?v=a-5fLkhfScQ&feature=emb_logo

Dickinson, Tim. "WTF is happening in the Flint water crisis explained." 22 January 2016. *Rolling Stone Magazine*. https://www.rollingstone.com/politics/politics-news/wtf-is-happening-in-the-flint-water-crisis-explained-227776/.

Euronews. "Bottled water is 3,500 times worse for the environment than tap water, say scientists." 8 August 2021. https://www.euronews.com/green/2021/08/05/bottled-water-is-3-500-times-worse-for-the-environment-than-tap-water-say-scientists

European Commission. "EU Water Legislation – Fitness Check" 26 July 2021. https://ec.europa.eu/environment/water/fitness_check_of_the_eu_water_legislation/index_en.htm

FloWater. https://www.drinkflowater.com.

Livingston, Amy. "Ways to Save Money by Conserving Water (Indoors & Outdoors)." 11 Aug 2021. Money Crashers. https://www.moneycrashers.com/ways-conserve-water/

Lusk, Tina, RN. "Missouri Water at Risk for Contaminants Detrimental to the Health of Its Inhabitants." University of Missouri, St. Louis. 10 May 2020.

Official Journal of the European Communities. "Directive 2000/60/EC of the European Parliament and of the Council of 23 October 2000 Establishing a Framework For Community Action in the Field of Water Policy." https://eur-lex.europa.eu/resource.html?uri=cellar:5c835afb-2ec6-4577-bdf8-756d3d694eeb.0004.02/DOC_1&format=PDF.

Pianin, Eric. "Flint is One of Many Lead-Polluted Water Systems in the US." 26 February 2016. *Fiscal Times*. https://www.thefiscaltimes.com/2016/02/28/Flint-One-Many-Lead-Polluted-Water-Systems-US

Plastic Soup Foundation. "The world's population consumes 1 million plastic bottles every minute." July 2017. https://www.plasticsoupfoundation.org/2017/07/the-worlds-population-consumes-1-million-plastic-bottles-every-minute/.

Ras, Bonnie Riva. "Flowater Raised $15 Million to Help Eradicate Plastic Water Bottles." 23 January 2019. Goodnet. https://www.goodnet.org/articles/flowater-raised-15-million-to-help-eradicate-plastic-water-bottles/

Schaper, David. "As infrastructure crumbles, trillions of gallons of water lost." *All Things Considered/National Public Radio*. 29 October 2014. http://www.npr.org/2014/10/29/359875321/as-infrastructure-crumbles-trillions-of-gallons-of-water-lost.

Smith, Amanda. "One year later: Are Sebring's water issues solved?" January 24, 2017; updated: April 3, 2017. WKBN.com. https://www.wkbn.com/news/one-year-later-are-sebrings-water-issues-solved/.

Solutions / Innovations

Waterscapes: What to Do When It Rains
Adkins, Adele. "River Lea." Music and lyrics. 24 June 2016 Release. LISTEN: https://www.facebook.com/IndonesianAdele/videos/river-lea-live-at-the-glastonbury-festival/1009159952486016/

Coombes, Peter J., Michael Smit, and Garth MacDonald. "A Case Study: Resolving boundary conditions in economic analysis of distributed solutions for water cycle management." *Australian Journal of Water Resources*, Volume 20, 2016, Issue 1. ISBN: 9781922107671. https://www.tandfonline.com/doi/full/10.1080/13241583.2016.1162762.

Department of Environmental Protection, Montgomery County, Maryland, U.S. "About RainScapes." https://www.montgomerycountymd.gov/water/rainscapes/about.html#types.

Hoering, Thomas. "The isotopic composition of the ammonia and the nitrate ion in rain." *Geochimica et Cosmochimica Acta*. Vol. 12, issues 1-2, 1957, 97-102. https://www.sciencedirect.com/science/article/abs/pii/0016703757900212

Johnston, K. "Youths create new rain garden at Broad Meadow Brook in Worcester." 6 September 2017. Worcester Youth Center. https://worcesteryouthcenter.org/2017/09/06/youths-create-new-rain-garden-at-broad-meadow-brook-in-worcester/

Smith, Amy. "Design: Mini-Project: Low-Cost Rainwater Harvesting." 18 February 2020. https://d-lab.mit.edu/news-blog/blog/design-mini-project-low-cost-rainwater-harvesting

Thames21. "Reedbeds." https://www.thames21.org.uk/project-reedbed-2/.

Verma, Piyush, "Rainwater harvesting in western Ghats of Maharastra, India: The case of Velhe Block, Pune District: A comprehensive multi-scalar approach." May 2020. https://dspace.mit.edu/handle/1721.1/127557

World Bank. 2013. World Bank Open Data. http://data.worldbank.org/

River From the Sky

Ghimire, Santosh R. and John M. Johnston. "Holistic impact assessment and cost savings of rainwater harvesting at the watershed level." 18 July 2017. Environmental Protection Agency. https://www.ncbi.nlm.nih.gov/pmc/articles/PMC6638562/.

Global Rain Harvesting Collective (GRWHC). United Nations Partnerships for SDGs Platform. https://sustainabledevelopment.un.org/partnership/?p=1646.

"Harvesting Innovations for People," Sustainable Innovations. https://www.si-usa.org

Living Circular. "Makoto Murase turns rainwater into a resource for Tokyo." 24 May 2016. https://www.livingcircular.veolia.com/en/eco-citizen/makoto-murase-turns-rainwater-resource-tokyo

Thames21. "New project to open up access to the Thames." 17 August 2020. Thames21.org. https://www.thames21.org.uk/2020/08/thames21-receives-funding-for-thames-connections-project/

UNEP. "Rainwater Harvesting and Utilisation: An Environmentally Sound Approach for Sustainable Urban Water Management. An Introductory Guide for Decision-makers." IETC Urban Environment Series (2). 2002. https://www.ircwash.org/sites/default/files/213.1-01RA-17421.pdf

Filter of the Future

Annan, Ebenezer, et al. "Clay Mixtures and the Mechanical Properties of Microporous and Nanoporous Ceramic Water Filters." *Journal of Materials in Civil Engineering* 28 (10):04016105. May 2016. https://ascelibrary.org/doi/abs/10.1061/%28ASCE%29MT.1943-5533.0001596

Sift for Success

Doty, Reiley. "New Brine Processor Increases Water Recycling on International Space Station." 26 February 2021. Johnson Space Center, Houston, TX. https://www.nasa.gov/feature/new-brine-processor-increases-water-recycling-on-international-space-station.

NASA. International Space Station Program Science Forum. "International Space Station: Benefits for Humanity," 87-91. NP-2018-06-013-JSC. https://www.nasa.gov/sites/default/files/atoms/files/benefits-for-humanity_third.pdf

Royal Academy of Engineering. "Tanzanian low-cost water filter wins innovation prize." 2 June 2015. BBC.com. https://www.bbc.com/news/world-africa-32973591.

Water From Space

Bradford, C.M., A.D. Bolatto, P.R. Maloney, J.E. Aguirre, et al. "The water vapor spectrum of APM 08279+5255: X-Ray heating and infrared pumping over hundreds of parsecs." arXiv.1106.4301 (astro-ph.CO). DOI: 10.1088/2041-8205/741/2/L37. https://arxiv.org/abs/1106.4301.

   Asteroids
Voosen, Paul. "A NASA mission is about to capture carbon-rich dust from a former water world." Science Magazine. 8 October 2020. https://www.sciencemag.org/news/2020/10/nasa-mission-about-capture-carbon-rich-dust-former-water-world OK

   Enceladus
Chang, Kenneth. "Under icy surface of a Saturn moon lies a sea of water, scientists say." 3 April 2014 *The New York Times*. https://www.nytimes.com/2014/04/04/science/space/a-moon-of-saturn-has-a-sea-scientists-say.html.

Hansen, Candice, J., L. Esposito, A.I.F. Steward, J. Colwell, A. Hendrix, W. Pryor, D. Shemansky, and R. West. "Enceladus' water plume," *Science* 311, no. 5766 (10 March 2006): 1422-1425. DOI:10.1126/science.1121254. https://science.sciencemag.org/content/311/5766/1422/tab-article-info

   Lunar
Dino, Jonas, "LCROSS impact data indicates water on moon." 13 November 2009. NASA Ames Research Center. https://space.nss.org/lcross-impact-data-indicates-water-on-moon/.

Honniball, C.I., P.G. Lucey, S. Li, et al., "Molecular water detected on the sunlit Moon by SOFIA." 26 October 2020. Nat. Astron (2020) https://doi.org/10.1038/s41550-020-01222-x.

Strickland, Ashley. "NASA mission finds water on the sunlit surface of the moon." 26 October 2020. CNN.com. https://www.cnn.com/2020/10/26/world/moon-water-nasa-announcement-scn-trnd/index.html.

Mars
NASA. "NASA confirms evidence that liquid water flows on today's Mars." 28 September 2015. https://www.nasa.gov/press-release/nasa-confirms-evidence-that-liquid-water-flows-on-today-s-mars

O'Callaghan, Jonathan. "Water on Mars: Discovery of three buried lakes intrigues scientists." 28 September 2020. *Nature.* https://www.nature.com/articles/d41586-020-02751-1.

Worth Its Salt
Crawford, Mark. "8 Engineering challenges for desalination technologies." 6 May 2020. American Society of Mechanical Engineers (ASME). https://www.asme.org/topics-resources/content/8-engineering-challenges-for-desalination-technologies?utm_source=facebook&utm_medium=social&utm_content=technology_and_society&utm_campaign=wk_050420

Jacobsen, Rowan. "Israel proves the desalination era is here: One of the driest countries on Earth now makes more freshwater than it needs." *Scientific American*, 29 July 2016. https://www.scientificamerican.com/article/israel-proves-the-desalination-era-is-here/

Jones, Edward, et al. "The state of desalination and brine production: A global outlook." April 2019. *Science of the Total Environment* 657 (2019) 1343-1356. https://pubmed.ncbi.nlm.nih.gov/30677901/

Kolyohin, Nick. "Feature: Israel aims to secure all of its water supply through desalination." 22 November 2019. Xinhuanet 22 November 2019. http://www.xinhuanet.com/english/20-19-11/c_138575940.htm

Siegel, Seth M. *Let There Be Water: Israel's Solution for a Water-Starved World.* New York: McMillan, 2015. ISBN: 9781466885448.

Siegel, Seth M. *Troubled Water: What's Wrong With What We Drink?* 2019. New York: Thomas Dunn Books. ISBN: 9781250132543.

Woo, Yun Chul, et al. "Co-axially electrospun superhydrophobic nanofiber membranes with 3D-hierarchically structured surface for desalination by long-term membrane distillation." *Journal of Membrane Science*, vol. 623 (2021). https://doi.org/10.1016/j.memsci.2020.119028. https://www.sciencedirect.com/science/article/pii/S0376738820316008

Ocean State's Lot
Beckham, Nancy. "Trees: finding their true value: pricing the environment." https://www.unep.org/news-and-stories/opinion/heatwaves-rising-seas-how-trees-defend-us

Lodge, Michael W. Remarks, UN Global Compact Action Platform for Sustainable Ocean Business, High Level meeting on Ocean. "Ocean as part of the solution – How industries can lead on delivering on the 17 SDGs and the opportunities of the Ocean in particular." 3 June 2019, Oslo, Norway. https://isa.org.jm/files/documents/En/SG-Stats/3_June_2019.pdf

United Nations Environment Programme. "From heatwaves to rising seas: How trees defend us." 11 September 2019. https://www.straitstimes.com/opinion/from-heatwaves-to-rising-seas-how-trees-defend-us .

Whitehouse, Sheldon, and Jack Reed. "Federal Delegation Announces Nearly $2 Billion to Bolster RI Coastline: Grants for Nature Conservancy and CRMC will protect homes, businesses from rising seas." 14 July 2017. https://www.reed.senate.gov/news/releases/federal-delegation-announces-nearly-2-million-to-bolster-ri-coastline

Waterfront City Squares
Epstein, Jonathan. "Condo Project Approved at Waterfront Village." *Buffalo News*, 22 January 2015. https://ciminelli.com/news/article/current/2015/01/22/100007/condo-project-approved-at-waterfront-village/

Inland Waterways International. "Promoting inland waterways." https://inlandwaterwaysinternational.org/

McClelland, Edward. "How Buffalo Got Its Waterfront Back: River restoration is influencing the city's economy, public space, and environmental health." Next City: Inspiring Better Cities. 5 December 2016. https://nextcity.org/features/view/buffalo-waterfront-redevelopment-economy/

Navigating a Changing Climate Partnership. https://navclimate.pianc.org/

UNESCO. "Historic Centre of Brugge: World Heritage Site." 2000. https://whc.unesco.org/en/list/996/

Floodscapes

Abraham, John. "Sea level rise is accelerating; how much it costs is up to us." *Guardian*, 11 March 2016. https://www.theguardian.com/environment/climate-consensus-97-per-cent/2016/mar/11/sea-level-rise-is-accelerating-how-much-it-costs-is-up-to-us

Aridi, Rasha. "Venice's Controversial Inflatable Floodgates Save City for the Second Time: The barriers may not be permanent solutions, but they've now protected Venice from two floods this month." 19 October 2020. *Smithsonian Magazine*. https://www.smithsonianmag.com/smart-news/venices-new-floodgates-deployed-second-time-shielding-city-potentially-destructive-floods-180976087/.

Bird, Winifred. "Rethinking urban landscapes to adapt to rising sea levels." https://e360.yale.edu/features/rethinking_urban_landscapes_to_adapt_to_rising_sea_levels_climate_change_new_york_city

Boettle, M., D. Dybski, J.P. Kropp. "Quantifying the effect of sea level rise and flood defence – a point process perspective on coastal flood damage." *National Hazards and Earth System Sciences: An interactive open-access journal of the European Geosciences Union*. Volume 16, issue 2. 29 February 2016. https://nhess.copernicus.org/articles/16/559/2016/ .

Brooke, Kathleen Lusk. "Rising Seas." May 2020. Building the World Blog. University of Massachusetts Boston. http://blogs.umb.edu/buildingtheworld/2020/05/09/water-pulitzer-prize-and-climate-change/

Hill, Kristina and Jared Green. "Interview with Kristina Hill." 2010. American Society of Landscape Architects. https://www.asla.org/ContentDetail.aspx?id=28548.

Kimmelman, Michael. "The Dutch Have Solutions to Rising Seas. It's an opportunity." Changing Climate, Changing Cities series, *New York Times*. 15 June 2017. https://www.nytimes.com/interactive/2017/06/15/world/europe/climate-change-rotterdam.html.

Neumann, Barbara, Athanasios T. Vafeidis, Juliane Zimmerman, Robert J. Nicholls. "Future coastal population growth and exposure to sea-level rise and coastal flooding – a global assessment." 11 March 2015. *PLOS ONE* 10(3):e0118571. https://pubmed.ncbi.nlm.nih.gov/25760037/.

Radford, Tim. "Scientists set out costs of sea level rise." 15 March 2016. *Climate News Network*. https://climatenewsnetwork.net/scientists-work-out-costs-of-sea-level-rise/

Ramirez, Rachel. "Floods are getting worse, and the number of people exposed is 10 times higher than previously thought." CNN.com. 4 August 2021. https://www.cnn.com/2021/08/04/weather/global-flood-risk-climate-change/index.html

Talaty, Urvi, Peter Howe, Matto Mildenberger, Jennifer Marlon, Anthony Leiserowitz. "Are hurricane-prone states more concerned about climate change?" 24 July 2020. Yale Program on Climate Change Communication. https://climatecommunication.yale.edu/publications/are-hurricane-prone-states-more-concerned-about-climate-change/

Union of Concerned Scientists. "Encroaching Tides: How sea level rise and tidal flooding threaten US East and Gulf Coast communities over the next 30 years." 2014. https://www.ucsusa.org/resources/encroaching-tides.

Verge Science. "This is what sea level rise will do to coastal cities." Video. 23 April 2019. https://www.youtube.com/watch?v=6tesHVSZJOg

Welby, Justin. "Our Moral Opportunity on Climate Change." 3 November 2017. *The New York Times*. https://www.nytimes.com/2017/11/03/opinion/faith-climate-change-justin-welby.html

Renewing Aquifers and Springs

Advanced Centre for Water Resources Development and Management (ACWADAM). http://www.acwadam.org

Environmental Protection Agency (EPA). "Aquifer Recharge and Aquifer Storage and Recovery." https://www.epa.gov/uic/aquifer-recharge-and-aquifer-storage-and-recovery

International Centre for Integrated Mountain Development (ICIMOD). https://www.icimod.org/

National Groundwater Association. "Managed Aquifer Recharge." https://www.ngwa.org.

Shrestha, Rajendra B. et al. *Protocol for Reviving Springs in the Hindu Kush Himalayas: A Practitioner's Manual*. ICIMOD Manual 2018/4. Kathmandu: ICIMOD. ISBN: 9789291156078. https://lib.icimod.org/record/34040

Reinventing the Toilet
Brueck, Hilary. "A $350 toilet powered by worms may be the ingenious future of sanitation that Bill Gates has been dreaming about." *Business Insider*. 13 January 2019. https://www.businessinsider.com/bill-gates-foundation-helps-invent-tiger-toilets-powered-by-worms-2019-1

Ecoloo Group. "Sustainable Toilet for All." https://www.ecoloogroup.com/

Gates Foundation. "Bill Gates Names Winners of the Reinvent the Toilet Challenge." August 2012. https://www.gatesfoundation.org/ideas/media-center/press-releases/2012/08/bill-gates-names-winners-of-the-reinvent-the-toilet-challenge.

Gates Foundation. "Reinvent the Toilet Challenge: A brief history." 2021. https://www.gatesfoundation.org/our-work/programs/global-growth-and-opportunity/water-sanitation-and-hygiene/reinvent-the-toilet-challenge-and-expo

Government of India, Ministry of Housing and Urban Affairs. "Swachh bharat." http://www.swachhbharaturban.in/sbm/home/#/SBM.

Mathewson, Samantha. "NASA's new $23 million space toilet is ready for launch, " 25 September 2020. *Space.com* https://www.space.com/nasa-space-toilet-ready-for-launch/.

Modi, Narendra. "Swachh Bharat Abhiyan." https://www.pmindia.gov.in/en/major_initiatives/swachh-bharat-abhiyan/

Rai, Arpan. "4,242 cities, 92 Ganga towns and 1.87 crore citizens: All you need to know about Swacch Survekshan 2020." 18 August 2020. *Hindustan Times*. https://www.hindustantimes.com/india-news/swachh-survekshan-2020-all-you-need-to-know-4-242-cities-92-ganga-towns-and-1-87-crore-citizens/story-bhOZzRPG5khHyL1VHanQ4K.html

World Health Organization (WHO). "WHO calls for increased investment to reach the goal of a toilet for all." 1 October 218. https://www.who.int/news/item/01-10-2018-who-calls-for-increased-investment-to-reach-the-goal-of-a-toilet-for-all.

United Nations, Department of Economic and Social Affairs (DESA). "The Sustainable Development Goals Explained: Clean Water and Sanitation." Leanne Burney, 17 September 2015. https://www.youtube.com/watch?v=LCKsU4bPFOQ

Water Credit
Salzman, James. *Drinking Water: A History*. 2012. Peter Mayer Publishers. ISBN: 9781468306750.

United Nations. "Sustainable Development Goals: 17 Goals to Transform Our World: Goal 6: Ensure access to water and sanitation for all." https://www.un.org/sustainabledevelopment/water-and-sanitation/

Water.org. "WaterCredit Toolkits for Financial Institutions." https://water.org/solutions/watercredit/ lending-for-water-sanitation/watercredit-toolkits/.

White, Gary. "Commencement Address, Missouri University of Science & Technology, December 13, 2013." See also, "An Interview With: Water.org's White," by Carlos David Mogollón, *WaterWorld*, 1 October 2009. https://www.waterworld.com/international/article/16217882/an-interview-with-waterorgs-gary-white.

Yunus, Muhammad. "Nobel Lecture." 10 December 2006. https://www.nobelprize.org/prizes/peace/ 2006/yunus/lecture.

Meat-Free Mondays
Hunt, Katie. "Why the search for the perfect vegan leather starts on the forest floor." CCN Style. 29 September 2020. https://www.cnn.com/style/article/vegan-leather-alternatives-fungi-biofabric-scn/index.html

McCartney, Paul. "Meat Free Monday." LISTEN to the song: https://www.youtube.com/watch?v=NnNFryHonQo

McCartney, Paul, Mary McCartney, Stella McCartney. "Meat Free Mondays: Global Campaigns." September 2020. https://meatfreemondays.com/global/

McCartney, Stella. "Materials and Innovation." https://www.stellamccartney.com/us/en/sustainability/sustainability.html.

Ramsing, Becky. "Food Trends for 2020 Show a Sustainability Focus." 7 January 2020. Johns Hopkins Center for a Livable Future. https://clf.jhsph.edu/viewpoints/food-trends-2020-show-sustainability-focus

Fashion Forward
Ellen MacArthur Foundation. "Redesigning the Future of Fashion." https://ellenmacarthurfoundation.org/topics/fashion/overview

McCartney, Stella. "Circular Fashion/Circular Economy." StellaMcCartney.com. https://www.stellamccartney.com/experience/en/sustainability/circularity-2/

Newbold, Alice. "Stella McCartney: Sustainability is the future of fashion, not just a trend." 30 September 2019. *Vogue.* https://www.vogue.co.uk/tags/stella-mccartney

Ralph Lauren Corporation. "Ralph Lauren Revolutionizes How the Fashion Industry Dyes Cotton." 22 March 2021. https://corporate.ralphlauren.com/pr_210322_ColorOnDemand.html

Water-Food-Energy Nexus
Lall, Upmanu. "Positive Water Sector Disruptions by 2030." 2 December 2018. Columbia University, Opinion paper prepared for the Inter-American Development Bank. https://www.researchgate.net/publication/331949159_Positive_Water_Sector_Disruptions_by_2030

McGrath, Matt. "Flexitarian Diets Key to Feeding people in a Warming World." 11 October 2018. BBC Science & Environment. https://www.bbc.com/news/science-environment-45814659 .

Spang, Edward. "New UC Davis Podcast Tackles Food Waste And Loss As A Way To Feed The Planet." 1 October 2019. https://spang.ucdavis.edu/news/new-uc-davis-podcast-tackles-food-waste-and-loss-way-feed-planet

Spang, Edward, et al., "Food-Energy-Water (FEW) Nexus: Informal Water Systems." https://spang.ucdavis.edu/food-energy-water-few-nexus.

Spang Lab. https://spang.ucdavis.edu

Springmann, Marco, et al. "Options for Keeping the Food System Within Environmental Limits." *Nature*, 11 October 2018. https://doi.org/10.1038/s41586-018-0594-0 .

United Nations. "Water, Food, and Energy." UN Water. https://www.unwater.org/water-facts/water-food-and-energy/

WEF Nexus Working Group. "(Re)Connect the Nexus." https://www.water-energy-food.org.

WEF Nexus Working Group. "Water, Energy, Food (WEF) Nexus Project." https://sjoseph.ucdavis.edu/ucdar.

Case Study: Colorado River Compact

Dineen, Sally. "Feds Slash Colorado River Release to Historic Lows." *National Geographic.* 16 August 2013. http://news.nationalgeographic.com/news/2013/08/130816-colorado-river-drought-lake-powell-mead-water-scarcity/.

Finley, Bruce. "Colorado River Water: Grand Bargain in the face of Climate Change." 25 August 2019. *The Denver Post.* https://www.denverpost.com/2019/08/25/colorado-river-water-grand-bargain-climate-change/.

Fountain, Henry. "In a first, U.S. Declares Shortage on Colorado River, Forcing Water Cuts." 16 August 2021, New York Times. https://www.nytimes.com/2021/08/16/climate/colorado-river-water-cuts.html

Gelt, Joe. "Sharing Colorado River Water: History, Public Policy and the Colorado River Compact." Summary of a conference held at the University of Arizona upon the 75th anniversary of the Colorado River Compact. *Arroyo*, August 1997, Volume 10, no. 1. Water Resources Research Center, College of Agriculture and Life Sciences, The University of Arizona. https://wrrc.arizona.edu/publications/ %20arroyo-newsletter/sharing-colorado-river-water-history-public-policy-and-colorado-river.

Healy, Meredith N. "Fluid Standing: Incorporating the Indigenous Rights of Nature Concept into Collaborative Management of the Colorado River Ecosystem." Colorado Natural Resources, Energy, and Environmental Law Review. 2019, volume 30: 2, pp. 327-360. https://www.colorado.edu/law/sites/default/files/attached-files/healy_web_edition_pdf.pdf

Helfgott, Alexandra. "Bilateral Water Management: Water Sharing between the US and Mexico along the Border." Mexico Institute, Wilson Center. 4 January 2021. https://www.wilsoncenter.org/article/bilateral-water-management-water-sharing-between-us-and-mexico-along-border

Kann, Drew, with video by Bryce Urbany and graphics by Renee Rigdon. "As a megadrought persists, new projections show a key Colorado River reservoir could sink to a record low later this year." 19 April 2021. https://www.cnn.com/2021/04/19/weather/western-drought-colorado-river-cutbacks-study/index.html

Karamanos, Keith. "Lake Mead: Benefits of the Largest Reservoir in the United States." California Polytechnic State University, San Louis Obispo, June 2010.

Kuhn, Eric and John Fleck. *Science Be Dammed: How Ignoring Inconvenient Science Drained the Colorado River.* University of Arizona Press, 2019. ISBN: 9789816540051.

Maffly, Brian. "Eco-groups sue feds, allege that Glen Canyon Dam plan ignores climate change." 1 October 2019. *Salt Lake Tribune.* https://www.sltrib.com/news/environment/2019/10/01/eco-groups-sue-feds/

Metz, Sam. "US West prepares for possible 1st water shortage declaration." 17 April 2021. https://apnews.com/article/business-science-general-news-government-and-politics-environment-and-nature-09302e61c5e0ef051f50459f3dcb771f

Ramirez, Rachel, with Drew Kann. "First-ever water cuts declared for Colorado River in historic drought." 16 August 2021. CNN.com. https://www.cnn.com/2021/08/16/us/lake-mead-colorado-river-water-shortage/index.html

Stone, Christopher D. "Should Trees Have Standing? - Towards Legal Rights for Natural Objects." *Southern California Law Review*, 1972, 45, 450-501. https://iseethics.files.wordpress.com/2013/02/stone-christopher-d-should-trees-have-standing.pdf.

Selection of Colorado River Laws and Agreements
1963 Arizona v. California, 373 US 546 (1963). https://supreme.justia.com/cases/federal/us/373/546/

1974 Colorado River Basin Salinity Control Act. https://www.usbr.gov/lc/region/g1000/pdfiles/crbsalct.pdf.

1992 Grand Canyon Protection Act, H.R. 814- 102nd Congress (1991-1992). https://www.congress.gov/bill/102nd-congress/house-bill/814/text .

AN ACT relating to water; prohibiting, with certain exceptions, the use of water. From the Colorado River to irrigate nonfunctional turf on certain properties. Southern Nevada Water Authority. Assembly Bill No. 356, 22 March 2021. https://www.leg.state.nv.us/Session/81st2021/Bills/AB/AB356_R1.pdf .

Bureau of Reclamation, U.S. Complete List of All Laws Regarding the Colorado River Compact. https://www.usbr.gov/lc/region/pao/lawofrvr.html .

Colorado River Compact of 1922. https://www.usbr.gov/lc/region/pao/pdfiles/crcompct.pdf

La Paz Agreement between the United States of America and Mexico. 14 August 1983. https://www.epa.gov/sites/production/files/2015-09/documents/lapazagreement.pdf

Law of the River. https://www.usbr.gov/lc/region/g1000/lawofrvr.html

Minute 319. International Boundary and Water Commission: United States and Mexico. 12 November 2012. http://www.ibwc.gov/Files/Minutes/Minute_319.pdf.

Utilization of the Waters of the Colorado and Tijuana Rivers and of the Rio Grande. Treaty between the United States of America and Mexico. 3 February 1944. https://www.usbr.gov/lc/region/pao/pdfiles/mextrety.pdf

Winters v. United States, 207 US 564 (1908). https://supreme.justia.com/cases/federal/us/207/564/

Rights
        Bolivia
Ley de Derechos de La Madre Tierra – Estado Plurinacional de Bolivia. https://www.scribd.com/document/44900268/Ley-de-Derechos-de-la-Madre-Tierra-Estado-Plurinacional-de-Bolivia

Cano Pecharromán, Lidia. "Rights of Nature: Rivers That Can Stand in Court." *Resources*, 2018, 7, 13. doi: 10:3390/resources7010013. https://www.mdpi.com/2079-9276/7/1/13

        Colombia
"Climate Change and Future Generations Lawsuit in Colombia: Key Excerpts from the Supreme Court's Decision." 13 April 2018. Dejusticia. https://www.dejusticia.org/en/climate-change-and-future-generations-lawsuit-in-colombia-key-excerpts-from-the-supreme-courts-decision/

        India
Daley, Jason. "India's Ganges and Yamuna Rivers Are Given the Rights of People." 23 March 2017. Smithsonian.com. https://www.smithsonianmag.com/smart-news/ganges-and-yamuna-rivers-given-rights-people-india-180962639/

Navajo
Calma, Justine. "The Navajo Nation Faced Water Shortages for Generations – and Then the Pandemic Hit." 6 July 2020. The Verge. https://www.theverge.com/2020/7/6/21311211/navajo-nation-covid-19-running-water-access

DigDeep. "Americans without Water." https://www.digdeep.org/

Navajo Nation Environmental Protection Agency (NNEPA). https://www.navajonationepa.org

New Zealand
New Zealand Parliament/Pāremata Aotearoa. "Innovative Bill Protects Whanganui River with Legal Personhood." *Te Awa Tupua* (Whanganui River Claims Settlement Bill). 28 March 2017. https://www.parliament.nz/en/get-involved/features/innovative-bill-protects-whanganui-river-with-legal-personhood/

SYSTEM DYNAMICS MODEL: WATER SYSTEMS—A MODEL OF USE

Adapted from: Saeed K, Mathisen P. Watershed Simulator. Presentation at Water Symposium. Worcester, MA: Worcester Polytechnic Institute, School of Arts and Sciences. March 31, 2014.

CONCLUSION
Ten Challenges and a Call to Action

Challenge 1: Clean Drinking Water and Safe Sanitation

Boulding, Kenneth E. Address to a joint meeting of the American Association for the Advancement of Science (AAAS) and the American Institute of Aeronautics and Astronautics (AIAA). 03 January 1980. San Francisco, CA.

Gates Foundation. "Reinvent the Toilet Challenge: A Brief History." 2020. https://www.gatesfoundation.org/our-work/programs/global-growth-and-opportunity/water-sanitation-and-hygiene/reinvent-the-toilet-challenge-and-expo

"There's Something in the Water." Documentary film by Ian Daniel, Elliot Page, and Ingrid Waldron. 2019. https://www.imdb.com/title/tt10864040/releaseinfo

Voice of America. "The Cost of Clean Water: $150B a Year, Says World Bank." 29 August 2017. https://www.voanews.com/science-health/cost-clean-water-150b-year-says-world-bank

Waldron, Ingrid. *There's Something in the Water: Environmental Racism in Indigenous & Black Communities*. Halifax & Winnipeg: Fernwood, 2018. ISBN: 9781773630571 (paper); Kindle: 9791773630595

Water.org. "An Economic Crisis." https://water.org/our-impact/water-crisis/economic-crisis/

Waldron, Ingrid. "Environmental Justice in Mi'kmaq & African Nova Scotian Communities." TEDxMSVUWomen, 2020. https://youtu.be/itRiNmo3hq8

Challenge 2: Contaminants—Three Factors to Watch

Factor #1: Plastics—Problems and Costs

Bailey, Richard, et al. "Breaking the Plastic Wave." Pew Charitable Trusts and SYSTEMIQ, 2020. https://www.pewtrusts.org/-/media/assets/2020/07/breakingtheplasticwave_report.pdf

Baldwin, Austin K., et al. "Plastic debris in 29 Great Lakes Tributaries: Relations to Watershed Attributes and Hydrology." *Environmental Science and Technology*, 2016, 50 (19): 10377-10385. DOI: 10.1021/acs.est.6b02917. https://www.researchgate.net/publication/308121939_Plastic_Debris_in_29_Great_Lakes_Tributaries_Relations_to_Watershed_Attributes_and_Hydrology

Brooke, Kathleen Lusk. "Water: Microplastic Filter Innovations." 2 August 2021. *Building the World* blog. https://blogs.umb.edu/buildingtheworld/2021/08/02/water-microplastic-filter-innovations/.

NOAA. "Garbage Patches." https://marinedebris.noaa.gov/info/patch.html

Petten, Laurens, et al., "Marine Plastic Pollution: The hefty cost of doing nothing." 2020. Deloitte. https://www2.deloitte.com/us/en/insights/topics/strategy/marine-plastic-pollution.html

Viool, Vincent, Abhishek Gupta, Laurens Petten, Jorg Schalekamp. Deloitte. "The Price Tag of Plastic Pollution." Pg. 10, Figure 2: "Economic impact per geographic region." https://www2.deloitte.com/content/dam/Deloitte/my/Documents/risk/my-risk-sdg14-the-price-tag-of-plastic-pollution.pdf

Weckhuysen Research Group. "Catalytic conversion of biomass, waste, and Co2." https://bertweckhuysen.com/research/.

Zhang, Fan, Manhao Zeng, Ryan D. Yappert, Jiakai Sun, Yu-Hsuan Lee, Anne M. LaPointe, Baron Peters, Mahdi M. Abu-Omar, Susannah L. Scott. "Polyethylene upcycling to long-chain alkylaromatics by tandem hydrogenolysis/aromatization." 23 October 2020. *Science*, vol. 370, no. 6515: 437-441.
DOI: 10.1126/science.abc5441. https://sciencemag.org/content/370/6515/437.full.

      Factor #2: Hydraulic Fracturing (Fracking)
Nikiforuk, Andrew. "Shale Gas: How often do fracked wells leak?" 10 January 2013. The Tyee, and Resilience.org.
https://www.resilience.org/stories/2013-01-10/shale-gas-how-often-do-fracked-wells-leak/

North Dakota State University. "A Guide to Plugging Abandoned Wells." July 2016. AE966. Revised by Tom Scherer.
https://www.ndinvasives.org/publications/landing-pages/environment-natural-resources/guide-to-plugging-abandoned-wells-ae966

Rogers, Nala. "2019: The Year Fracking Earthquakes Turned Deadly." 21 February 2020. Inside Science.
https://www.insidescience.org/news/2019-year-fracking-earthquakes-turned-deadly

SGK Planet. "Magazine: All about Fracking." https://sgkplanet.com/en/magazine-all-about-fracking/

Townsend, Dina. "The legal status of fracking worldwide: An environmental law and human rights perspective." Global Network for Human Rights and the Environment. 6 January 2020.
https://gnhre.org/2020/01/06/the-legal-status-of-fracking-worldwide-an-environmental-law-and-human-rights-perspective/.

      Factor #3: Deep Seabed Mining
Ballard, Barclay. "Deep-sea mining could provide access to a wealth of valuable minerals." 13 May 2019. *The New Economy*. https://www.theneweconomy.com/energy/deep-sea-mining-could-provide-access-to-a-weath-of-valuable-minerals.

Deep Sea Conservation Coalition. "Deep-Seabed Mining: The Main Players." 2020
http://www.savethehighseas.org/deep-sea-mining/the-main-players/

Gallagher, M. B. "Understanding the Impact of Deep-Sea Mining." 5 December 2019. MIT News. With VIDEO.
https://news.mit.edu/2019/understanding-impact-deep-sea-mining-1206

Heffernan, Olive. "Seabed mining is coming -bringing minerals riches and fears of epic extinctions." 24 July 2019. *Nature*.
https://www.nature.com/articles/d41586-019-02242-y

International Seabed Authority. www.isa.org.jm.

International Union for Conservation of Nature (IUCN). "Deep-sea mining." https://www.iucn.org/resources/issues-briefs/deep-sea-mining.

MarketWatch. "2021 Deep Sea Mining Technology Market Top Vendor Performance Analysis with Impact of COVID-19, Manufacturer Strategies, Recent Developments, Growth Overview, Latest Trends, Opportunities, and Forecast to 2026." 11 June 2021. https://www.marketwatch.com/press-release/2021-deep-sea-mining-technology-market-top-vendor-performance-analysis-with-impact-of-covid-19-manufacturer-strategies-recent-developments-growth-overview-latest-trends-opportunities-and-forecast-to-2026-2021-06-11

Miller, K.A., et al., "Challenging the Need for Deep Seabed Mining From the Perspective of Metal Demand, Biodiversity, Ecosystems Services, and Benefit Sharing." 29 July 2021. Frontiers in Marine Science.
https://doi.org/10.3389/fmars.2021.706161, and
https://www.frontiersin.org/articles/10.3389/fmars.2021.706161/full

Shukman, David. "Companies back moratorium on deep sea mining." 3 April 2021. BBC. com.
https://www.bbc.com/news/science-environment-56607700

United Nations. "United Nations Convention on the Law of the Sea." https://www.un.org/depts/los/convention_agreements/texts/unclos/unclos_pdf.

World Wildlife Fund. "In too deep: What we know, and don't know, about deep seabed mining." 09 February 2021.
https://www.worldwildlife.org/publications/in-too-deep-what-we-know-and-don-t-know-about-deep-seabed-mining

Challenge 3: Infrastructure—Leaking or Lacking?
American Society of Civil Engineers. "Drinking Water: Infrastructure Report Card, 2017."
https://www.infrastructurereportcard.org/cat-item/drinking_water/

Fluence. "Aging Water Infrastructure in the US." 31 May 2018. Fluence News. https://www.fluencecorp.com/aging-water-infrastructure-in-the-us/

Graham-Rowe, Duncan. "Self-Healing Pipelines." 21 December 2006. *Technology Review*. https://www.technologyreview.com/2006/12/21/130692/self-healing-pipelines/.

Hares, Sophie. "The cost of clean water: $150 billion a year, says World Bank." 28 August 2017. Thomas Reuters Foundation. https://www.reuters.com/article/us-global-water-health-idUSKCN1B812E

Molle, François. "Water Pricing in Thailand: Theory and Practice." Doras Center-Delta Project: Research Report #7, Kasetsart University/IRD. 2001. ISBN: 9475538981. https://citeseerx.ist.psu.edu/viewdoc/download?doi=10.1.1.578.7869&rep=rep1&type=pdf

Ramm, Klara, Chair, EurEau Committee on Economic and Legal Affairs. "Time to invest in Europe's water infrastructure." 2 May 2018. Euractiv. https://www.euractiv.com/section/energy-environment/opinion/time-to-invest-in-europes-water-infrastructure

Sukphisit, Suthon. "Troubled Waters." 28 July 2019. *Bangkok Post*. https://www.bangkokpost.com/ life/social-and-lifestyle/170327/troubled-waters.

Tabuchi, Hiroko. "$300 Billion War Beneath the Street: Fighting to Replace America's Water Pipes." 10 November 2017. *New York Times*. https://www.nytimes.com/2017/11/10/climate/water-pipes-plastic-lead.html.

Thomson, Amy. "NASA Just sent a New $23 Million Space Toilet to the International Space Station." 9 October 2020. Smithsonian Magazine. https://www.smithsonianmag.com/science-nature/nasa-just-sent-new-23-million-space-toilet-international-space-station-180976037/

Tiseo, Ian. "Global Water Industry – Statistics & Facts." Statista/Energy & Environment/Water & Wastewater. 29 October 2020. https://www.statista.com/topics/1575/water/

Wray, Dianna. "City of Houston has Lifted the Boil Water Notice." 17 February 2021. *Houstonia Magazine*. https://www.houstoniamag.com/news-and-city-life/2021/02/city-of-houston-has-issued-a-boil-water-notice

Challenge 4: Rising Seas
Bayraktarov, Elisa, et al. Data from "The cost and feasibility of marine coastal restoration." https://esajournals.onlinelibrary.wiley.com/doi/full/10.1890/15-1077. For data See Dryad: http://dx.doi.org/10.5061/dryad.rc0jn

Bjarke Ingels Group (BIG). "The Big U." 2017. https://big.dk/#projects.

Breuck, Hilary. "The heart of Paris is underwater." 29 January 2018. *Business Insider*. https://www.businessinsider.com/see-paris-underwater-as-the-seine-floods-the-streets-hundred-year-flood-2018-1.

Brooke, Kathleen Lusk. "Year 2020: Climate Conservation Corps." Building the World Blog, University of Massachusetts Boston. https://blogs.umb.edu/buildingtheworld/year-2020-climate-conservation-corps-ccc/.

Center for Coastal Environmental Sensing Networks. "Near shore environments less than 30 meters." Scholarworks, University of Massachusetts Boston. https://scholarworks.umb.edu/cesn/

Chen, Robert F. "CP24G – Transdisciplinary Research and Education in Coastal Systems Posters," and "Social-Ocean Science Interactions and SDGs." 18 February 2020. *Ocean Sciences Meeting*, San Diego, CA, U.S. https://agu.confex.com/agu/osm20/meetingapp.cgi/Session/85229

Church, J. A., et al., *Climate change 2013: The Physical Science Basis. Contribution of Working Group to the Fifth Assessment Report of the Intergovernmental Panel on Climate Change*. UK: Cambridge University Press, 2013.

Dal Cin, Francesca, Fransje Hooimeijer, and Maria Matos Silva. "Planning the Urban Waterfront Transformation, from Infrastructures to Public Space Design in a Sea-Level Rise Scenario: The European Union Prize for Contemporary Architecture Case." 18 January 2021. *Water* 2021, 13(2), 218. https://doi.org/10.3390/w13020218.

Duvat, Virginia K. E., et al., "Risks to future atoll habitability from climate-driven environmental changes." 23 December 2020. WIREs Climate Change/Wiley. DOI: 10.1002/wcc.700. https://onlinelibrary.wiley.com/doi/epdf/10.1002/wcc.700.

Edwards-May, David. "French Waterways." https://www.french-waterways.com/waterways/canals-rivers-france/

European Environment Agency. "Global and European sea level rise." 11 December 2020. https://www.eea.europa.eu/data-and-maps/indicators/sea-level-rise-7/assessment/.

Flavelle, Christopher. "Climate Change Could Cut World Economy by $23 Trillion in 2040, Insurance Giant Warns." 23 April 2021. *New York Times*. For the study, see: Swiss Re. "The economics of climate change." 22 April 2021. https://www.swissre.com/institute/research/topics-and-risk-dialogues/climate-and-natural-catastrophe-risk/expertise-publication-economics-of-climate-change.html

Flavelle, Christopher, quoting Donald L. Griffin of the American Property Casualty Insurance Association, in "US Disaster Costs Doubled in 2020, Reflecting Costs of Climate Change." 7 January 2021. *New York Times*. https://www.nytimes.com/2021/01/07/climate/2020-disaster-costs.html

IOP Publishing. "Rising sea levels could cost the world $14 trillion a year by 2100." 3 July 2018. https://www.sciencedaily.com/releases/2018/07/180703190745.htm.

Jones, Jessica. "Hurricane Network." Pivot to Growth. www.pivottogrowth.com.

Kirezci, Ebru, et al., "Projections of global-scale extreme sea levels and resulting episodic coastal flooding over the 21st Century." *Sci Rep* 10, 11629 (2020). https://doi.org/10.1038/s41598-020-67736-6

Kirshen, Paul, et al., "Integrated assessment of storm surge barrier systems under present and future climates and comparison to alternatives: a case study of Boston, USA." 13 July 2020. *Climatic Change* (2020) 162:445-464. https://doi.org/10.1007/s10584-020-02781-8

Knowlton, Nancy of Smithsonian Museum of Natural History talks with Gwen Ifill. "Storms, Starfish Wiped out Half of the Great Barrier Reef Coral." PBS NewsHour. VIDEO: https://www.youtube.com/watch?v=M7b6gRUi820

Kulp, Scott A. and Benjamin H. Strauss. "Author Correction: New elevation data triple estimates of global vulnerability to sea-level rise and coastal flooding." December 2019. https://www.nature.com/articles/s41467-019-13552-0

Kulp, Scott. A. and Benjamin H. Strauss. "New elevation data triple estimates of global vulnerability to sea-level rise and coastal flooding." *Nat. Commun* 10, 4844 (Oct. 2019). https://doi.org/10.1038/s41467-019-12808-z.

Lempérière, François and Luc Deroo. "Peut-on éviter les inondations à Paris?" 25 January 2018. Comité français des barrages et reservoirs (CFBK).

Litwin, Evan. "The Climate Diaspora: Indo-Pacific Emigration from Small Island Developing States." 1 May 2011. Thesis. McCormack Graduate School of Policy and Global Studies. University of Massachusetts Boston.

Mashal, Mujib, and Hari Kumar. "Glacier Bursts in India, Leaving More Than 100 Missing in Floods." 7 February 2021. *New York Times*. https://www.nytimes.com/2021/02/07/world/asia/india-glacier-flood-uttarakhand.html.

Morrison, Jim. "Who Will Pay for the Huge Costs of Holding Back Rising Seas?" Yale Environment 360. 5 August 2019. https://e360.yale.edu/features/who-will-pay-for-the-huge-costs-of-holding-back-rising-seas.

Penn, Allison Rebecca. "What Climate Change means for Coastal Real Estate Values and Property Investors." 27 June 2019. All Property Management. https://www.allpropertymanagement.com/blog/post/what-climate-change-means-for-coastal-real-estate-values/.

Schinko, Thomas, et al., "Economy-wide effects of coastal flooding due to sea level rise." 2020 Environ. Res. Commun. 2.015002. https://iopscience.iop.org/article/10.1088/2515-7620/ab6368/.

Sever, Megan. "Economic costs of rising seas will be steeper than we thought, unless we prepare. A study estimates 4 percent in annual global GDP losses by 2100 unless coast regions prepare." https://www.sciencenews.org/article/climate-economic-costs-rising-seas-will-be-steeper-than-thought

Shaw, Jonathan. "Controlling the Global Thermostat." November-December 2020. *Harvard Magazine*, pp. 42 -47, 82 -83. https://www.harvardmagazine.com/2020/11/features-controlling-global-thermostat

Stone Living Lab. https://www.stonelivinglab.org

Sustainable Solutions Lab. "Feasibility of Harbor-wide Barrier Systems: Preliminary Analysis of Boston Harbor." Principal Investigator: Paul Kirshen. May 2018. University of Massachusetts Boston. https://www.umb.edu/editor_uploads/images/centers_institutes/sustainable_solutions_lab/umb_rpt_BosHarbor_5.18_15-optimized.pdf

Wuebbles, D. J., et al., editors. National Climate Assessment (NCA4). "Climate Science Special Report: Fourth National Climate Assessment (NCA4), Volume I." US Global Change Research Program. https://science2017.globalchange.gov/

Challenge 5: Droughts and Fires
Carlowicz, Michael. "Drought Threatens Millions in South Africa." 1 December 2019.
https://earthobservatory.nasa.gov/images/146015/drought-threatens-millions-in-southern-africa.

Davidson, Frank P., Kathleen Lusk Brooke, with design and illustrations by Cherie E. Potts. *Building the Future.* "Lake Hope." pp. 14-20. Boston, 8 August 2012. LOC Reg. No. TXU001842617

Ghosh, Pallab. "Climate change boosted Australia bushfire risk by at least 30%." 4 March 2020. BBC.com.
https://www.bbc.com/news/science-environment-51742646 .

Lindqvist, A.N., Fornell, R., Prade, T. Tufvesson, L, Khalil, S. and Kopainsky, B. "Human-Water Dynamics and their Role for Seasonal Water Scarcity: A Case Study." *Water Resources Management* 35, (2021), 3043–3061.
https://doi.org/10.1007/s11269-021-02819-1

Challenge 6: Water from Space
Brooke, Kathleen Lusk. "SPACE: Here's looking at you, Earth." 10 August 2020. *Building the World Blog.* University of Massachusetts Boston.
https://blogs.umb.edu/buildingtheworld/2020/08/10/space-heres-looking-at-you-earth/

Fishman, Charles. "Scientists Discover The Oldest, Largest Body of Water In Existence – In Space." 29 July 2011. *Fast Company.*
https://www.fastcompany.com/1769468/scientists-discover-oldest-largest-body-water-existence-space.

Rasmussen, Carol and Alan Buis. "The Fingerprints of Sea Level Rise." 26 August 2015. Jet Propulsion Laboratory (JPL).
https://www.jpl.nasa.gov/news/the-fingerprints-of-sea-level-rise

Challenge 7: Renewal
Annan, Ebenezer, et al. "Clay Mixtures and the Mechanical Properties of Microporous and Nanoporous Ceramic Water Filters." *Journal of Materials in Civil Engineering* 28 (10), May 2016.
https://www.researchgate.net/publication/302918873_Clay_Mixtures_and_the_Mechanical_
Properties_of_Microporous_and_Nanoporous_Ceramic_Water_Filters.
https://ascelibrary.org/doi/10.1061/%28ASCE%29MT.1943-5533.0001596

Chang, Kenneth. "Under Icy Surface of a Saturn Moon Lies a Sea of Water, Scientists Say." 3 April 2014. *New York Times.*
https://www.nytimes.com/2014/04/04/science/space/a-moon-of-saturn-has-a-sea-scientists-say.html

Davidson, Frank P. and Kathleen Lusk Brooke. "Founding of Cyrene," pages 11-21; "Aqueducts of Rome," pages 21-35. In *Building the World: An Encyclopedia of the Great Engineering Projects in History.* Volume One. Greenwood Press, ABC-CLIO, Bloomsbury, 2006. ISBN: 0313333734.

IDE Technologies. https://www.IDE-tech.com/en/

Jacobsen, Rowan. "Israel proves the desalination era is here." 29 July 2016. *Scientific American.*
https://www.scientificamerican.com/article/israel-proves-the-desalination-era-is-here/.

Massachusetts Institute of Technology. "Rainwater Harvesting." WATER FOR ALL. Mission 2017: Global Water Security.
http://12.000.scripts.mit.edu/mission2017/

Shrestha, Rajendra, Jayesh Desai, Aditi Mukherji, Madhav Dhakal. "Protocol for Reviving Springs in the Hindu Kush Himalayas: A Practitioner's Manual." September 2018. *International Centre for Integrated Mountain Development (ICIMOD).* ISBN: 9789291156078. https://lib.icimod.org/record/34040

Talbot, David. "Megascale Desalination: The world's largest and cheapest reverse-osmosis desalination plant is up and running in Israel." *Technology Review.* https://www.technologyreview.com/technology/megascale-desalination/

United Nations. Convention to Combat Desertification. "The Great Green Wall Initiative." 2020.
https://www.unccd.int/actions/great-green-wall-initiative

Woo, Yun Chul, et al. "Co-axially electrospun superhydrophobic nanofiber membranes with 3D-hierarchically structured surface for desalination by long-term membrane distillation." *Journal of Membrane Science,* vol. 623, 1 April 2021, 119028. https://doi.org/10.1016/j.memsci.2020.119028

Challenge 8: Global/Regional
Brundtland, Gro Harlem. "Conversations with History: Interview with Gro Harlem Brundtland." With Gro Harlem Brundtland and Harry Kreisler. 29 April 2014. Institute of International Studies, University of California, Berkeley. University of California Television (UCTV). https://youtu.be/pHBW_Ng62QI

See also: https://theelders.org/profile/gro-harlem-brundtland

Cash, David W., and Susanne C. Moser. "Linking global and local scales: designing dynamic assessment and management processes." 14 April 2000. *Global Environmental Change* 10 (2000), 109-120. https://doi.org/10.1016/S0959-3780(00)00017-0

Chen, R. F. "Energy and Natural Resources." Chapter. In *Teaching Energy Across the Sciences: K-12*. Jeffrey Nordine, ed. National Science Teachers Association (NSTA) Press, 2015 . ISBN 9781941316016.

Eckstein, Gabriel. "International Law and Transboundary Aquifers." In *Routledge Handbook of Water Law and Policy*. Edited by Alistair Rieu-Clarke, Andrew Allan, Sarah Hendry. Pp. 217-233. New York: Routledge, 2017. ISBN: 9781138121201.

Hardin, Garrett. "The Tragedy of the Commons." *Science* 13 December 1968. Volume 162, Issue 3859, pp. 1243-1248. https://www.science.org/doi/abs/10.1126/science.162.3859.1243.

Langley, Winston E., Editor. "General Assembly Resolution 1803 (XVII) of 14 December 1962, Permanent Sovereignty Over Natural Resources," pp. 343 – 345, in *Human Rights: Sixty Major Global Instruments*. Jefferson, North Carolina and London: McFarland & Company, 1992. ISBN: 0899506690.

Litwin, George H., John J. Bray, Kathleen Lusk Brooke. *Mobilizing the Organization: Bringing Strategy to Life*. London: Prentice Hall/Pearson, 1996. ISBN: 0131488910.

MacNeill, Jim. "Brundtland Revisited." 4 February 2021. Open Canada. https://opencanada.org/brundtland-revisited/.

Organisation for Economic Co-operation and Development (OECD). "Development finance institutions and private sector development." https://www.oecd.org/development/development-finance-institutions-private-sector-development.htm.

Ostrom, Elinor. *Governing the Commons: The Evolution of Institutions for Collective Action*. New York: Cambridge University Press, 1990. ISBN: 9780521405997.

United Nations. Audiovisual Library of International Law. https://legal.un.org/avl/pdf/ha/ga_1803/ga_1803_ph_e.pdf

United Nations. "Declaration of the United Nations Conference on the Human Environment." Stockholm, Sweden, 5-16 June 1972. https://www.ipcc.ch/apps/njlite/srex/njlite_download.php?id=6471

United Nations. "General Assembly Resolution 1803 (XVII) Permanent Sovereignty Over Natural Resources." 1962.

United Nations. "Right to exploit freely natural wealth and resources." 21 December 1952. A/RES/626(VII), https://digitallibrary.un.org/record/211441

United Nations. "United Nations Conference on Environment and Development (UNCED) – Rio Declaration," 3-14 June 1992 Rio de Janeiro, Brazil." https://www.un.org/en/events/pastevents/UNCED_1992.shtml

United Nations. "World Charter for Nature (1982) https://digitallibrary.un.org/record/39295?ln=en

World Commission on Environment and Development (WCED). "Our Common Future, From One Earth to One World: An Overview." (Also referred to as "The Brundtland Report.") Oxford: Oxford University Press, 1987. ISBN: 019282080X. Available online: https://digitallibrary.un.org/record/129811

Challenge 9: Respect
Budds, Diana. "How Pantone Became the Definitive Language of Color." 18 September 2015. *Fast Company*. https://www.fastcompany.com/3050240/how-pantone-became-the-definitive-language-of-color

Glass, Philip. "Itaipú: Singing Stone," see: https://www.wisemusicclassical.com/work/6072/Itaipu--Philip-Glass/

Glass, Philip. *Itaipú*. Guaraní text of libretto translated by Daniela Thomas. Copyright 1988 Dunvagen Music Publishers, Sony Cat. #: 46352. ASIN: B00000277F.

Houtz, Jolayne. "Buying pink: How much of your purchase goes to breast-cancer research?" 10 October 2006. *The Seattle Times*. https://www.seattletimes.com/life/lifestyle/buying-pink-how-much-of-your-purchase-goes-to-breast-cancer-research/

Karlinksy, Malia. "Pantone's Color of the Year expert lives on Bainbridge Island." *Seattle Refined*. 11 January 2021. http://seattlerefined.com/lifestyle/pantone-colors-of-the-year-2021

"Pantone Color of the Year 2021." Video. https://www.youtube.com/watch?v=pu9zLAKpntM.

Sandler, Emma. "Butter London Sees Brand Awareness Opportunity with Pantone Color of the Year." 6 December 2018. https://www.glossy.co/platform-effect/butter-london-sees-brand-awareness-opportunity-with-pantone-color-of-the-year/

Shearer, Arial. "Meet the Seattle-area Woman Behind Pantone's 2020 Color of the Year." December 2019, *Seattle Magazine*. https://www.seattlemag.com/life-style/meet-seattle-area-woman-behind-pantones-2020-color-year

Talkeu Tounouga, Camille, translated by Odile Brock. "Water in Sub-Saharan Africa: A Cultural Approach." *Leonardo*. International Society for the Arts, Sciences, and Technology (ISAST). Volume 36, Number 4, August 2003, page 283. MIT Press.

Zerubavel, Eviatar. *The Seven Day Circle: The History and Meaning of the Week*. New York: Free Press, 1985. Chicago: University of Chicago Press, reprinted 1989. ISBN: 0226981657.

Challenge 10: Rights

Challe, Tiffany. "The Rights of Nature – Can an Ecosystem Bear Legal Rights?" 22 April 2021. Sabin Center for Climate Change Law, Columbia Climate School, Columbia University, New York, USA. https://news.climate.columbia.edu/2021/04/22/rights-of-nature-lawsuits/

Davidson, Frank P. and Kathleen Lusk Brooke. *Building the World: An Encyclopedia of Great Engineering Projects in History*. Volumes 1 and 2. Contains texts of original laws including Roman Aqueducts, Grand Canal of China, New River of England, Colorado River Compact, and others. Westport: Greenwood Press/ABC-CLIO, 2006. ISBN-10 : 9780313333545.

Eckstein, Yoram, and Gabriel E. Eckstein. "Transboundary Aquifers: Conceptual Models for Development of International Law." National Groundwater Association. *Groundwater*. Volume 43, Issue 5. Pages 679-690. https://ngwa.onlinelibrary.wiley.com/doi/abs/10.1111/j.1745-6584.2005.00098.x .

Hutchinson, Carrie. "An underwater museum is opening inside the world's most famous reef." 29 April 2020. CNBC.com, includes video. https://www.cnbc.com/2020/04/29/museum-of-underwater-art-to-open-inside-australia-great-barrier-reef.html

ImageStone, Christopher D. "Should Trees Have Standing – Toward Legal Rights for Natural Objects." *Southern California Law Review* 45 (1972): 450-501. https://iseethics.files.wordpress.com/2013/02/stone-christopher-d-should-trees-have-standing.pdf.

Lepore, Jill. "The elephant who could be a person." 16 November 2021. *The Atlantic*. https://www.theatlantic.com/ideas/archive/2021/11/happy-elephant-bronx-zoo-nhrp-lawsuit/620672/?utm_campaign=mb&utm_medium=newsletter&utm_source=morning_brew

Laws and Links

Bolivia. "La Ley de Derechos de Madre Tierra." Ley 071. 21 December 2010. Text in Spanish. http://extwprlegs1.fao.org/docs/pdf/bol144985.pdf .

Bolivia. "Revised Framework of Ley de Derechos de Madre Tierra – La Ley Marco de la Madre Tierra y Desarrollo Integral para Vivir Bien." Ley 300. 15 October 2012.

Canada. Conseil Des Innu De Ekuanitshit. "919-082/919-01-18" 18 January 2021. http://files.harmonywithnatureun.org/upload1072.pdf

Ecuador. "Constitución Política de la República del Ecuador." Asamblea Constituyente. Text in Spanish. https://pdba.georgetown.edu/Parties/Ecuador/Leyes/constitucion.pdf

Ecuador. "Constitution of the Republic of Ecuador, 20 October 2008. English language translation: https://pdba.georgetown.edu/Constitutions/Ecuador/english08.html.

India and Bangladesh. "Treaty between the Government of the Republic of India and the Government of the People's Republic of Bangladesh on sharing of the Ganga/Ganges waters at Farakka." 12 December 1996. https://iea.uoregon.edu/treaty-text/1040

"Lake Erie Bill of Rights." Jason A. Hill, CCM, CCE, Court Administrator, Sixth District Court of Appeals. LEBOR. https://farmoffice.osu.edu/blog-tags/lake-erie-bill-rights.

Municipalité Régionale de Comté de Minganie. "Résolution 025-21: Reconnaissance de la personnalité juridique et des droits de la rivière Magpie – Mutehekau Shipu." 16 February 2021. http://files.harmonywithnatureun.org/uploads/upload1069.pdf

New Zealand Parliament. "Te Awa Tupua (Whanganui River Claims Settlement) Act, 2017. 20 March. Reprint 7 August 2020. https://www.legislation.govt.nz/act/public/2017/0007/latest/whole.html

United Nations. Convention on the Law of the Non-navigational Uses of International Watercourses, 1997. Entered into force in 2014. https://legal.un.org/ilc/texts/instruments/english/conventions/8_3_1997.pdf

United Nations. World Charter for Nature, 1982. See: UN Document A/37/L.4, and ADD.1. https://digitallibrary.un.org/record/39295?LN=EN .

United States Congress. Colorado River Compact. Signed At Santa Fe, New Mexico, November 24, 1922. https://www.usbr.gov/lc/region/g1000/pdfiles/crcompct.pdf

Yurok Tribe. "Yurok Tribe, et al., Plaintiffs, v. U.S. Bureau of Reclamation. et al., Defendants." United States District Court Northern District of California, 29 May 2020. Case No. 19-cv-04405-WHO (N.C. Cal. May.29, 2020) Court of Appeals. https://casetext.com/case/yurok-tribe-v-us-bureau-of-reclamation-3

Poem
Dickinson, Emily. *The Poems of Emily Dickinson*. Edited by R. W. Franklin, 1998. Poem no. 1638, p. 597. Cambridge, MA: Harvard University Press. ISBN: 9780674676220.

ABOUT THE AUTHOR

Kathleen Lusk Brooke, founder of the Center for the Study of Success, taught seminars at Harvard and MIT on Failure and Success. Previous books include *Mobilizing the Organization*, nominated for the Financial Times Best Global Business Book, and *Building the World*, exploring how engineering, scientific, and technical success shaped civilization. In addition to recognition from the Copernicus Society, Fulbright Foundation, and Woodrow Wilson Foundation, Kathleen Lusk Brooke was named one of the Beautiful Minds of the Millennium.

CPSIA information can be obtained
at www.ICGtesting.com
Printed in the USA
BVHW020045200123
656708BV00016B/87

9 798985 035919